A GUIDE TO
GOLF COURSES IN
BRITAIN & IRELAND

Produced by AA Publishing
Editorial: lifestyleguides@theAA.com
Prelim pictures have been sourced from Corbis UK
Design/repro Jamie Wiltshire, Basingstoke
Printed and bound by Trento, Italy
Published by AA Publishing, which is a trading name of
Automobile Association Developments Limited, whose
registered office is Fanum House, Basingstoke, Hampshire
RG21 4EA

Registered number 1878835
A CIP catalogue record for this book is available from
the British Library

ISBN-10: 07495 47073
ISBN-13: 9780 7495 47073
A02637

CONTENTS

How to use the Guide

Sample Entry

1 — Anytown

2 — **Anywhere Golf Club**
Any Street AB01 2CD
3 — ☎ 0123 456 789 📄 0123 456 789

4 — **A gently undulating parkland course.**

5 — 18 holes, 6079yds, Par 71, SSS 70, Course record 65.

6 — **Club membership:** 590. **Visitors:** with member only at
7 — weekends. **Societies:** Wed & Fri normally booked 6 — 8
mths ahead. **Green Fees:** £30 per round weekdays — 9
10 — (£46 weekends). **Cards:** 💳 💳 💳 **Prof:** Colin
Clingan **Course Designer:** Sandy Herd **Facilities:** ⑨ — 11
by prior arrangement ⑩ by prior arrangement 🍴 ☕ 🍷
12 — 🚹 🏪 ⛳ 🛺 ⛳ **Conf:** Corporate Hospitality Days
available **Location:** 2m W of M1 junc 13 — 13

Hotel
★★★69% **Anyplace Hotel,**
Any Street, ANYTOWN — 14
☎ 0123 456 789 – 39 en suite 27 annexe en suite

1 Location name The directory is organised alphabetically by
county then town or village name.
2 Club name Check any details with the club in advance.
3 Contact details
4 Description A brief description of the course or courses, with
significant features highlighted.
5 Course statistics The number of holes, yardage, par, Standard
Scratch Score, Course Record, and number of club members.
6 Visitor information Details of booking requirements or
restrictions.
7 Society information Booking requirements or restrictions for
societies.
8 Green fees The most up-to-date green fees are given,
including any variations or restrictions. Where green fees are
not confirmed, contact the club for current details. An asterisk
* denotes 2005 fees.
9 Credit cards symbols The credit cards accepted by the club.
10 Professional The name of the club professional(s).
11 Facilities Please see the key to symbols on the right.
12 Conference facilities The available conference facilities are
noted, and corporate hospitality days.
13 Location The location of the club is given in relation to the
nearest town or motorway junction. Contact the club for
further details.
14 Accommodation AA recognised hotel or guest
accommodation is provided for most entries. Contact details
and the number of rooms are given.

Championship courses

Major championship courses have a
full-page entry more extensive details.
A selection of AA recognised hotels is given
for these courses.

Hotels & guest accommodation

Most course entries are followed by details of a
nearby AA recognised hotel or guest
accommodation. This does not imply that the hotel
offers special terms for the golf club. To find out
more about AA ratings and awards, please see our
website www.TheAA.com.
Where golf courses offer club accommodation the
bed symbol appears under Facilities. This is listed
as an option for readers wishing to stay at the
course. Unless the club accommodation has an AA
Star or Diamond classification, the only AA
recognised accommodation is the hotel or guest
house that follows the entry.

Key to symbols

☎	Telephone number
📄	Fax number
€	Euro (Republic of Ireland only)
⑨	Lunch
⑩	Dinner
🍴	Bar snacks
☕	Tea/coffee
🍷	Bar open midday and evenings
◇	Accommodation at club
🚹	Changing rooms
🏪	Well-stocked shop
⛳	Clubs for hire
⛳	Motorised cart/trolley for hire
🛺	Buggies for hire
⛳	Trolley for hire
⛳	Driving range
🎣	Fishing
🎾	Hard court tennis
🎾	Grass court tennis
🏊	Heated indoor swimming pool
🏊	Heated outdoor swimming pool
🐎	Horse riding
★	AA Star classification for hotels
◎	AA Rosette award for food
◆	AA Diamond for guest houses
🏨	Town House Hotel
🏨	Country House Hotel
🏨	Restaurant with rooms
Ⓤ	Hotel not yet rated by the AA

ENGLAND

BEDFORDSHIRE

ASPLEY GUISE

Aspley Guise & Woburn Sands
West Hill MK17 8DX
☎ 01908 583596 📄 01908 583596 (Secretary)

A fine undulating course in expansive heathland interspersed with many attractive clumps of gorse, broom and bracken. Some well-established silver birch are a feature. The 7th, 8th and 9th are really tough holes to complete the first half.

18 holes, 6079yds, Par 71, SSS 70, Course record 65.

Club membership: 590. **Visitors:** with member only at weekends. **Societies:** Wed & Fri normally booked 6 mths ahead. **Green Fees:** £30 per round weekdays (£46 weekends). **Cards:** 💳 💳 💳 **Prof:** Colin Clingan **Course Designer:** Sandy Herd **Facilities:** ⑪ by prior arrangement 🍴 by prior arrangement 🏌 ⚑ 🍴 🎯 🏠 ⚑ 🚗 ✦ **Conf:** Corporate Hospitality Days available **Location:** 2m W of M1 junc 13

Hotel
★★★69% **Moore Place Hotel,**
The Square, ASPLEY GUISE
☎ 01908 282000 – 39 en suite 27 annexe en suite

DUNSTABLE

Dunstable Downs
Whipsnade Rd LU6 2NB
☎ 01582 604472 📄 01582 478700
e-mail: dunstabledownsgc@btconnect.com

A fine downland course set on two levels with far-reaching views and frequent sightings of graceful gliders. The 9th hole is one of the best short holes in the country.

18 holes, 6251yds, Par 70, SSS 70, Course record 64.

Club membership: 600. **Visitors:** welcome Mon, Tue, Thur and Fri, weekends with member only. Handicap certificate required. **Societies:** apply in advance. **Green Fees:** £30 per round. **Prof:** Michael Weldon **Course Designer:** James Braid **Facilities:** ⑪ 🍴 🏌 ⚑ 🍴 🏠 🚗 ✦ **Conf:** Corporate Hospitality Days available **Location:** 2m S off B4541

Hotel
★★★63% **Old Palace Lodge,** Church St, DUNSTABLE
☎ 01582 662201 – 68 en suite

BERKSHIRE

ASCOT

Berkshire
Swinley Rd SL5 8AY
☎ 01344 621495 📄 01344 623328

Two classic heathland courses, with splendid tree-lined fairways, that have remained the same since they were constructed in 1928. The Red Course, on slightly higher ground, is a little longer than the Blue. It has an unusual assortment of holes, six par 3s, six par 4s and six par 5s, the short holes, particularly the 10th and 16th, being the most intimidating. The Blue Course starts with a par 3 and shares with the 16th the reputation of being the finest holes of the 18.

Red Course: 18 holes, 6379yds, Par 72, SSS 71.
Blue Course: 18 holes, 6260yds, Par 71, SSS 71.

Visitors: by prior arrangement **Societies:** applications in writing only and must be registered. **Green Fees:** £110 per day, £80 per round. **Cards:** 💳 💳 💳 **Prof:** P Anderson **Course Designer:** H Fowler **Facilities:** ⑪ 🏌 ⚑ 🍴 🏠 🍴 🎯 ⚑ 🚗 ✦ **Conf:** Corporate Hospitality Days available **Location:** 2.5m NW of M3 jct 3 on A332

Hotel
★★★★ 66% **The Berystede,**
Bagshot Rd, Sunninghill, ASCOT
☎ 0870 400 8111 – 90 en suite

Swinley Forest
Coronation Rd SL5 9LE
☎ 01344 874979 (Secretary) 📄 01344 874733
e-mail: swinleyfgc@aol.com

An attractive and immaculate course of heather and pine situated in the heart of Swinley Forest. The 17th is as good a short hole as will be found, with a bunkered plateau green, and the 12th hole is one of the most challenging par 4s.

18 holes, 6100yds, Par 69, SSS 70, Course record 62.

Club membership: 350.
Visitors: on introduction of a member or by invitation only. **Societies:** must contact in writing. **Green Fees:** not confirmed. **Cards:** 💳 💳 💳 💳 **Prof:** Stuart Hill **Course Designer:** Harry Colt **Facilities:** ⑪ 🏌 ⚑ 🍴 🏠 🍴 ⚑ 🚗 ✦ Video studio. **Conf:** Corporate Hospitality Days available **Location:** 2m S of Ascot, off A330

Hotel
★★★★ 66% **The Berystede,**
Bagshot Rd, Sunninghill, ASCOT
☎ 0870 400 8111 – 90 en suite

CROWTHORNE

East Berkshire
Ravenswood Ave RG45 6BD
☎ 01344 772041 📄 01344 777378
e-mail: thesecretary@eastberksgc.fsnet.co.uk

An attractive heathland course with an abundance of heather and pine trees. Walking is easy and the greens are exceptionally good. Some fairways become tight where the heather encroaches on the line of play. The course is testing and demands great accuracy.

Continued 5

18 holes, 6236yds, Par 69, SSS 70.

Club membership: 766.

Visitors: must contact in advance and have a handicap certificate; must play with member at weekends & bank holidays. Societies: telephone for availability. Green Fees: £45 per day. Prof: Jason Brant Course Designer: P Paxton Facilities: ⑪ ⓛ ▬ ☎ ⚑ ⚐ ⌂ ☐ ⚑ ✆ Location: W side of town centre off B3348

Hotel
★★★★★ Pennyhill Park Hotel & The Spa, London Rd, BAGSHOT
☎ 01276 471774 – 26 en suite 97 annexe en suite

MAIDENHEAD

Maidenhead
Shoppenhangers Rd SL6 2PZ
☎ 01628 624693 📄 01628 780758
e-mail: manager@maidenheadgolf.co.uk

A pleasant parkland course with excellent greens and some challenging holes. The long par 4 4th and short par 3 13th are only two of the many outstanding aspects of this course.

18 holes, 6364yds, Par 70, SSS 70.

Club membership: 750.

Visitors: may not play after noon on Fri or at weekends. Must contact in advance and have a handicap certificate. Societies: must contact in writing. Green Fees: £35 per day; £30 per round. Cards: ⬤ ▭ VISA ▬ ▬ 🔄 Prof: Steve Geary Course Designer: Alex Simpson Facilities: ⑪ ⓘ ⓛ ▬ ☎ ⚑ ⌂ ☐ ⚑ ✆ Conf: facilities available Location: S side of town centre off A308

Hotel
★★★★ Fredrick's Hotel Restaurant Spa, Shoppenhangers Rd, MAIDENHEAD
☎ 01628 581000 – 34 en suite

Temple
Henley Rd, Hurley SL6 5LH
☎ 01628 824795 📄 01628 828119
e-mail: templegolfclub@btconnect.com

An open parkland course offering extensive views over the Thames Valley. Firm, relatively fast

greens, natural slopes and subtle contours provide a challenging test to golfers of all abilities. Excellent drainage assures play during inclement weather.

18 holes, 6266yds, Par 70, SSS 70.

Club membership: 480.

Visitors: must contact in advance, limited weekend access. Societies: contact Secretary for details. Green Fees: £50 per day; £40 per round (£60/£50 weekends). Cards: ⬤ ▭ VISA ▬ ▬ 🔄 Prof: James Whiteley Course Designer: Willie Park (Jnr) Facilities: ⑪ ⓛ ▬ ☎ ⚑ ⌂ ☐ ⚑ ✆ ✆ Conf: Corporate Hospitality Days available Location: Exit M4 jct 8/9 take A404M then A4130,or M40 exit junct 4 take A404 then A4130, signposted Henley

Hotel
★★★★ 71% The Compleat Angler, Marlow Bridge, MARLOW
☎ 0870 400 8100 – 64 en suite

MORTIMER

Wokefield Park
Wokefield Park RG7 3AE
☎ 0118 933 4029 📄 0118 933 4031
e-mail: wokefieldgolf@initialstyle.co.uk

Set in a prime location amid the peaceful and picturesque Berkshire countryside. The course architect has retained the numerous mature trees, and these, together with the winding streams, nine lakes and large bunkers, contribute to the beauty and challenge of this championship course.

18 holes, 6579yds, Par 72, SSS 72, Course record 65.

Club membership: 350.

Visitors: subject to availability. Phone pro-shop on 118 933 4072/4078 to book tee times. Societies: apply in writing/telephone in advance Green Fees: £50 per day; £30 per round; £18 per 9 holes (£65/£45/£25 weekends). Cards: ⬤ ▭ VISA ▬ ▬ 🔄 Prof: Gary Smith Course Designer: Jonathan Gaunt Facilities: ⑪ ⓘ ⓛ ▬ ☎ ⚑ ⌂ ☐ ⚑ ✆ ✆ ▬ ✆ ⚑ ⊙ ☕ ⚓ sauna, gymnasium, jacuzzi. Conf: facilities available Corporate: Hospitality Days available Location: M4 junct 11, A33 towards Basingstoke. 1st rdbt, 3rd exit towards Grazeley and Mortimer. After 2.5m and sharp right bend club on right

Hotel
★★★ 72% Romans Country House Hotel, Little London Rd, SILCHESTER
☎ 0118 970 0421 – 11 en suite 14 annexe en suite

READING

Calcot Park
Bath Rd, Calcot RG31 7RN
☎ 0118 942 7124 📄 0118 945 3373
e-mail: info@calcotpark.com

A delightfully sporting, slightly undulating

Continued

Berkshire **SUNNINGDALE**

Sunningdale

Ridgemount Rd SL5 9RR
☎ 01344 621681 📠 01344 624154

The Old Course, founded in 1900, was designed by Willie Park. It is a classic course at just 6308 yards long, with gorse and pines, silver birch, heather and immaculate turf. The New Course is no less a challenge, created by H S Holt in 1922 at 6443 yards. There's a long wait to become a member of this prestigious club, and its location within easy reach of London is an attraction in itself. Visitors playing two rounds have to alternate onto the other course in the afternoon. Short rounds may be played by finishing at the 10th or 13th green on the Old Course, and the 10th or 11th green on the New Course. On Monday one course is designated the two-ball course until 3pm – check when booking a tee time.

WHERE TO STAY NEARBY

★★★★★
Pennyhill Park Hotel & The Spa, London Rd, BAGSHOT
☎ 01276 471774; 26 en suite 97 annexe en suite

★★★★66%
The Berystede, Bagshot Rd, Sunninghill, ASCOT
☎ 0870 400 8111 📠 01344 872301 90 en suite

★★★★71%
The Royal Berkshire Ramada Plaza, London Rd, Sunninghill, ASCOT
☎ 01344 623322 📠 01344 627100 63 en suite

★★66%
Brockenhurst Hotel, Brockenhurst Rd, SOUTH ASCOT
☎ 01344 621912 📠 01344 873252 12 en suite 5 annexe en suite

Old Course
18 holes, 6308yds, Par 70, SSS 70

New Course
18 holes, 6443yds, Par 71, SSS 72

Club Membership
1000

Visitors
Not Fri–Sun, bank holidays; must contact in advance; handicap certificate (less than 18) and letter of introduction

Societies
Tue, Wed, Thu, by arrangement

Green Fees
Old Course £145 per round; New Course £110 per round. 36 holes £185

Cards

Professional
Keith Maxwell

Course Designer
W Park

Facilities

Corporate
Hospitality Days available

Location
1m S off A30

parkland course just outside the town, which celebrated its 75th anniversary in 2005. The subtle borrows on the greens challenge all categories of golfer. Hazards include streams, a lake and many trees. The 6th is a 503-yard par 5, with the tee-shot hit downhill over cross-bunkers to a well-guarded green; the 7th (156 yards) is played over the lake to an elevated green and the 13th (also 156 yards) requires a carry across a valley to a plateau green.

18 holes, 6216yds, Par 70, SSS 70, Course record 63.

Club membership: 730. Visitors: must have handicap certificate or letter of introduction from club. May play weekdays only, excluding bank holidays. Societies: must apply in writing. Green Fees: £50 per day/round. Enquire for off peak rates. Prof: Mark Grieve Course Designer: H S Colt Facilities: ⑪ ⑩ 📍 ⬛📧🗔 ⤴ 🖾 ✂ 🥄 Conf: Corporate Hospitality Days available Location: 1.5m from M4 junct 12 on A4 towards Reading

Hotel
★★★ 72% The Copper Inn Hotel & Restaurant, PANGBOURNE
☎ 0118 984 2244 – 14 en suite 8 annexe en suite

SONNING

Sonning
Duffield Rd RG4 6GJ
☎ 0118 969 3332 📄 0118 944 8409
e-mail: secretary@sonning-golf-club.co.uk

A quality parkland course and the scene of many county championships. Wide fairways, not over-bunkered, and very good greens. Holes of changing character through wooded belts. Four challenging par 4s over 450 yards.

18 holes, 6366yds, Par 70, SSS 70, Course record 65.

Club membership: 750. Visitors: weekdays only. Handicap certificate or proof of membership of another club required. Societies: must apply in writing. Wed only, min 16. Green Fees: £40.50 before 10.30am or £30.50 after 10.30am. Prof: R McDougall Course Designer: Hawtree Facilities: ⑪ ⑩ 📍 ⬛📧🗔 ⤴ 🖾 🥄 Conf: facilities available Corporate: Hospitality Days available Location: 1m S off A4

Hotel
★★★ 78% The French Horn, SONNING ON THAMES
☎ 0118 969 2204 – 13 en suite 8 annexe en suite

STREATLEY

Goring & Streatley
RG8 9QA
☎ 01491 873229 📄 01491 875224
e-mail: secretary@goringgc.org

A parkland/moorland course that requires 'negotiating'. Four well-known first holes lead up to the heights of the 5th tee, to which there is a 300ft climb. Wide fairways, not over-bunkered,

with nice rewards on the way home down the last few holes. A delightful course that commands magnificent views of the Ridgeway and the River Thames.

18 holes, 6355yds, Par 71, SSS 70, Course record 65.

Club membership: 740. Visitors: must contact in advance, with member only at weekends. Handicap certificate required. Societies: telephone in advance. Green Fees: not confirmed. Cards: 💳 💳 💳 💳 💳 Prof: Jason Hadland Course Designer: Tom Morris Facilities: ⑪ ⑩ 📍 ⬛📧🗔 ⤴ 🖾 ✂ Location: N of village off A417

Hotel
★★★★ 69% The Swan at Streatley, High St, STREATLEY
☎ 01491 878800 – 46 en suite

BRISTOL

BRISTOL

Bristol and Clifton
Beggar Bush Ln, Failand BS8 3TH
☎ 01275 393474 📄 01275 394611
e-mail: mansec@bristolgolf.co.uk

Utilising the aesthetics and hazards of a former quarry, a valley, stone walls and spinneys of trees, the course is a stern challenge but one always in tiptop condition, due in summer to the irrigation and in winter to the natural draining land upon which it is situated. Par 3s from 120 to 220 yards, dog-legs which range from the gentle to the brutal and a collection of natural obstacles and hazards add to the charm of the layout.

18 holes, 6387yds, Par 70, SSS 71, Course record 63.

Club membership: 850. Visitors: must have a handicap certificate. Weekends restricted. Societies: telephone to enquire. Green Fees: £38 per day (£45 weekends). Cards: 💳 💳 💳 💳 Prof: Paul Mitchell Facilities: ⑪ ⑩ 📍 ⬛📧🗔 ⤴ 🖾 🥄 ✂ ✂ 🌳 chipping green, practice bunkers. Conf: facilities available Corporate: Hospitality Days available Location: M5 junct 19, follow A369 for 4m, then take B3129. Club 1m on right

Hotel
★★★ 68% Corus Hotel Bristol, Beggar Bush Ln, Failand, BRISTOL
☎ 0870 609 6144 – 112 en suite

Henbury
Henbury Hill, Westbury-on-Trym BS10 7QB
☎ 0117 950 0044 & 950 2121 (Prof)
📄 0117 959 1928
e-mail: thesecretary@henburygolfclub.co.uk

18 holes, 6007yds, Par 69, SSS 70, Course record 65.

Location: 3m NW of city centre on B4055 off A4018 Telephone for further details

Hotel
Henbury Lodge Hotel, Station Rd, Henbury, BRISTOL
☎ 0117 950 2615 – 12 en suite 9 annexe en suite

Knowle
West Town Ln, Brislington BS4 5DF
☎ 0117 977 0660 📠 0117 972 0615

A parkland course with nice turf. The first five holes climb up and down hill but the remainder are on a more even plane.

18 holes, 6006yds, Par 69, SSS 69, Course record 61.

Club membership: 700. **Visitors:** must have handicap certificate, must telephone professional 0117 977 9193 for weekends. **Societies:** Thu only, apply in writing or telephone. **Green Fees:** not confirmed.
Prof: Robert Hayward **Course Designer:** Hawtree/J H Taylor **Facilities:** 🏤 🕖 🛏 🍺 🍴 ⚑ 👜 ⚑ 🏌 🛒 ♂
Location: 3m SE of city centre off A37

Hotel
★★★★🏚 79% **Hunstrete House Hotel,** HUNSTRETE
☎ 01761 490490 – 25 en suite

BUCKINGHAMSHIRE

AYLESBURY

Ellesborough
Wendover Rd, Butlers Cross HP17 0TZ
☎ 01296 622114 📠 01296 622114
e-mail: admin@ellesboroughgolf.co.uk

Once part of the property of Chequers, and under the shadow of the famous Coombe monument at the Wendover end of the Chilterns. A downland course, it is rather hilly with most holes enhanced by far-ranging views over the Aylesbury countryside.

18 holes, 6360yds, Par 71, SSS 71, Course record 64.

Club membership: 700. **Visitors:** welcome on weekdays, handicap certificate required. **Societies:** Wed & Thu only, by prior arrangement with General Manager. **Green Fees:** not confirmed. **Prof:** Mark Squire **Course Designer:** James Braid **Facilities:** 🏤 🛏 🍺 🍴 👜 👜 ♂ **Conf:** Corporate Hospitality Days available **Location:** 1m W of Wendover on B4010 towards Princes Risborough

Hotel
⌂ **Innkeeper's Lodge Aylesbury South,** 40 Main St, Weston Turville, AYLESBURY
☎ 01296 613131 & 0870 243 0500 📠 01296 616902
16 en suite

BEACONSFIELD

Beaconsfield
Seer Green HP9 2UR
☎ 01494 676545 📠 01494 681148
e-mail: secretary@beaconsfieldgolfclub.co.uk

An interesting and, at times, testing tree-lined and parkland course which frequently plays longer than appears on the card! Each hole differs to a considerable degree and here lies the charm. Walking is easy, except perhaps to the 6th and 8th. Well bunkered.

18 holes, 6506yds, Par 72, SSS 71, Course record 63.

Club membership: 850. **Visitors:** must contact in advance and have a handicap certificate. May not play weekends. **Societies:** phone for details **Green Fees:** £60 per day; £50 per round (with member only at weekend & bank holidays). **Prof:** Michael Brothers **Course Designer:** H S Colt **Facilities:** 🏤 🕖 🛏 🍺 🍴 👜 👜 ⚑ ♂ 🏌 **Conf:** Corporate Hospitality Days available **Location:** Exit M40 junct 2, adjacent to Seer Green railway station

Hotel
⌂ **Innkeeper's Lodge,** Aylesbury End, BEACONSFIELD
☎ 01494 671211 – 32 en suite

BURNHAM

Burnham Beeches
Green Ln SL1 8EG
☎ 01628 661448 📠 01628 668968
e-mail: enquiries@bbgc.co.uk

A wooded parkland course on the edge of the historic Burnham Beeches Forest with a good variety of holes.

18 holes, 6449yds, Par 70, SSS 71, Course record 66.

Club membership: 670. **Visitors:** must contact in advance. May play only play weekends as guest of member. Handicap certificate required. **Societies:** welcome Apr-Oct, write or telephone for information. **Green Fees:** £40 per round weekdays. **Prof:** Ronnie Bolton **Facilities:** 🏤 🕖 🛏 🍺 🍴 👜 👜 ⚑ 🏌 🛒 ♂
Location: 0.5m NE of Burnham

Hotel
★★★ 65% **Burnham Beeches Hotel,**
Grove Rd, BURNHAM
☎ 0870 609 6124 – 82 en suite

DENHAM

Denham
Tilehouse Ln UB9 5DE
☎ 01895 832022 📠 01895 835340
e-mail: club.secretary@denhamgolfclub.co.uk

A beautifully maintained parkland/heathland course, home of many county champions. Slightly hilly and calling for good judgement of distance in the wooded areas.

18 holes, 6462yds, Par 70, SSS 71, Course record 66.

Club membership: 790. **Visitors:** must contact in advance & have handicap certificate. Must play with member Fri-Sun. **Societies:** Tue-Thu. Must book in advance. **Green Fees:** £55 per round. **Prof:** Stuart

Buckinghamshire **LITTLE BRICKHILL**

Woburn Golf & Country Club

MK17 9LJ

☎ 01908 370756   📠 01908 378436

e-mail: enquiries@woburngolf.com

Easily accessible from the M1, Woburn is famed not only for its golf courses but also for the magnificent stately home and wildlife park, which are both well worth a visit. Charles Lawrie of Cotton Pennink designed two great courses here among trees and beautiful countryside. From the back tees they are rather long for the weekend amateur golfer. The Duke's Course is a tough challenge for golfers at all levels. The Duchess Course, although relatively easier, still demands a high level of skill to negotiate the fairways guarded by towering pines. The Duke's has become the home of the increasingly popular Weetabix Women's British Open, held here since 1990. The town of Woburn and the abbey are in Bedfordshire, while the golf and country club are over the border in Buckinghamshire.

WHERE TO STAY NEARBY

★★★
Menzies Flitwick Manor,
Church Rd, FLITWICK
☎ 01525 712242; 17 en suite

★★★73%
The Inn at Woburn,
George St, WOBURN
☎ 01525 290441   📠 01525 290432
50 en suite 7 annexe en suite

★★★69%
Moore Place Hotel,
The Square, ASPLEY GUISE
☎ 01908 282000   📠 01908 281888
39 en suite 27 annexe en suite

Duke's Course
18 holes, 6973yds, Par 72, SSS 74, Course record 62

Duchess Course
18 holes, 6651yds, Par 72, SSS 72

Marquess Course
18 holes, 7214yds, Par 72, SSS 74

Visitors
Mid-week by arrangement; handicap certificate required (gentlemen 24, ladies 36).

Societies
must contact in advance

Green Fees
Duke's/Duchess £66 per round, Marquess £96 per round (Aug–Oct £95/£110 including lunch). 36 holes including lunch: Duke's/Duchess £130, Marquess £150

Cards

Professional
Luther Blacklock

Course Designer
Charles Lawrie

Facilities
🍴 🍺 ☕ 🍷 ⛳ 🏠 🎪 🏌 🚜 🏌 🏒 🚿 🏊

Corporate
Hospitality Days available

Location
M1 junct 13, 4m W off A5130

Campbell **Course Designer:** H S Colt **Facilities:** ⊕ 🍽 🛢 ➡ 🏌 ♨ 🏠 🔞 ⛳ Conf: Corporate Hospitality Days available **Location:** 0.5m N of North Orbital Road, 2m from Uxbridge

Hotel
★★★ 71% **Barn Hotel,** West End Rd, RUISLIP
☎ 01895 636057 – 59 en suite

GERRARDS CROSS
Gerrards Cross

Chalfont Park SL9 0QA
☎ 01753 883263 (Sec) & 885300 (Pro)
📄 01753 883593
e-mail: secretary@gxgolf.co.uk

A wooded parkland course which has been modernised in recent years and is now a very pleasant circuit with infinite variety. The best part lies on the plateau above the clubhouse where there are some testing holes.

18 holes, 6212yds, Par 69, SSS 70, Course record 64.

Club membership: 700. **Visitors:** must contact professional in advance, a handicap certificate is required, may not play Tue, weekends or public holidays. **Societies:** booking well in advance necessary, handicap certificates required, packages to suit. **Green Fees:** £53 per day, £40 per round. **Cards:** 💳 💳 💳 💳 **Prof:** Matthew Barr **Course Designer:** Bill Pedlar **Facilities:** ⊕ 🍽 🛢 ➡ 🏌 ♨ 🏠 ⛳ ⛳ **Location:** NE side of town centre off A413

Hotel
★★★ 69% **Bull Hotel,** Oxford Rd, GERRARDS CROSS
☎ 01753 885995 – 123 en suite

STOKE POGES
Stoke Park Club

Stoke Park, Park Rd SL2 4PG
☎ 01753 717171 📄 01753 717181
e-mail: info@stokeparkclub.com

Judgement of the distance from the tee is all important on this classic parkland course. Fairways are wide and the challenge seemingly innocuous – testing par 4's, superb bunkering and fast putting surfaces. The 7th hole is the model for the well-known 12th hole at Augusta.

Course 1: 18 holes, 6721yds, Par 71, SSS 72, Course record 65.
Course 2: 18 holes, 6551yds, Par 72, SSS 73.
Course 3: 18 holes, 6318yds, Par 71, SSS 70.

Club membership: 2500. **Visitors:** must contact in advance. **Societies:** telephone in advance. **Green Fees:** £125 per 18 holes (£200 weekends). **Cards:** 💳 💳 💳 💳 💳 **Prof:** Stuart Collier **Course Designer:** Harry Shapland Colt **Facilities:** ⊕ 🍽 🛢 ➡ 🏌 ♨ 🏠 🔞 ♨ ⛳ ⛳ ⛳ 🏊 🏌 sauna, gymnasium, indoor tennis courts. treatment room spa. **Conf:** facilities available **Corporate:** Hospitality Days

available **Location:** Turn off A4 at Slough into Stoke Poges Lane B416, club is 1.5m on left

Hotel
★★★★ 70% **Slough/Windsor Marriott Hotel,** Ditton Rd, Langley, SLOUGH
☎ 0870 400 7244 – 382 en suite

STOWE
Silverstone

Silverstone Rd MK18 5LH
☎ 01280 850005 📄 01280 850156
e-mail: proshop@silverstonegolfclub.co.uk

Set in the rolling North Buckinghamshire countryside, the course offers an interesting challenge for both experienced players and those with a higher handicap. Fairly flat parkland course with water features on 9 holes.

18 holes, 6472yrds, Par 72, SSS 71, Course record 65.

Club membership: 432. **Visitors:** no restrictions. **Societies:** may play weekdays/weekends after noon. Telephone to book. **Green Fees:** terms on application. **Cards:** 💳 💳 💳 💳 **Prof:** Rodney Holt **Course Designer:** David Snell **Facilities:** ⊕ 🍽 🛢 ➡ 🏌 🏠 ⛳ 🚗 ⛳ 🏌 **Conf:** facilities available **Corporate:** Hospitality Days available **Location:** from Silverstone village follow signs to the Grand Prix track. Golf club 1m past the entrance on right

Hotel
★★★★ 65% **Villiers Hotel,**
3 Castle St, BUCKINGHAM
☎ 01280 822444 – 46 en suite

CAMBRIDGESHIRE

BAR HILL
Cambridgeshire Moat House

Moat House Hotel, Bar Hill CB3 8EU
☎ 01954 780098 & 249971 📄 01954 780010
18 holes, 6734yds, Par 72, SSS 73, Course record 68.

Location: M11/A14, then B1050 (Bar Hill) Telephone for further details

Hotel
★★★★ 76% **Hotel Felix,**
Whitehouse Ln, CAMBRIDGE
☎ 01223 277977 – 52 en suite

CAMBRIDGE
Gog Magog

Shelford Bottom CB2 4AB
☎ 01223 247626 📄 01223 414990
e-mail: secretary@gogmagog.co.uk

Situated just outside the centre of the university town, Gog Magog, established in 1901, is known as the nursery of Cambridge undergraduate golf. The chalk downland courses are on high ground, and it is said that if you stand on the highest point and could see far enough to the east the next highest ground would be the Ural Mountains! The courses are open but there are enough trees and other hazards to provide plenty of problems. Views from the high parts are superb. The nature of the ground ensures good winter golf. The area has been designated a Site of Special Scientific Interest.

Old Course: 18 holes, 6398yds, Par 70, SSS 70, Course record 62.
Wandlebury: 18 holes, 6735yds, Par 72, SSS 72, Course record 67.

Club membership: 1400. **Visitors:** Must contact in advance. Mon-Fri only. Weekends and bank holidays by special arrangement with secretary. **Societies:** Tue & Thu by reservation. **Green Fees:** £44 per day, £37 per round (£60 per round weekends and bank holidays). **Prof:** Ian Bamborough **Course Designer:** Hawtree Ltd **Facilities:** ⑪ ⑩ 🏌 ⬛ 🚩 🏌 👤 🏠 🛒 🏌 🏌 **Conf:** Corporate Hospitality Days available **Location:** 3m SE on A1307

Hotel
★★★ 71% **Gonville Hotel,**
Gonville Place, CAMBRIDGE
☎ 01223 366611 & 221111 🖹 01223 315470
78 en suite

GIRTON

Girton
Dodford Ln CB3 0QE
☎ 01223 276169 🖹 01223 277150
e-mail: secretary@girtongolfclub.sagehost.co.uk

Flat, open parkland course with many trees and ditches. Easy walking.

18 holes, 6012yds, Par 69, SSS 69, Course record 66.

Club membership: 800. **Visitors:** with member only at weekends. Contact professional in advance (01223 276991). **Societies:** apply in writing. **Green Fees:** £22 weekdays. **Prof:** Scott Thomson **Course Designer:** Allan Gow **Facilities:** ⑪ ⑩ 🏌 ⬛ 🚩 👤 🏠 🚩 🏌 **Location:** 3m from Cambridge. Just off junct 31 of A14

Hotel
★★★★ 76% **Hotel Felix,**
Whitehouse Ln, CAMBRIDGE
☎ 01223 277977 – 52 en suite

CHESHIRE

DELAMERE

Delamere Forest
Station Rd CW8 2JE
☎ 01606 883264 & 883800 🖹 01606 889444
e-mail: info@delameregolf.co.uk

Played mostly on undulating open heath there is great charm in the way this course drops down into the occasional pine sheltered valley. Six of the first testing nine holes are between 420 and 455 yards in length.

18 holes, 6328yds, Par 72, SSS 70, Course record 63.

Club membership: 500. **Visitors:** must contact in advance. Only 2 ball games at weekends. **Societies:** apply in writing or by telephone. **Green Fees:** £50 per day; £36 per round weekdays. **Prof:** Ellis B Jones **Course Designer:** H Fowler **Facilities:** ⑪ ⑩ by prior arrangement 🏌 ⬛ 🚩 👤 🏠 🛒 🏌 🏌 **Conf:** Corporate Hospitality Days available **Location:** 1.5m NE, off B5152

Hotel
★★ 64% **Hartford Hall,**
School Ln, Hartford, NORTHWICH
☎ 01606 780320 – 20 en suite

KNUTSFORD

Mere Golf & Country Club
Chester Rd, Mere WA16 6LJ
☎ 01565 830155 🖹 01565 830713
e-mail: enquiries@meregolf.co.uk

A gracious parkland championship course designed by James Braid in the Cheshire sand belt, with several holes close to a lake. The round has a tight finish with four testing holes.

18 holes, 6817yds, Par 71, SSS 73, Course record 64.

Club membership: 550. **Visitors:** by prior arrangement only, not able to play Wed, Fri, Sat & Sun.

Societies: apply by telephone to Karen Gallagher. Green Fees: £70 per day (£50 Oct-Mar). Cards: ⬤ 🟦 VISA D ⬛ ⬛ Prof: Peter Eyre Course Designer: James Braid/George Duncan Facilities: ⬤ 🍽 ⬛ ⬛ ⬛ ⬛ ⬛ ⬛ ⬛ ⬛ squash, sauna, solarium, gymnasium. Conf: facilities available Corporate: Hospitality Days available Location: 1m E of M6 junct 19, 1m W of M56 junct 7

Hotel
★★★★ 71% **Cottons Hotel & Spa,** Manchester Rd, KNUTSFORD ☎ 01565 650333 – 109 en suite

MACCLESFIELD

Tytherington
Dorchester Way, Tytherington SK10 2JP ☎ 01625 506000 📠 01625 506040 e-mail: tytherington.events@clubhaus.com

Modern championship course in beautiful, mature parkland setting with eight water features and over 100 bunkers. Testing holes, notably the signature 12th hole (par 5), played from an elevated tee with adjacent snaking ditch and a lake guarding the green.

18 holes, 6765yds, Par 72, SSS 74.

Club membership: 4800. Visitors: subject to availability and may not play weekends am. Societies: telephone and apply in writing. Green Fees: not confirmed. Cards: ⬤ ⬛ 🟦 VISA ⬛ ⬛ Prof: Gavin Beddon Course Designer: Dave Thomas/Patrick Dawson Facilities: ⬤ 🍽 ⬛ ⬛ ⬛ ⬛ ⬛ ⬛ ⬛ squash, sauna, solarium, gymnasium. Location: 1m N of Macclesfield off A523

Hotel
★★★★ 68% **Shrigley Hall Hotel Golf & Country Club,** Shrigley Park, Pott Shrigley, MACCLESFIELD ☎ 01625 575757 – 150 en suite

PRESTBURY

Prestbury
Macclesfield Rd SK10 4BJ ☎ 01625 828241 📠 01625 828241 e-mail: office@prestburygolfclub.com

Undulating parkland course, with many plateau greens. The 9th hole has a challenging uphill 3-tier green and the 17th is over a valley. Host to county and inter-county championships, including hosting an Open qualifying event annually until 2009.

18 holes, 6359yds, Par 71, SSS 71, Course record 64.

Club membership: 702. Visitors: must contact in advance and have an introduction from own club, with member only at weekends. Societies: apply in writing, Thu only. Green Fees: £45 per round. Cards: ⬤ ⬛ VISA Prof: Nick Summerfield Course Designer: Harry S Colt Facilities: ⬤ 🍽 ⬛ ⬛ ⬛ ⬛ ⬛ Conf: Corporate Hospitality Days available Location: S side of village off A538

Hotel
★★★★ 69% **De Vere Mottram Hall,** Wilmslow Rd, Mottram St Andrew, Prestbury, ☎ 01625 828135 – 132 en suite

SANDIWAY

Sandiway
Chester Rd CW8 2DJ ☎ 01606 883247 (Secretary) 📠 01606 888548 e-mail: info@sandiwaygolf.fsnet.co.uk

Delightful undulating wood and heathland course with long hills up to the 8th, 16th and 17th holes. Many dog-legged and tree-lined holes give opportunities for the deliberate fade or draw. True championship test and one of the finest inland courses in north-west England.

18 holes, 6404yds, Par 70, SSS 71, Course record 65.

Club membership: 750. Visitors: book through Secretary, members have reserved tees 8.30-9.30 and 12.30-1.30 (11.30-12.30 winter). Handicap certificate required Societies: book in advance through Secretary/Manager. Green Fees: £55 per day, £45 per round (£60 per round weekends). Prof: William Laird Course Designer: Ted Ray Facilities: ⬤ 🍽 ⬛ ⬛ ⬛ ⬛ ⬛ Location: 2m W of Northwich on A556

Hotel
★★ 64% **Hartford Hall,** School Ln, Hartford, NORTHWICH ☎ 01606 780320 – 20 en suite

WARRINGTON

Leigh
Kenyon Hall, Broseley Ln, Culcheth WA3 4BG ☎ 01925 762943 (Secretary) 📠 01925 765097 e-mail: golf@leighgolf.fsnet.co.uk

This is a compact parkland course, which has benefited in recent years from an intensive tree planting programme and extra drainage. An interesting course to play with narrow fairways making accuracy from the tees essential.

18 holes, 5853yds, Par 69, SSS 69, Course record 64.

Continued

Club membership: 850. Visitors: contact professional for details. Societies: Mon (ex bank holidays), Tue & Fri, apply by telephone. Green Fees: Summer: £32 (£40 weekends) Winter: £20 (£27 weekends). Prof: Andrew Baguley Course Designer: Harold Hilton Facilities: ⊕ ⏣ 🖳 💺 🏴 🏌 🔩 🍴 ✎ Conf: Corporate Hospitality Days available Location: 5m NE off A579

Hotel
★★★ 72% Fir Grove Hotel, Knutsford Old Rd, WARRINGTON
☎ 01925 267471 – 52 en suite

WILMSLOW

Wilmslow
Great Warford, Mobberley WA16 7AY
☎ 01565 872148 📠 01565 872172
e-mail: info@wilmslowgolfclub@co.uk

Peaceful parkland course, in the heart of the mid-Cheshire countryside, offering golf at all levels.

18 holes, 6607yds, Par 72, SSS 72, Course record 62.

Club membership: 850. Visitors: must contact in advance. Societies: Tue & Thu only, application in writing or telephone in advance. Green Fees: £55 per day; £45 per round (£65/£55 weekends & bank holidays). Cards: 💳 💳 📇 💳 Prof: John Nowicki Facilities: ⊕ ⏣ 🖳 💺 🏴 🏌 🔩 🍴 ✎ Conf: Corporate Hospitality Days available Location: 2m SW off B5058

Hotel
★★★ 77% Alderley Edge Hotel, Macclesfield Rd, ALDERLEY EDGE
☎ 01625 583033 – 52 en suite

CORNWALL & ISLES OF SCILLY

CAMELFORD

Bowood Park Hotel
Lanteglos PL32 9RF
☎ 01840 213017 📠 01840 212622
e-mail: golf@bowoodpark.com

A rolling parkland course set in 230 acres of ancient deer park once owned by the Black

Prince. Here 27 lakes and ponds test the golfer and serve as a haven for a variety of wildlife.

Bowood Park Golf Course: 18 holes, 6736yds, Par 72, SSS 72, Course record 68.

Club membership: 3500. Visitors: booking system in operation, contact in advance. Societies: contact for details. Green Fees: £30 per round (£40 weekends). Cards: 💳 💳 💳 📇 📇 💳 Prof: John Phillips Course Designer: Sandow Facilities: ⊕ ⏣ 🖳 💺 🏴 🏌 🔩 🍴 ✎ 🏌 🔩 🐎 🚶 masseur available. Conf: facilities available Corporate: Hospitality Days available Location: Through Camelford, 0.5m turn right Tintagel/Boscastle B3266, 1st left at garage

Hotel
★★★ 66% Bowood Park Hotel & Golf Course, Lanteglos, CAMELFORD
☎ 01840 213017 – 31 en suite

CARLYON BAY

Carlyon Bay Hotel
Sea Rd PL25 3RD
☎ 01726 814250 & 814228 (pro shop)
📠 01726 814250
e-mail: golf@carlyonbay.co.uk

Championship-length, cliff-top parkland course running east to west and back again and also uphill and down a fair bit. The fairways stay in excellent condition all year as they have since the course was laid down in 1925. Magnificent views from the course across St Austell Bay; particularly from the ninth green, where an approach shot remotely to the right will plummet over the cliff edge.

18 holes, 6597yds, Par 72, SSS 71, Course record 63.

Club membership: 500. Visitors: must contact in advance (pro shop 01726 814228) Societies: must contact in advance. Green Fees: from £25-£42 per round depending on season. Cards: 💳 💳 📇 📇 💳 Prof: Mark Rowe Course Designer: Hamilton Stutt Facilities: 🖳 💺 🏴 🏌 🔩 🍴 ✎ 🏌 🔩 🐎 🚶 ♨ sauna, solarium, 9-hole par 3 course. Conf: Corporate: Hospitality Days available Location: 3m SE of St Austell

Hotel
★★★★ 75% Carlyon Bay Hotel, Sea Rd, Carlyon Bay, ST AUSTELL
☎ 01726 812304 – 87 en suite

CONSTANTINE BAY

Trevose
PL28 8JB
☎ 01841 520208 📠 01841 521057
e-mail: info@trevose-gc.co.uk

Well-known links course with early holes close to the sea on excellent springy turf. A championship course affording varying degrees of difficulty appealing to both the professional and higher handicap player. It is a good test with well-positioned bunkers and a meandering stream, and the wind playing a decisive role in preventing low scoring. Self-catering accommodation is available at the club.

Championship Course: 18 holes, 6863yds, Par 72, SSS 73, Course record 66.
New Course: 9 holes, 3031yds, Par 35.
Short Course: 9 holes, 1360yds, Par 29.

Club membership: 1650. Visitors: subject to reservations, handicap certificate required for championship course. Advisable to contact in advance. Societies: telephone or write to the secretary. Green Fees: terms on application. Cards: 🖸 🟦 🟨 🔳 🈹 Prof: Peter Green Course Designer: H S Colt Facilities: ⑪ ⑩ ⚑ ⬛ ⬛ 🎿 🏠 ⚙ ◇ ⚘ ⬛ ⚘ ⚘ 🕳 ⚑ self-catering accommodation & a la carte restaurant. Location: 4m W of Padstow on B3276, to St Merryn, proceed 500yds past crossroads and take right turn, signposted

LELANT

West Cornwall
TR26 3DZ
☎ 01736 753401 📠 01736 753401
e-mail: ian@westcornwallgolfclub.fsnet.co.uk

A seaside links with sandhills and lovely turf adjacent to the Hayle estuary and St Ives Bay. A real test of the player's skill, especially 'Calamity

Corner' starting at the 5th on the lower land by the River Hayle.

18 holes, 5884yds, Par 69, SSS 69, Course record 63.

Club membership: 813. Visitors: must prove handicap certificate, be a member of a club affiliated to the EGU, advisable to contact in advance. Societies: must apply in writing/telephone in advance. Green Fees: not confirmed. Cards: 🖸 🟦 🟨 🔳 🈹 Prof: Jason Broadway Course Designer: Reverend Tyack Facilities: ⑪ ⑩ ⚑ ⬛ ⬛ 🎿 🏠 ⚙ ◇ snooker. Location: N side of village off A3074

Hotel
★★ 72% Pedn-Olva Hotel,
West Porthminster Beach, ST IVES
☎ 01736 796222 – 30 en suite

MULLION

Mullion
Cury TR12 7BP
☎ 01326 240685 (sec) & 241176 (pro)
📠 01326 240685
e-mail: secretary@mulliongolfclub.plus.com

Founded in 1895, a clifftop and links course with panoramic views over Mounts Bay. A steep downhill slope on 6th and the 10th descends to the beach with a deep ravine alongside the green. Second most southerly course in the British Isles.

18 holes, 6083yds, Par 70, SSS 70.

Club membership: 750. Visitors: preferable to contact in advance, restricted during club competitions. Handicap certificate required. Societies: must contact in advance. Green Fees: £30 per day, £25 per round (£35/£30 weekends & bank holidays). Prof: Ian Harris Course Designer: W Sich Facilities: ⑪ ⑩ ⚑ ⬛ ⬛ 🎿 🏠 ⚙ ⬛ ◇ indoor computerised teaching academy. Location: 1.5m NW of Mullion, off A3083

Hotel
★★★ 71% Polurrian Hotel, MULLION
☎ 01326 240421 – 39 en suite

ROCK

St Enodoc
PL27 6LD
☎ 01208 863216 📠 01208 862976
e-mail: stenodocgolfclub@aol.com

Classic links course with huge sand hills and rolling fairways. James Braid laid out the original 18 holes in 1907 and changes were made in 1922 and 1935. On the Church, the 10th is the toughest par 4 on the course and on the 6th is a truly enormous sandhill known as the Himalayas. The Holywell is not as exacting as the Church; it is less demanding on stamina but still a real test of skill for golfers of any handicap.

Church Course: 18 holes, 6243yds, Par 69, SSS 70, Course record 64.

Championship Course

St Mellion Hotel

Golf & Country Club PL12 6SD
☎ 01579 351351 📄 01579 350537
e-mail: stmellion@crown-golf.co.uk

Set among 450 acres of glorious Cornish countryside, St Mellion with its two outstanding courses is heralded as the premier golf and country club in the south-west. The Old Course is perfect for golfers of all abilities. Complete with well-sited bunkers, strategically tiered greens and difficult water features, this is definitely not a course to be overlooked. But if you really want to test your game, then head to the renowned Nicklaus Course, designed by the great man himself. On its opening in 1998 Jack declared, 'St Mellion is potentially the finest golf course in Europe'. The spectacularly sculptured fairways and carpet greens of the Nicklaus Course are a challenge and an inspiration to all golfers.

WHERE TO STAY NEARBY

★★★68%
St Mellion International,
ST MELLION
☎ 01579 351351
39 annexe en suite

★★
Well House Hotel, St Keyne,
LISKEARD
☎ 01579 342001 📄 01579 343891
9 en suite

★★★67%
China Fleet Country Club,
SALTASH
☎ 01752 848668 📄 01752 848456
40 en suite

Nicklaus Course
18 holes, 6592yds, Par 72, SSS 74, Course record 63

The Old Course
18 holes, 5782yds, Par 68, SSS 68, Course record 60

Club Membership
2850

Visitors
Phone in advance
01579 352002

Societies
Apply in writing or phone in advance

Green Fees
Nicklaus Course £80 per day, £57 per round; Old Course £70 per day, £39 per round

Cards
💳💳💳💳💳💳💳

Professional
David Moon

Course Designers
Old Course H J Stutt, Jack Nicklaus

Facilities
squash, sauna, solarium, gymnasium.

Conference
Facilities available

Corporate
Hospitality Days available

Location
A38 to Saltash, onto A388 to Callington

Holywell Course: 18 holes, 4142yds, Par 63, SSS 61.

Club membership: 1300. **Visitors:** may not play on bank holidays. Must have a handicap certificate of 24 or below for Church Course. Must contact in advance. **Societies:** must contact in writing/telephone. **Green Fees:** not confirmed. **Cards:** 💳💳💳💳💳 **Prof:** Nick Williams **Course Designer:** James Braid **Facilities:** ⒶⓄ 🍴 🏌 ♣ 📧 🅿 🏌 ⚑ **Location:** W side of village

Hotel
★★ 63% **The Molesworth Arms Hotel,**
Molesworth St, WADEBRIDGE
☎ 01208 812055 – 16 rms (14 en suite)

CUMBRIA

APPLEBY-IN-WESTMORLAND

Appleby
Brackenber Moor CA16 6LP
☎ 017683 51432 📠 017683 52773
e-mail: appleby.gc@tiscali.co.uk

This remotely situated heather and moorland course offers interesting golf with the rewarding bonus of several long par 4 holes that will be remembered and challenging par 3s. There are superb views of the Pennines and the Lakeland hills. Renowned for the excellent greens and very good drainage.

18 holes, 5901yds, Par 68, SSS 68, Course record 62.

Club membership: 800. **Visitors:** phone for details. May not play before 3pm weekends/competition days. **Societies:** must contact in advance by letter/phone. **Green Fees:** £25 per day; £20 per round (£30/£24 weekends and bank holidays). **Prof:** James Taylor **Course Designer:** Willie Fernie **Facilities:** ⒶⓄ 🏌 ♣ 📧 🅿 🏌 ⚑ **Conf:** Corporate Hospitality Days available **Location:** 2m E of Appleby 0.5m off A66

Hotel
★★★ 78% **Appleby Manor Country House Hotel,**
Roman Rd, APPLEBY-IN-WESTMORLAND
☎ 017683 51571 – 23 en suite 7 annexe en suite

BOWNESS-ON-WINDERMERE

Windermere
Clearbarrow LA23 3NB
☎ 015394 43123 📠 015394 43123
e-mail: windermeregc@btconnect.com

Located in the heart of the Lake District, just 2 miles from Lake Windermere. The course offers some of the finest views in the country. Not a long course but makes up for its lack of distance with heather and tight undulating fairways. The 6th hole has a nerve wracking but exhilarating blind shot – 160 yards over a rocky face to a humpy fairway with a lake to avoid on the second shot.

18 holes, 5122yds, Par 67, SSS 65, Course record 58.

Club membership: 890. **Visitors:** contact pro shop 7 days before day of play, 10-12 & 1.30-4.30 or before 9am by arrangement. **Societies:** by arrangement contact the secretary. **Green Fees:** £30 per round (£37 weekends & bank holidays). **Cards:** 💳💳💳 **Prof:** W S M Rooke **Course Designer:** G Lowe **Facilities:** ⒶⓄ 🏌 ♣ 📧 🅿 🏌 ⚑ **Conf:** **Corporate:** Hospitality Days available **Location:** B5284 1.5m from Bowness

Hotel
★★★ 68% **Famous Wild Boar Hotel,**
Crook, WINDERMERE
☎ 015394 45225 – 36 en suite

BRAMPTON

Brampton
Tarn Rd CA8 1HN
☎ 016977 2255 📠 01900 827852
e-mail: secretary@bramptongolfclub.com

Challenging golf across glorious rolling fell country demanding solid driving and many long second shots. A number of particularly fine holes, the pick of which may arguably be the lengthy 3rd and 11th. The challenging nature of the course is complemented by unrivalled panoramic views from a number of vantage points.

18 holes, 6407yds, Par 72, SSS 71, Course record 65.

Club membership: 800. **Visitors:** visitors intending to play at weekends are recommended to telephone in advance. **Societies:** apply in writing to I J Meldrum (Secretary), 17 Helvellyn Close, Cockermouth, Cumbria CA13 9BJ or telephone 01900 827985. **Green Fees:** £30 per day; £26 per round (£38/£32 weekends & bank holidays). **Cards:** 💳💳💳💳💳 **Prof:** Stewart Wilkinson **Course Designer:** James Braid **Facilities:** ⒶⓄ 🏌 ♣ 📧 🅿 🏌 ⚑ games room. **Conf:** Corporate Hospitality Days available **Location:** 1.5m SE of Brampton on B6413

Hotel
★★★★ ⌂ **Farlam Hall Hotel,** BRAMPTON
☎ 016977 46234 – 11 en suite 1 annexe en suite

CARLISLE

Carlisle
Aglionby CA4 8AG
☎ 01228 513029 (secretary) 📠 01228 513303
e-mail: secretary@carlislegolfclub.org

Majestic looking, long-established parkland course with great appeal providing a secure habitat for red squirrels and deer. A complete but not too severe test of golf, with fine turf, natural hazards, a stream and many beautiful trees; no two holes are similar.

18 holes, 6263yds, Par 71, SSS 70, Course record 63.

Club membership: 800. Visitors: may not play before 9am and between 12 and 1.30 and when tee is reserved. Very limited play Sun and with member only Sat and Tue. Societies: Mon, Wed & Fri, contact Secretary in advance for details on 01228 513029. Green Fees: £45 per day; £35 per round (£45 weekends). Prof: Graeme Lisle Course Designer: Mackenzie Ross Facilities: ⑪ ⑥ ⓛ ⓔ ⓣ ⓛ △ ⓔ ⓟ 🚬 ⚙ Conf: facilities available Corporate Hospitality Days available Location: On A69 0.5m E of M6 junct 43

Hotel
★★★ 71% **Crown Hotel**, Wetheral, CARLISLE
☎ 01228 561888 – 49 en suite 2 annexe en suite

GRANGE-OVER-SANDS

Grange Fell
Fell Rd LA11 6HB
☎ 015395 32536

A fell-side course with no excessive climbing and dependant on how straight you hit the ball. Fine views in all directions.

9 holes, 5292yds, Par 70, SSS 66, Course record 65.

Club membership: 300. Visitors: may normally play Mon-Sat. Green Fees: £15 per day (£20 weekends & bank holidays). Facilities: ⓔ ⓣ ⓛ △ Location: 1m W on Grange-Over-Sands/Cartmel road

Hotel
★★★ 75% **Netherwood Hotel**,
Lindale Rd, GRANGE-OVER-SANDS
☎ 015395 32552 – 32 en suite

PENRITH

Penrith
Salkeld Rd CA11 8SG
☎ 01768 891919 ▤ 01768 891919

A beautiful and well-balanced course, always changing direction, and demanding good length from the tee. It is set on rolling moorland with occasional pine trees and some fine views.

18 holes, 6047yds, Par 69, SSS 69, Course record 63.

Club membership: 850. Visitors: contact in advance. Handicap certificate required. Societies: telephone in advance. Green Fees: £31 per day; £26 per round (£36/£31 weekends). Prof: Garry Key Facilities: ⑪ ⑥ ⓛ ⓔ ⓣ △ ⓔ ⓟ ⚙ ⚒ Conf: facilities available Location: M6 junct 41, follow A6 to Penrith, left after 30mph sign and follow signs for golf club

Hotel
★★ 67% **Brantwood Country Hotel**,
Stainton, PENRITH
☎ 01768 862748 – 7 en suite

SEASCALE

Seascale
The Banks CA20 1QL
☎ 019467 28202 ▤ 019467 28202
e-mail: seascalegolfclub@aol.com

A tough links requiring length and control. The natural terrain is used to give a variety of holes and considerable character. Undulating greens add to the challenge. Fine views over the Western Fells, the Irish Sea and Isle of Man.

18 holes, 6416yds, Par 71, SSS 71, Course record 64.

Club membership: 700. Visitors: no restrictions, but advisable to contact for tee reservation times. Societies: telephone to make provisional booking. Green Fees: £30 per day; £25 per round (£35/£30 weekends & bank holidays). Prof: Sean Rudd Course Designer: Willie Campbell Facilities: ⑪ ⑥ ⓛ ⓔ ⓣ △ ⓔ ⓟ ⚙ ⚒ Conf: facilities available Location: NW side of village off B5344

Hotel
★★ 76% **Low Wood Hall Hotel & Restaurant**,
NETHER WASDALE
☎ 01946 726100 – 6 rms (5 en suite) 6 annexe en suite

SILLOTH

Silloth on Solway
The Clubhouse CA7 4BL
☎ 016973 31304 ▤ 016973 31782
e-mail: sillothgolfclub@lineone.net

Billowing dunes, narrow fairways, heather and gorse and the constant subtle problems of tactics and judgement make these superb links on the Solway an exhilarating and searching test. The 13th is a good long hole. Superb views.

18 holes, 6070yds, Par 72, SSS 70, Course record 59.

Club membership: 700. Visitors: must contact in advance. Societies: telephone for times available. Green Fees: £33 per day (£45 per round weekends). Cards: ⬛ 🟦 🟥 🔳 🔲 Prof: J Graham Course Designer: David Grant/Willie Park Jnr Facilities: ⑪ ⑥ ⓛ ⓔ ⓣ △ ⓔ ⚙ Conf: facilities available Location: S side of village off B5300

Hotel
★★ 67% **Golf Hotel**, Criffel St, SILLOTH
☎ 016973 31438 – 22 en suite

ULVERSTON

Ulverston
Bardsea Park LA12 9QJ
☎ 01229 582824 ▤ 01229 588910
e-mail: enquiries@ulverstongolf.co.uk

Inland golf with many medium length holes on undulating parkland. The 17th is a testing par 4. Overlooking Morecambe Bay the course offers extensive views to the Lakeland Fells.

18 holes, 6201yds, Par 71, SSS 70, Course record 64.

Club membership: 808. **Visitors:** must contact in advance, be a member of an accredited golf club with a handicap certificate. Restricted on Tue – Ladies day. **Societies:** by arrangement in writing. **Green Fees:** terms on application. **Cards:** 💳 VISA 🔵 🔴 💳 💳 **Prof:** M R Smith **Course Designer:** A Herd/H S Colt **Facilities:** ⑪ ⑩ ⬛ ⬛ ⬛ ⬛ ⬛ ⬛ ⬛ practice ball dispensing machine. **Conf:** Corporate Hospitality Days available **Location:** 2m S off A5087

Hotel
★★★ 67% **Whitewater Hotel,**
The Lakeland Village, NEWBY BRIDGE
☎ 015395 31133 – 35 en suite

DERBYSHIRE

Cavendish
Gadley Ln SK17 6XD
☎ 01298 79708 📠 01298 79708
e-mail: admin@cavendishgolfcourse.com

This parkland/moorland course with its comfortable clubhouse nestles below the rising hills. Generally open to the prevailing west wind, it is noted for its excellent surfaced greens which contain many deceptive subtleties. Designed by Dr Alastair McKenzie, good holes include the 8th, 9th and 18th.

18 holes, 5721yds, Par 68, SSS 68, Course record 61.

Club membership: 650. **Visitors:** must contact in advance, weekends are restricted by competitions. Ladies day Thu **Societies:** telephone professional on 01298 25052. **Green Fees:** terms on application. **Cards:** VISA **Prof:** Paul Hunstone **Course Designer:** Dr Mackenzie **Facilities:** ⑪ ⬛ ⬛ ⬛ ⬛ ⬛ ⬛ **Location:** 0.75m W of town centre off A53

Hotel
★★★ 77% **Best Western Lee Wood Hotel,**
The Park, BUXTON
☎ 01298 23002 – 35 en suite 5 annexe en suite

Kedleston Park
DE22 5JD
☎ 01332 840035 📠 01332 840035
e-mail: secretary@kedlestonpark.fsnet.co.uk

The course is laid out in flat mature parkland with fine trees and background views of historic Kedleston Hall (National Trust). Many testing holes are included in each 9 and there is an excellent modern clubhouse.

18 holes, 6675yds, Par 72, SSS 72, Course record 64.

Club membership: 731. **Visitors:** must contact in advance. **Societies:** weekdays only, apply in writing. **Green Fees:** £55 per day; £45 per round. **Cards:** 💳 💳 VISA 🔴 💳 💳 💳 **Prof:** Paul Wesselingh **Course Designer:** James Braid **Facilities:** ⑪ ⑩ ⬛ ⬛ ⬛ ⬛ ⬛ ⬛ ⬛ sauna. **Conf:** Corporate Hospitality Days available **Location:** Signposted Kedleston Hall from A38

Hotel
★★★ 63% **International Hotel,**
288 Burton Rd, DERBY
☎ 01332 369321 – 41 en suite 21 annexe en suite

DEVON

East Devon
Links Rd EX9 6DG
☎ 01395 443370 📠 01395 445547
e-mail: secretary@edge.co.uk

An interesting course with downland turf, much heather and gorse, and superb views over the bay. Laid out on cliffs 250 to 400 feet above sea level, the early holes climb to the cliff edge. The downhill 17th has a heather section in the fairway, leaving a good second to the green. In addition to rare orchids, the course enjoys an abundance of wildlife including deer and peregrine falcons.

18 holes, 6231yds, Par 70, SSS 70, Course record 61.

Club membership: 850. **Visitors:** advisable to contact in advance, no visitors before 9am. Visitors must be member of a recognised club and must produce proof of handicap. **Societies:** Thu only, must contact in advance. **Green Fees:** £45 per 27/36 holes; £36 per 18 holes. **Cards:** 💳 💳 ⬛ VISA 🔴 💳 💳 **Prof:** Trevor Underwood **Facilities:** ⑪ ⑩ ⬛ ⬛ ⬛ ⬛ ⬛ ⬛ **Conf:** Corporate Hospitality Days available **Location:** W side of town centre

Hotel
★★ 74% **Barn Hotel,**
Foxholes Hill, Marine Dr, EXMOUTH
☎ 01395 224411 – 11 en suite

CHURSTON FERRERS

Churston
Dartmouth Rd TQ5 0LA
☎ 01803 842751 & 842218 📄 01803 845738
e-mail: manager@churstongc.freeserve.co.uk
18 holes, 6219yds, Par 70, SSS 70, Course record 64.

Location: NW side of village on A379
Telephone for further details

Hotel
★★★ 67% **Berryhead Hotel,**
Berryhead Rd, BRIXHAM
☎ 01803 853225 – 32 en suite

MORETONHAMPSTEAD

Bovey Castle
TQ13 8RE
☎ 01647 445009 📄 01647 440961
e-mail: richard.lewis@boveycastle.com

**This enjoyable parkland course has enough
hazards to make any golfer think. Most hazards
are natural such as the Rivers Bowden and Bovey
which meander through the first eight holes.**

18 holes, 6303yds, Par 70, SSS 70, Course record 63.

Club membership: 130. **Visitors:** must contact in
advance and pre-arrange starting times. **Societies:**
must telephone for reservation in advance. **Green
Fees:** £117.50 per round any time. **Cards:** 💳 💳 💳
💳 📇 📇 **Prof:** Richard Lewis **Course
Designer:** J Abercrombie **Facilities:** 🏌 🍴 🛍 🍺 🍸
🛋 🏠 🏌 ◇ 🏌 🛍 🏌 🏌 ♨ 🏋 🏌 🏌 sauna,
solarium, gymnasium. **Conf:** facilities available
Corporate Hospitality Days available **Location:** 2m W
of Moretonhampstead, off B3212

Hotel
★★★★★ 70% **Bovey Castle,**
MORETONHAMPSTEAD
☎ 01647 445000 – 65 en suite

SAUNTON

Saunton
EX33 1LG
☎ 01271 812436 📄 01271 814241
e-mail: info@sauntongolf.co.uk

**Two traditional championship links courses.
Windy, with natural hazards.**

East Course:
18 holes, 6427yds, Par 71, SSS 71, Course record 64.
West Course:
18 holes, 6138yds, Par 71, SSS 70, Course record 63.

Club membership: 1450. **Visitors:** prior booking
recommended and must have handicap certificate.
Societies: must apply in advance, handicap certificates
required. **Green Fees:** £75 per day; £55 per round.
Cards: 💳 💳 💳 **Prof:** A T MacKenzie **Course
Designer:** F Pennick/W H Fowler **Facilities:** 🏌 🍴 🛍
🍺 🍸 🛋 🏠 🏌 ◇ 🏌 **Conf:** Corporate Hospitality
Days available **Location:** S side of village off B3231

Hotel
★★★★ 74% **Saunton Sands Hotel,** SAUNTON
☎ 01271 890212 – 92 en suite

TAVISTOCK

Tavistock
Down Rd PL19 9AQ
☎ 01822 612344 📄 01822 612344
e-mail: tavygolf@hotmail.org

**Set on Whitchurch Down in south-west Dartmoor
with easy walking and magnificent views over
rolling countryside into Cornwall. Downland turf
with some heather, and interesting holes on
undulating ground.**

18 holes, 6495yds, Par 71, SSS 71, Course record 60.

Club membership: 700. **Visitors:** advisable to
contact in advance. **Societies:** by arrangement with
secretary. **Green Fees:** £28 per day/round (£35
weekends). **Prof:** D Rehaag **Course Designer:** H
Fowler **Facilities:** 🏌 🍴 🛍 🍺 🍸 🛋 🏠 ◇
Location: 1m SE of town centre, on Whitchurch Down

Hotel
★★★ 64% **Bedford Hotel,** 1 Plymouth Rd, TAVISTOCK
☎ 01822 613221 – 30 en suite

TEIGNMOUTH

Teignmouth
Haldon Moor TQ14 9NY
☎ 01626 777070 📄 01626 777304
e-mail: tgc@btconnect.com

**This fairly flat heathland course is high up with
fine panoramic views of sea, moors and river
valley. Good springy turf with some heather and
an interesting layout makes for very enjoyable
holiday golf. Designed by Dr Alister MacKenzie,
the world famous architect who also designed
Augusta GC USA.**

18 holes, 6200yds, Par 71, SSS 69, Course record 63.

Club membership: 900. **Visitors:** handicap certificate
required. Phone pro shop to book on 01626 772894.
Societies: Thu only, telephone in advance and confirm

in writing. **Green Fees:** £30 per round (£35 weekends). **Cards:** 💳 💳 💳 **Prof:** Rob Selley **Course Designer:** Dr Alister Mackenzie **Facilities:** 🍴 🏠 ⛳ ☕ 🧺 🏌 **Conf:** Corporate Hospitality Days available **Location:** 2m NW off B3192

Hotel
★★★ 70% **Ness House Hotel,**
Ness Dr, Shaldon, TEIGNMOUTH
☎ 01626 873480 – 7 en suite 5 annexe en suite

THURLESTONE

Thurlestone
TQ7 3NZ
☎ 01548 560405 📠 01548 562149
e-mail: info@thurlestonegc.co.uk
Situated on the edge of the cliffs with typical downland turf and good greens. The course, after an interesting opening hole, rises to higher land with fine sea views, and finishes with an excellent 502-yard downhill hole to the clubhouse.

18 holes, 6340yds, Par 71, SSS 70, Course record 65.

Club membership: 770. **Visitors:** must contact in advance & have handicap certificate from a recognised club. **Green Fees:** £34 per day/round. **Cards:** 💳 💳 💳 💳 **Prof:** Peter Laugher **Course Designer:** Harry S Colt **Facilities:** 🍴 🍽 by prior arrangement 🏠 ⛳ 🧺 ☕ 🏌 🎾 🎱 **Location:** S side of village

Hotel
★★★★ 72% **Thurlestone Hotel,** THURLESTONE
☎ 01548 560382 – 64 en suite

TIVERTON

Tiverton
Post Hill EX16 4NE
☎ 01884 252187 📠 01884 251607
e-mail: tivertongolfclub@lineone.net
A parkland course where the many different species of tree are a feature and where the lush pastures ensure some of the finest fairways in the south-west. The undulating ground provides plenty of variety and there are a number of interesting holes which visitors will find a real challenge.

18 holes, 6236yds, Par 71, SSS 71, Course record 65.

Club membership: 750. **Visitors:** must contact in advance & have a current handicap certificate. **Societies:** apply in writing or telephone. **Green Fees:** £32 per 18 holes. **Prof:** Michael Hawton **Course Designer:** Braid **Facilities:** 🍴 🍽 by prior arrangement 🏠 ⛳ 🧺 ☕ 🏌 **Conf:** Corporate Hospitality Days available **Location:** 3m E of Tiverton, M5 junct 27, proceed through Sampford Peverell and Halberton

Hotel
★★★ 70% **The Tiverton Hotel,**
Blundells Rd, TIVERTON
☎ 01884 256120 – 69 en suite

WESTWARD HO!

Royal North Devon
Golf Links Rd EX39 1HD
☎ 01237 473817 📠 01237 423456
e-mail: info@royalnorthdevongolfclub.co.uk
Oldest links course in England with traditional links features and a museum in the clubhouse.

18 holes, 6716yds, Par 72, SSS 72, Course record 65.

Club membership: 1150. **Visitors:** advisable to telephone and book tee time, handicap certificate preferred or letter of introduction from club. **Societies:** apply in writing or telephone. **Green Fees:** £44 per day; £38 per round (£50/£44 weekends & bank holidays). **Cards:** 💳 💳 💳 **Prof:** Iain Parker **Course Designer:** Old Tom Morris **Facilities:** 🍴 🏠 🍽 🧺 ⛳ ☕ 🏌 🎾 Museum of Golf Memorabilia, snooker. **Location:** N side of village off B3236

Guesthouse
◆◆◆◆ **Culloden House,**
Fosketh Hill, WESTWARD HO!
☎ 01237 479421 – 5 en suite

YELVERTON

Yelverton
Golf Links Rd PL20 6BN
☎ 01822 852824 📠 01822 854869
e-mail: secretary@yelvertongc.co.uk

An excellent course on Dartmoor with plenty of gorse and heather. Tight lies in the fairways, fast greens and challenging hazards. Boasts three of the best holes in Devon (12th, 13th and 16th). Outstanding views.

18 holes, 6353yds, Par 71, SSS 71, Course record 64.

Club membership: 650. **Visitors:** must have handicap certificate and subject to availability, contact in advance. No visitors on Sun. **Societies:** must book in advance, by telephone initially. **Green Fees:** £30 per day. **Cards:** 💳 💳 💳 💳 💳 💳 **Prof:** Tim McSherry **Course Designer:** Herbert Fowler **Facilities:** 🍴 🍽 🏠 🧺 ⛳ ☕ 🏌 🎾 indoor golf academy. **Conf:** facilities available **Corporate:** Hospitality Days available **Location:** 1m S of Yelverton, off A386

Hotel
★★★ 72% **Moorland Links Hotel,** YELVERTON
☎ 01822 852245 – 45 en suite

DORSET

BERE REGIS

Dorset Golf & Country Club

BH20 7NT

☎ 01929 472244 📠 01929 471294

e-mail: admin@dorsetgolfresort.com

Lakeland is the longest course in Dorset. Designed by Martin Hawtree with numerous inter-connected water features, carefully planned bunkers and sculptured greens. A player who completes a round within handicap has every reason to celebrate! The Woodland Course, although shorter, is equally outstanding with rhododendron and tree-lined fairways.

Lakeland Course: 18 holes, 6580yds, Par 72, SSS 73, Course record 69.

Woodland Course: 9 holes, 5032yards, Par 66, SSS 64.

Club membership: 600. Visitors: must book in advance Societies: apply in advance. Green Fees: Lakeland: £36 (£40 weekends). Woodland: £24 (£28 weekends). Cards: 💳 💳 💳 💳 💳 Prof: Scott Porter Course Designer: Martin Hawtree Facilities: 🏌️🅿️🍴🍺💈🏺🎯⛳🎱🏌️🛒 Conf: facilities available Corporate: Hospitality Days available Location: 5m from Bere Regis on Wool Road

Hotel

★★ 69% **Kemps Country House Hotel,**
East Stoke, WAREHAM

☎ 01929 462563

5 rms (4 en suite) 10 annexe en suite

BROADSTONE

Broadstone (Dorset)

Wentworth Dr BH18 8DQ

☎ 01202 692595 📠 01202 642520

e-mail: admin@broadstonegolfclub.com

Undulating and demanding heathland course with the 2nd, 7th, 13th and 16th being particularly challenging holes.

18 holes, 6315yds, Par 70, SSS 70, Course record 65.

Club membership: 620. Visitors: restricted at weekends & bank holidays. Must contact in advance. Handicap certificate required. Societies: contact in

advance. Green Fees: £70 per 27/36 holes, £45 per round (£55 per round weekends & bank holidays). Cards: 💳 💳 💳 💳 💳 Prof: Nigel Tokely Course Designer: Colt/Dunn Facilities: 🏌️🅿️🍴🍺💈🎯🏌️ 🏺🅿️🎱🎯 Conf: Corporate Hospitality Days available Location: N side of village off B3074

Guesthouse

◆◆◆◆ **Ashton Lodge, 10 Oakley Hill, WIMBORNE**

☎ 01202 883423 – 5 rms (2 en suite)

DORCHESTER

Came Down

Came Down DT2 8NR

☎ 01305 813494 (manager) 📠 01305 813494

e-mail: manager@camedowngolfclub.co.uk

Scene of the West of England Championships on several occasions, this fine course lies on a high plateau commanding glorious views over Portland. Three par 5 holes add interest to a round. The turf is of the springy, downland type.

18 holes, 6255yds, Par 70, SSS 70.

Club membership: 750. Visitors: advisable to phone in advance, must have handicap certificate. May play after 9am weekdays and after 11am Sun. Societies: by arrangement Green Fees: £26 per day weekdays (£30 weekends). Cards: 💳 💳 💳 💳 💳 💳 Prof: Nick Rodgers Course Designer: J H Taylor/H S Colt Facilities: 🏌️🅿️🍴🍺🍴🎯🏺🎱 Location: 2m S off A354

Guesthouse

◆◆◆◆◆ **Yalbury Cottage Hotel & Restaurant,**
Lower Bockhampton, DORCHESTER

☎ 01305 262382 – 8 en suite

FERNDOWN

Ferndown

119 Golf Links Rd BH22 8BU

☎ 01202 874602 📠 01202 873926

e-mail: ferndowngc@lineone.net

Fairways are gently undulating amongst heather, gorse and pine trees, giving the course a most attractive appearance. There are a number of dog-leg holes.

Championship Course: 18 holes, 6501yds, Par 71, SSS 71, Course record 65.

Presidents Course: 9 holes, 5604yds, Par 70, SSS 68.

Club membership: 600. Visitors: must contact in advance and have handicap certificate, no visitors on Thu except on Presidents Course, numbers restricted at weekends. Societies: welcome Tue & Fri only, telephone in advance. Green Fees: Championship: £80 per day, £60 per round (£90/£70 weekends). Cards: 💳 💳 💳 💳 💳 Prof: Neil Pike Course Designer: Harold Hilton Facilities: 🏌️🅿️🍴🍺🍴 🎯🏺🏌️🎱 Conf: Corporate Hospitality Days available Location: S side of town centre off A347

Hotel
⚲ Premier Travel Inn Bournemouth/Ferndown,
Ringwood Rd, Tricketts Cross, FERNDOWN
☎ 08701 977102 – 32 en suite

Parkstone
Links Rd, Parkstone BH14 9QS
☎ 01202 707138 📄 01202 706027
e-mail: admin@parkstonegolfclub.co.uk

Very scenic heathland course with views of Poole Bay. Designed in 1909 by Willie Park Jnr and enlarged in 1932 by James Braid. The result of this highly imaginative reconstruction was an intriguing and varied test of golf set among pines and heather fringed fairways where every hole presents a different challenge.

18 holes, 6250yds, Par 72, SSS 70, Course record 63.

Club membership: 700. Visitors: must contact in advance and have handicap certificate. Societies: apply in writing/telephone in advance. Handicap certificates must be provided. Green Fees: £75 per day; £50 per round (£85/£60 weekends & bank holidays). Cards: 💳 🏧 Prof: Martyn Thompson Course Designer: Willie Park Jnr Facilities: 🏨 🍴 🛎 ⛳ Conf: Corporate Hospitality Days available Location: E side of town centre off A35

Hotel
★★★ 64% Salterns Harbourside Hotel,
38 Salterns Way, Lilliput, POOLE
☎ 01202 707321 – 20 en suite

Sherborne
Higher Clatcombe DT9 4RN
☎ 01935 814431 📄 01935 814218
e-mail: sherbornegc@btconnect.com

Beautiful mature parkland course to the north of Sherborne on the Dorset/Somerset border, with extensive views. Recently extended to 6414yds.

18 holes, 6414yds, Par 72, SSS 71, Course record 62.

Club membership: 600. Visitors: must contact in advance & have handicap certificate. Societies: prior booking (Tue & Wed only). Green Fees: £30 per day, £25 per round (£36 per round weekends). Prof: Alistair Tresidder Course Designer: James Braid (part) Facilities: 🏨 🍴 🛎 ⛳ Location: 2m N off B3145

Hotel
★★★ 72% Eastbury Hotel, Long St, SHERBORNE
☎ 01935 813131 – 22 en suite

Isle of Purbeck
BH19 3AB
☎ 01929 450361 & 450354 📄 01929 450501
e-mail: enquiries@purbeckgolf.co.uk

A heathland course sited on the Purbeck Hills with grand views across Swanage, the Channel and Poole Harbour. Holes of note include the 5th, 8th, 14th, 15th, and 16th where trees, gorse and heather assert themselves. The very attractive clubhouse is built of the local stone.

Purbeck Course: 18 holes, 6295yds, Par 70, SSS 70, Course record 66.
Dene Course: 9 holes, 4014yds, Par 60.

Club membership: 500. Visitors: advisable to telephone. Societies: must contact in advance. Green Fees: not confirmed. Cards: 💳 🏧 Prof: Ian Brake Course Designer: H Colt Facilities: 🏨 🍴 by prior arrangement 🛎 ⛳ Location: 2.5m N on B3351

Hotel
★★★ 69% The Pines Hotel,
Burlington Rd, SWANAGE
☎ 01929 425211 – 49 en suite

CO DURHAM

Barnard Castle
Harmire Rd DL12 8QN
☎ 01833 638355 📄 01833 695551
e-mail: sec@barnardcastlegolfclub.org.uk

Perched high on the steep bank of the River Tees, the extensive remains of Barnard Castle, with its splendid round tower, date back to the 12th and 13th centuries. The parkland course is flat and lies in open countryside. Its delightful plantations and natural water features add colour and interest to this classic course.

18 holes, 6406yds, Par 73, SSS 71, Course record 63.

Club membership: 650. **Visitors:** must contact in advance, restricted at weekends. Handicap certificate required. **Societies:** apply in writing. **Green Fees:** £22 per round (£32 weekends and bank holidays). **Prof:** Darren Pearce **Course Designer:** A Watson **Facilities:** ⊕ ⊗ ⊾ ⬛ ⊟ ⚓ ⚑ ⚓ ⚔ **Conf:** Corporate Hospitality Days available **Location:** 1m N of town centre on B6278

Hotel
★★ Rose & Crown Hotel, ROMALDKIRK
☎ 01833 650213 – 7 en suite 5 annexe en suite

BISHOP AUCKLAND
Bishop Auckland
High Plains, Durham Rd DL14 8DL
☎ 01388 661618 ▤ 01388 607005
e-mail: enquiries@bagc.co.uk

A rather hilly parkland course with many well-established trees offering a challenging round. A small ravine adds interest to several holes including the short 7th, from a raised tee to a green surrounded by a stream, gorse and bushes. Pleasant views down the Wear Valley and over the residence of the Bishop of Durham. Has the distinction of having three consecutive par 5 holes and two consecutive par 3s.

18 holes, 6379yds, Par 72, SSS 70, Course record 63.

Club membership: 950. **Visitors:** parties must contact in advance. Handicap certificate advisable. Dress rules apply. **Societies:** weekdays only; must contact in advance. **Green Fees:** £24 per round (£30 per round weekends). **Cards:** ⬛ ⬛ ⬛ ⬛ ⬛ **Prof:** David Skiffington **Course Designer:** James Kay **Facilities:** ⊕ ⊗ ⊾ ⬛ ⊟ ⚓ ⬛ ⚔ snooker. **Location:** 1m NE on A689

Hotel
★★★ 74% Whitworth Hall Country Park Hotel, Stanners Ln, SPENNYMOOR
☎ 01388 811772 – 29 en suite

EAGLESCLIFFE
Eaglescliffe and District
Yarm Rd TS16 0DQ
☎ 01642 780238 (office) ▤ 01642 780238
e-mail: eaglescliffegcsec@tiscali.co.uk

An undulating wooded parkland course with views over the river Tees to the Cleveland Hills. A tee on the riverbank makes for a daunting tee shot at the 14th signature hole.

18 holes, 6275yds, Par 72, SSS 70, Course record 64.

Club membership: 970. **Visitors:** restricted Tue, Thu, Fri & weekends. Contact pro on 01642 790122 **Societies:** must contact in advance, apply to Secretary on 01642 780238 **Green Fees:** £40 per day; £30 per round (£50/£36 weekends). **Prof:** Graeme Bell **Course Designer:** J Braid/H Cotton **Facilities:** ⊕ ⊗ ⊾ ⬛ ⊟ ⚓ ⚑ ⚓ ⚔ **Location:** On eastern side of A135 between Yarm and Stockton-on-Tees

Hotel
★★★ 72% Parkmore Hotel & Leisure Park, 636 Yarm Rd, Eaglescliffe, STOCKTON-ON-TEES
☎ 01642 786815 – 55 en suite

HARTLEPOOL
Hartlepool
Hart Warren TS24 9QF
☎ 01429 274398 ▤ 01429 274129

18 holes, 6200yds, Par 70, SSS 70, Course record 62.

Course Designer: Partly Braid **Location:** N of Hartlepool, off A1086
Telephone for further details

Hotel
⇧ Premier Travel Inn Hartlepool, Maritme Av, Hartlepool Marina, HARTLEPOOL
☎ 08701 977127 – 40 en suite

MIDDLETON ST GEORGE
Dinsdale Spa
Neasham Rd DL2 1DW
☎ 01325 332297 ▤ 01325 332297

A mainly flat, parkland course on high land above the River Tees with views of the Cleveland Hills. Water hazards in front of 10th tee and green; the prevailing west wind affects the later holes. There is a practice area by the clubhouse.

18 holes, 6099yds, Par 71, SSS 69, Course record 65.

Club membership: 870. **Visitors:** welcome Mon & Wed-Fri, contact for further details. **Societies:** bookings through office, no weekends or Tue. Apply in writing or telephone. **Green Fees:** £25 per day. **Prof:** Neil Metcalfe **Facilities:** ⊕ ⊗ ⊾ ⬛ ⊟ ⚓ ⬛ ⚔ **Location:** 1.5m SW

Hotel
★★★ 69% The Croft, Croft-on-Tees, DARLINGTON
☎ 01325 720319 – 20 en suite

SEATON CAREW
Seaton Carew
Tees Rd TS25 1DE
☎ 01429 261040 ▤ 01429 267952

A championship links course taking full advantage of its dunes, bents, whins and gorse. Renowned for its par 4 17th; just enough fairway for an accurate drive followed by another precise shot to a pear-shaped, sloping green that is severely trapped.

The Old Course: 18 holes, 6622yds, Par 72, SSS 72.
Brabazon Course: 18 holes, 6857yds, Par 73, SSS 73.

Club membership: 761. **Visitors:** restricted until after 10am at weekends and bank holidays,and after 9.30am midweek. **Societies:** must apply in writing/elephone in advance. **Green Fees:** terms on application. **Prof:** Mark Rogers **Course Designer:** McKenzie **Facilities:** ⊕ ⍩ ⏛ ⬚ ⬛ ⍩ 𝅘 ⌂ ⛳ ⚑ 𝆕 🏌 ⚐ **Location:** SE side of village off A178

Hotel
⬆ **Premier Travel Inn Hartlepool,**
Maritme Av, Hartlepool Marina, HARTLEPOOL
☎ 08701 977127 – 40 en suite

ESSEX

Abridge Golf and Country Club
Epping Ln, Stapleford Tawney RM4 1ST
☎ 01708 688396 ▤ 01708 688550
e-mail: info@abridgegolf.com

A parkland course with easy walking. The quick drying course is by no means easy to play. This has been the venue of several professional tournaments. Abridge is a Golf and Country Club and has all the attendant facilities.

18 holes, 6704yds, Par 72, SSS 72, Course record 67.

Club membership: 600. **Visitors:** must have current handicap certificate, contact in advance. May not play Tue but may play weekends after 2pm. **Societies:** telephone in advance. May play Mon, Wed and Fri. **Green Fees:** £35 per 18 holes (£45 weekends). **Cards:** 💳 💳 💳 💳 **Prof:** Stuart Layton **Course Designer:** Henry Cotton **Facilities:** ⊕ ⏛ ⬛ ⍩ 𝅘 ⌂ ⚑ 𝆕 🏌 ⚐ ⛳ ⚑ sauna, 5 short practice holes. **Conf:** facilities available **Location:** 1.75m NE

Hotel
⬆ **Premier Travel Inn Romford West,** Whalebone Ln North, Chadwell Heath, ROMFORD
☎ 0870 9906450 – 40 en suite

Chelmsford
Widford Rd CM2 9AP
☎ 01245 256483 ▤ 01245 256483
e-mail: office@chelmsfordgc.co.uk

An undulating parkland course, hilly in parts, with three holes in woods and four difficult par 4s. From the reconstructed clubhouse there are fine views over the course and the wooded hills beyond.

18 holes, 5981yds, Par 68, SSS 69, Course record 63.

Club membership: 650. **Visitors:** must contact in advance. Society days Wed/Thu, Ladies Day Tue. With member only at weekends. **Societies:** must contact in advance. **Green Fees:** not confirmed. **Prof:** Mark Welch **Course Designer:** Tom Dunn **Facilities:** ⊕ ⏛ ⬛ ⍩ 𝅘 ⌂ ⛳ 🏌 𝆕 **Location:** 1.5m S of town centre off A12

Hotel
★★★ 72% **Pontlands Park Country Hotel,**
West Hanningfield Rd, Great Baddow, CHELMSFORD
☎ 01245 476444 – 36 en suite

Chigwell
High Rd IG7 5BH
☎ 020 8500 2059 ▤ 020 8501 3410
e-mail: info@chigwellgolfclub.co.uk

18 holes, 6279yds, Par 71, SSS 70, Course record 66.

Course Designer: Hawtree/Taylor **Location:** 0.5m S on A113
Telephone for further details

Hotel
⬆ **Premier Travel Inn Romford East,**
Mercury Gardens, ROMFORD
☎ 08701 977220 – 40 en suite

Thorndon Park
CM13 3RH
☎ 01277 810345 ▤ 01277 810645
e-mail: tpgc@btclick.com

Course built on clay substructure and playable even at the wettest time of the year. Holes stand on their own surrounded by mature oaks, some of which are more than 700 years old. The lake in the centre of the course provides both a challenge and a sense of peace and tranquillity. The Palladian magnificence of Thorndon Hall, site of the old clubhouse, is the backdrop to the closing hole.

18 holes, 6492yds, Par 71, SSS 71, Course record 68.

Club membership: 600. **Visitors:** must contact in advance, at weekends with member only except after 1pm Sun. **Societies:** welcome Mon, Tue and Fri but must apply in writing. **Green Fees:** terms on application. **Prof:** Brian White **Course Designer:** Colt/Alison **Facilities:** ⊕ ⍩ by prior arrangement ⏛ ⬛ ⍩ 𝅘 ⌂ ⚑ 𝆕 **Conf:** Corporate Hospitality Days available **Location:** W side of village off A128

Hotel
★★★ 70% **Weald Park Hotel, Golf & Country Club,** Coxtie Green Rd, South Weald, BRENTWOOD
☎ 01277 375101 – 32 annexe en suite

ORSETT

Orsett

Brentwood Rd RM16 3DS
☎ 01375 891352 📠 01375 892471
e-mail: enquiries@orsettgolfclub.co.uk

A very good test of golf – this heathland course with its sandy soil is quick drying and provides easy walking. Close to the Thames estuary it is seldom calm and the main hazards are the prevailing wind and thick gorse. Any slight deviation can be exaggerated by the wind and result in a ball lost in the gorse. The clubhouse has been modernised to a very high standard.

18 holes, 6614yds, Par 72, SSS 72, Course record 65.

Club membership: 770. **Visitors:** weekdays only. Must contact in advance and have a handicap certificate. **Societies:** must contact in advance. **Green Fees:** £30 per round. **Prof:** Paul Joiner **Course Designer:** James Braid **Facilities:** ⊕ ⏀ ☕ 🖼 ⚑ 🏌 ⚐ coaching. **Conf:** Corporate Hospitality Days available **Location:** At junct of A13 off A128, towards Chadwell St Mary

Hotel
★★★ 67% **Lakeside Moat House,**
High Rd, North Stifford, GRAYS
☎ 01708 719988 – 97 en suite

THEYDON BOIS

Theydon Bois

Theydon Rd CM16 4EH
☎ 01992 812460 & 813054 📠 01992 813054
e-mail: theydongolf@hotmail.com

The course was originally nine holes built into Epping Forest. It was later extended to 18 holes which were well-planned and well-bunkered but in keeping with the 'Forest' tradition. The old nine in the Forest are short and have two bunkers between them, but even so a wayward shot can be among the trees. The autumn colours here are truly magnificent.

18 holes, 5490yds, Par 68, SSS 67, Course record 64.

Club membership: 600. **Visitors:** may not play Wed, Thu, Sat & Sun mornings, ring 01992 812460 in advance to be sure tee is available. **Societies:** book through the Secretary. **Green Fees:** not confirmed. **Cards:** 💳 💳 💳 💳 💳 **Prof:** R Hall **Course Designer:** James Braid **Facilities:** ⊕ ⏀ 🖼 ⚑ ⚐ 🏌 ☕ **Location:** 2m from junct 26 on M25

Hotel
⌂ **Travelodge Harlow East (Stansted),**
A414 Eastbound, Tylers Green, North Weald, HARLOW
☎ 08700 850 950 – 60 en suite

GLOUCESTERSHIRE

CHIPPING SODBURY

Chipping Sodbury

BS37 6PU
☎ 01454 319042 📠 01454 320052
e-mail: info@chippingsodburygolfclub.co.uk

New Course:
18 holes, 6912yds, Par 73, SSS 73, Course record 65.

Course Designer: Hawtree **Location:** 0.5m N Telephone for further details

Hotel
★★ 71% **Compass Inn,** TORMARTON
☎ 01454 218242 & 218577 📠 01454 218741
26 en suite

COALPIT HEATH

The Kendleshire

Henfield Rd BS36 2UY
☎ 0117 956 7007 📠 0117 957 3433
e-mail: info@kendleshire.co.uk

Opened in 1997, the course boasts 27 holes with water coming into play on 18 holes. Notable holes are the 11th, the 16th and the 27th. The 11th is a short hole with an island green set in a 3-acre lake and the 16th has a second shot played over water. The course is never short of interest and the greens have been built to USGA specification.

18 holes, 6550, Par 71, SSS 71, Course record 63.
18 holes, 6249, Par 71, SSS 70, Course record 68.
18 holes, 6353, Par 70, SSS 70, Course record 68.

Club membership: 900. **Visitors:** must contact in advance and wear soft spikes. **Societies:** telephone in advance **Green Fees:** £32 per round (£38 weekends). **Cards:** 💳 💳 💳 💳 💳 **Prof:** Mike Bessell **Course Designer:** A Stiff/P McEvoy **Facilities:** ⊕ ⏀ 🖼 ⚑ ⚐ 🏌 ☕ **Conf:** facilities available Corporate Hospitality Days available **Location:** off M32 junct 1 on Avon Ring Road.

Hotel
★★★★ 65% **Jurys Bristol Hotel,** Prince St, BRISTOL
☎ 0117 923 0333 – 191 en suite

DURSLEY

Stinchcombe Hill

Stinchcombe Hill GL11 6AQ
☎ 01453 542015 📠 01453 549545
e-mail: stinchcombehill@golfers.net

High on the hill with splendid views of the Cotswolds, the River Severn and the Welsh hills. A downland course with good turf, some trees and an interesting variety of greens. Protected greens make this a challenging course in windy conditions.

18 holes, 5734yds, Par 68, SSS 68, Course record 63.

Club membership: 550. **Visitors:** restricted at weekends. Must contact professional in advance 01453 543878. **Societies:** must apply in advance. **Green Fees:** not confirmed. **Prof:** Paul Bushell **Course Designer:** Arthur Hoare **Facilities:** ⒯ �𝄞 ⌂ ☕ ⑨ ⋔ ⚑ ✎ **Conf:** Corporate Hospitality Days available **Location:** 1m W off A4135

Hotel
★★★ 65% **Prince of Wales Hotel,**
Berkeley Rd, BERKELEY
☎ 01453 810474 – 43 en suite

GLOUCESTER

Ramada Hotel & Resort Gloucester
Matson Ln, Robinswood Hill GL4 6EA
☎ 01452 525653 📠 01452 307212

Undulating, wooded course, built around a hill with superb views over Gloucester and the Cotswolds. The 12th is a drive straight up a hill, nicknamed 'Coronary Hill'.

18 holes, 6170yds, Par 70, SSS 69, Course record 65.

Club membership: 600. **Visitors:** can book up to 7 days in advance. **Societies:** telephone in advance. **Green Fees:** not confirmed. **Cards:** 💳 VISA 📇 💲 **Prof:** John Whiddon **Facilities:** ⒯ ⌂ ☕ ⑨ ⋔ ◇ ✎ ⚑ squash, sauna, solarium, gymnasium. **Location:** 2.5m SE of Gloucester, off B4073

Hotel
Ⓤ **Ramada Hotel & Resort Gloucester,**
Matson Ln, Robinswood Hill, GLOUCESTER
☎ 01452 525653 – 107 en suite

TEWKESBURY

Tewkesbury Park Hotel Golf & Country Club
Lincoln Green Ln GL20 7DN
☎ 01684 295405 📠 01684 292386
e-mail: tewkesburypark@corushotels.com

The course offers many interesting and testing holes, with wooded areas and water hazards early in the round, opening up onto spacious fairways on the back nine holes of the undulating course.

18 holes, 6533yds, Par 73, SSS 72, Course record 66.

Club membership: 550. **Visitors:** must book in advance via pro shop/hotel reservations. **Societies:** telephone initially. **Green Fees:** terms on application. **Cards:** 💳 VISA 💳 📇 💲 **Prof:** Charlie Boast **Course Designer:** Frank Pennick **Facilities:** ⒯ ⌂ ⑨ ☕ ⋔ ◇ ✎ 🏇 ♨ ≋ squash, sauna, solarium, gymnasium. **Conf:** facilities available Corporate Hospitality Days available **Location:** 1m SW off A38

Hotel
★★★ 67% **The Tewkesbury Park Hotel Golf & Country Club,** Lincoln Green Ln, TEWKESBURY
☎ 0870 609 6101 – 80 en suite

WICK

The Gloucestershire
Tracy Park Estate, Bath Rd BS30 5RN
☎ 0117 937 2251 📠 0117 937 4288
e-mail: golf@thegloucestershire.com

Two 18-hole championship courses on the south-western escarpment of the Cotswolds, affording fine views. Both courses present a challenge to all levels of player, with water playing a part on a number of occasions. The clubhouse dates back to 1600 and is a building of great beauty and elegance, set in the 221-acre estate of this golf and country club.

Crown Course: 18 holes, 6252yds, Par 69, SSS 70.
Cromwell Course: 18 holes, 6246yds, Par 71, SSS 70.

Club membership: 600. **Visitors:** no restrictions, must book tee time (0117 937 2251) **Societies:** must telephone/write to Robert Ford **Green Fees:** terms on application. **Cards:** 💳 VISA 💳 📇 💲 **Prof:** David Morgan **Facilities:** ⒯ ⌂ ⑨ ☕ ⋔ ⚑ ◇ ✎ 🏇 ◇ ✎ **Conf:** facilities available Corporate Hospitality Days available **Location:** S side of village off A420

Hotel
★★★ **The Queensberry Hotel,** Russel St, BATH
☎ 01225 447928 – 29 en suite

GREATER LONDON

ADDINGTON

The Addington
205 Shirley Church Rd CR0 5AB
☎ 020 8777 1055 📠 020 8777 6661
e-mail: addingtogolf@btconnect.com

This heather and woodland course is possibly one of the best laid out courses in Southern England with the world famous 13th, par 3 at 230 yards. A good test of golfing ability with no two holes the same.

Continued

18 holes, 6338yds, Par 68, SSS 71, Course record 66.

Visitors: handicap certificate required. **Societies:** weekdays only, telephone for prior arrangement. **Green Fees:** £75 (£95 weekends after 10.30am). **Cards:** 💳 💳 💳 🉐 **Course Designer:** J F Abercromby **Facilities:** 🛈 🍴 🛒 🏌 🎽 ⚒ Conf: Corporate Hospitality Days available **Location:** 3m from Centre of Croydon off M25 junct 4/7

Hotel
★★★★ 67% **Selsdon Park Hotel & Golf Course,** Addington Rd, Sanderstead, CROYDON
☎ 020 8657 8811 – 204 en suite

BECKENHAM

Langley Park
Barnfield Wood Rd BR3 6SZ
☎ 020 8658 6849 📠 020 8658 6310
e-mail: manager@langleyparkgolf.co.uk

This is a pleasant, but difficult, well-wooded, parkland course with natural hazards including a lake at the par 3 18th hole. Although most fairways are bordered by woodland, they are wide with forgiving rough and friendly bunkers.

18 holes, 6488yds, Par 69, SSS 71, Course record 65.

Club membership: 700. **Visitors:** must contact in advance and may not play weekends. **Societies:** Wed & Thu only or by special arrangement, telephone to book. **Green Fees:** £45 per day, £35 per round. **Cards:** 💳 💳 💳 💳 💳 🉐 **Prof:** Colin Staff **Course Designer:** J H Taylor **Facilities:** 🛈 🍴 🛒 🏌 🎽 🛒 📷 ⚒ Conf: Corporate Hospitality Days available **Location:** 0.5m N of Beckenham on B2015

Hotel
★★★ 71% **Bromley Court Hotel,** Bromley Hill, BROMLEY
☎ 020 8461 8600 – 114 en suite

BROMLEY

Sundridge Park
Garden Rd BR1 3NE
☎ 020 8460 0278 📠 020 8289 3050
e-mail: gm@spgc.co.uk

The East Course is longer than the West but many think the shorter of the two courses is the more difficult. The East is surrounded by trees while the West is more hilly, with good views. Both are certainly a good test of golf. An Open qualifying course with year round irrigation of fairways.

East Course:
18 holes, 6516yds, Par 71, SSS 71, Course record 63.
West Course:
18 holes, 6019yds, Par 69, SSS 69, Course record 65.

Club membership: 1200. **Visitors:** may only play on weekdays. Must contact in advance and must have a handicap certificate. No advance booking necessary.

Societies: must contact well in advance. **Green Fees:** £85 per day, £65 per round - weekdays only. **Cards:** 💳 💳 🉐 **Prof:** Stuart Dowsett **Course Designer:** Willie Park **Facilities:** 🛈 🍴 🛒 🏌 🎽 🛒 📷 ⚒ 🐾 🛒 ⚒ **Conf:** facilities available Corporate Hospitality Days available **Location:** N side of town centre off A2212

Hotel
★★★ 71% **Bromley Court Hotel,** Bromley Hill, BROMLEY
☎ 020 8461 8600 – 114 en suite

CROYDON

Shirley Park
194 Addiscombe Rd CR0 7LB
☎ 020 8654 1143 📠 020 8654 6733
e-mail: secretary@shirleyparkgolfclub.co.uk

This parkland course lies amid fine woodland with good views of Shirley Hills. The more testing holes come in the middle section of the course. The remarkable 7th hole calls for a 187-yard iron or wood shot diagonally across a narrow valley to a shelved green set right-handed into a ridge. The 13th hole, 160 yards, is considered to be one of the finest short holes in the county.

18 holes, 6210yds, Par 71, SSS 70, Course record 64.

Club membership: 600. **Visitors:** should contact in advance. With member only on Saturdays. **Societies:** by arrangement. **Green Fees:** £40 weekday (£48 Sun). **Cards:** 💳 💳 🉐 **Prof:** Michael Taylor **Course Designer:** Tom Simpson/Herbert Fowler **Facilities:** 🛈 🍴 🛒 🏌 🎽 🛒 📷 ⚒ ⚒ **Location:** E side of town centre on A232

Hotel
★★★★ 67% **Selsdon Park Hotel & Golf Course,** Addington Rd, Sanderstead, CROYDON
☎ 020 8657 8811 – 204 en suite

HADLEY WOOD

Hadley Wood
Beech Hill EN4 0JJ
☎ 020 8449 4328 & 4486 📠 020 8364 8633
e-mail: gen.mgr@hadleywoodgc.com

A parkland course on the northwest edge of London. The gently undulating fairways have a friendly width inviting the player to open his

shoulders, though the thick rough can be very punishing to the unwary. The course is pleasantly wooded and there are some admirable views.

18 holes, 6514yds, Par 72, SSS 71, Course record 67.

Club membership: 600. Visitors: handicap certificate required, may not play Tue mornings & weekends. Must contact in advance. Societies: must contact in advance. Green Fees: terms on application. Prof: Peter Jones Course Designer: Alistair Mackenzie Facilities: ⑪ ⍾ ⓘ ⓘ 里 里 ⓘ 公 🏠 ⓘ 𝆑 ☟ Conf: Corporate Hospitality Days available Location: E side of village

Hotel
★★★★★🏡 73% **West Lodge Park Hotel,**
Cockfosters Rd, HADLEY WOOD
☎ 020 8216 3900 – 46 en suite 13 annexe en suite

KINGSTON UPON THAMES
Coombe Hill
Golf Club Dr, Coombe Ln West KT2 7DF
☎ 020 8336 7600 🖨 020 8336 7601
e-mail: thesecretary@coombehillgolf.demon.co.uk

A splendid course in wooded terrain. The undulations and trees make it an especially interesting course of great charm. And there is a lovely display of rhododendrons in May and June.

18 holes, 6293yds, Par 71, SSS 71, Course record 67.

Club membership: 550. Visitors: must contact in advance. With member only at weekends. Societies: must book in advance. Green Fees: Weekdays only: £100 per 36 holes, £80 per 18 holes. Cards: 💳 💳 Prof: Craig Defoy Course Designer: J F Abercromby Facilities: ⑪ ⍾ ⓘ 里 里 ⓘ 公 🏠 ⓘ 🛒 𝆑 sauna. Conf: Corporate: Hospitality Days available Location: 1.75m E on A238

Hotel
⌂ **Travelodge London Kingston,**
21-23 London Rd, KINGSTON UPON THAMES
☎ 08700 850 950 – 72 en suite

NORTHWOOD
Northwood
Rickmansworth Rd HA6 2QW
☎ 01923 821384 🖨 01923 840150
e-mail: secretary@northwoodgolf.co.uk

A high quality parkland course in the heart of Middlesex. The course provides a good test of golf to the experienced golfer and can hold many surprises for the unsuspecting. The par 4 10th hole, 'Death or Glory', has wrecked many good cards in the past, while the long par 4 5th hole requires two very good shots to make par.

18 holes, 6535yds, Par 71, SSS 71, Course record 67.

Club membership: 650. Visitors: must contact in advance. May not play weekends. Societies: must

apply in writing or by phone. Green Fees: £50 per day, £36 per round. Cards: 💳 💳 💳 💳 𝆑 Prof: C J Holdsworth Course Designer: James Braid Facilities: ⑪ ⍾ ⓘ 里 里 ⓘ 公 🏠 𝆑 Conf: Corporate Hospitality Days available Location: On main A404

Hotel
★★★ 68% **Quality Harrow Hotel,**
12-22 Pinner Rd, HARROW
☎ 020 8427 3435 – 79 en suite 23 annexe en suite

Sandy Lodge
Sandy Lodge Ln HA6 2JD
☎ 01923 825429 🖨 01923 824319
e-mail: info@sandylodge.co.uk

A links-type, very sandy, heathland course.

18 holes, 6347yds, Par 71, SSS 71, Course record 64.

Club membership: 780. Visitors: must contact in advance, may not play at weekends. Handicap certificate required. Societies: must telephone in advance. Green Fees: £40 per round. Cards: 💳 💳 𝆑 Prof: Jeff Pinsent Course Designer: H Vardon Facilities: ⑪ ⍾ ⓘ 里 里 ⓘ 公 🏠 𝆑 🛒 𝆑 ☟ Conf: Corporate Hospitality Days available Location: N side of town centre off A4125 close to M1 & M25

Hotel
★★★ 67% **The White House,**
Upton Rd, WATFORD
☎ 01923 237316 – 57 en suite

RICHMOND (UPON THAMES)
Richmond
Sudbrook Park, Petersham TW10 7AS
☎ 020 8940 4351 (office) & 8940 7792 (shop)
🖨 8940 8332/7914
e-mail: admin@richmondgolfclub.co.uk

A beautiful and historic wooded, parkland course on the edge of Richmond Park, with six par 3 holes. The 4th is often described as the best short hole in the south. Low scores are uncommon because cunningly sited trees call for great accuracy. The clubhouse is one of the most distinguished small Georgian mansions in England.

18 holes, 6100yds, Par 70, SSS 70, Course record 65.

Club membership: 650. Visitors: may not play weekends before 3.30pm. Societies: must apply in writing. Green Fees: £40/£45 per 18 holes weekday. Cards: 💳 💳 💳 💳 💳 𝆑 Prof: Steve Burridge Course Designer: Tom Down Facilities: ⑪ ⍾ by prior arrangement ⓘ 里 里 ⓘ 公 🏠 ⓘ 🛒 𝆑 ☟ Conf: facilities available Corporate: Hospitality Days available Location: 1.5m S off A307

Hotel
★★★ 69% **The Richmond Hill Hotel,**
Richmond Hill, RICHMOND UPON THAMES
☎ 020 8940 2247 – 138 en suite

Royal Mid-Surrey
Old Deer Park TW9 2SB
☎ 020 8940 1894 📠 020 8939 0150
e-mail: secretary@rmsgc.co.uk

A long playing parkland course. The flat fairways are cleverly bunkered. The 1st hole at 245 yards from the medal tees is a tough par 3 opening hole. The 18th provides an exceptionally good par 4 finish with a huge bunker before the green to catch the not quite perfect long second. The Inner Course, while shorter than the Outer, offers a fair challenge to all golfers. Again the 18th offers a strong par 4 finish with bunkers threatening from the tee. A long second to a sloping, well bunkered green will reward the accurate player.

Outer Course: 18 holes, 6343yds, Par 69, SSS 70, Course record 63.
Inner Course: 18 holes, 5544yds, Par 68, SSS 67.

Club membership: 1400. Visitors: may not play at weekends. Must contact in advance and bring a handicap certificate. Societies: must apply in writing. Green Fees: terms on application. Cards: 💳 💳 💳 💳 Prof: Philip Talbot Course Designer: J H Taylor Facilities: ⊕ 🏐 🍴 ➕ 🏊 📷 🅿️ ⚷ 🛒 ⛳ Conf: facilities available Corporate: Hospitality Days available Location: 0.5m N of Richmond upon Thames off A316

Hotel
★★★ 69% The Richmond Hill Hotel,
Richmond Hill, RICHMOND UPON THAMES
☎ 020 8940 2247 – 138 en suite

Romford
Heath Dr, Gidea Park RM2 5QB
☎ 01708 740986 📠 01708 752157

A many-bunkered parkland course with easy walking. It is said there are as many bunkers as there are days in the year. The ground is quick drying making a good course for winter play when other courses might be too wet.

18 holes, 6410yds, Par 72, SSS 70, Course record 64.

Club membership: 693. Visitors: with member only weekends & bank holidays. Must contact professional in advance & have handicap certificate. Societies: must telephone in advance. Green Fees: not confirmed. Prof: Chris Goddard Course Designer: H Colt Facilities: ⊕ 🍴 🏐 ➕ 🍴 🏊 📷 ⚷ Location: 1m NE on A118

Hotel
⌂ Premier Travel Inn Romford East,
Mercury Gardens, ROMFORD
☎ 08701 977220 – 40 en suite

GREATER MANCHESTER

Bolton
Lostock Park, Chorley New Rd BL6 4AJ
☎ 01204 843067 & 843278 📠 01204 843067
e-mail: boltongolf@lostockpark.fsbusiness.co.uk

This well-maintained heathland course is always a pleasure to visit. The 12th hole should be treated with respect and so too should the final four holes which have ruined many a card.

18 holes, 6237yds, Par 70, SSS 70, Course record 64.

Club membership: 612. Visitors: not able to play Tue before 4pm or on competition days or before 10am and between 12-2pm. Societies: write or telephone in advance, not accepted Tue, Sat or Sun. Green Fees: £25 (winter £20). Prof: R Longworth Facilities: ⊕ 🍴 🏐 ➕ 🍴 🏊 📷 ⚷ Conf: facilities available Corporate: Hospitality Days available Location: 3m W of Bolton, on A673

Hotel
⌂ Premier Travel Inn Bolton,
991 Chorley New Rd, Horwich, BOLTON
☎ 08701 977282 – 40 en suite

Manchester
Hopwood Cottage, Rochdale Rd M24 6QP
☎ 0161 643 3202 📠 0161 643 9174
e-mail: mgc@zen.co.uk

Moorland golf of unique character over a spaciously laid out course with generous fairways sweeping along to large greens. A wide variety of holes will challenge the golfer's technique, particularly the testing last three holes.

18 holes, 6519yds, Par 72, SSS 72, Course record 63.

Club membership: 650. Visitors: must contact in advance, limited play weekends and Wed. Societies: telephone in advance. Green Fees: not confirmed. Cards: 💳 💳 💳 Prof: Brian Connor Course Designer: Shapland Colt Facilities: ⊕ 🍴 🏐 ➕ 🍴 🏊 📷 ⚷ 🛒 ⚷ 🎱 snooker. Conf: facilities available Corporate: Hospitality Days available Location: 2.5m N off A664. M62 junct 20

Hotel
★★★★ 62% Norton Grange Hotel,
Manchester Rd, Castleton, ROCHDALE
☎ 01706 630788 – 51 en suite

Swinton Park
East Lancashire Rd M27 5LX
☎ 0161 794 0861 📠 0161 281 0698
e-mail: info@spgolf.com

One of Lancashire's longest inland courses. Designed and laid out in 1926 by James Braid.

18 holes, 6472yds, Par 73, SSS 71.

Club membership: 600. **Visitors:** may not play weekends or Thu. Must contact in advance and have handicap certificate. **Societies:** apply by letter. **Green Fees:** £30 per day/round. **Prof:** James Wilson **Course Designer:** James Braid **Facilities:** ⓣ ⓞ ⓛ ⓑ ⓦ ⓣ ⓛ ⓔ ⓕ **Conf:** facilities available **Location:** 1m W off A580

Hotel
★★★ 63% **Novotel Manchester West,**
Worsley Brow, WORSLEY
☎ 0161 799 3535 – 119 en suite

HAMPSHIRE

Barton-on-Sea
Milford Rd BH25 5PP
☎ 01425 615308 📄 01425 621457

Though not strictly a links course, it is situated on a coastal cliff with views over the Solent to the Isle of Wight. With 27 holes (three loops of nine), sea breezes often add to the test.

9 holes, 3012yds, Par 36.
Needles: 9 holes, 3078yds, Par 35.
Stroller: 9 holes, 2989yds, Par 36.

Club membership: 940. **Visitors:** must contact in advance. Must contact in advance. **Societies:** must telephone in advance. **Green Fees:** not confirmed. **Cards:** 💳 💳 💳 💳 💳 **Prof:** Peter Rodgers **Course Designer:** Hamilton Stutt **Facilities:** ⓣ ⓞ by prior arrangement ⓑ ⓦ ⓣ ⓛ ⓔ ⓕ ⓔ ⓕ snooker tables. **Conf:** Corporate Hospitality Days available **Location:** B3058 SE side of town

Hotel
★★★★★★📄🏰 **Chewton Glen Hotel,**
Christchurch Rd, NEW MILTON
☎ 01425 275341 – 58 en suite

Basingstoke
Kempshott Park RG23 7LL
☎ 01256 465990 📄 01256 331793
e-mail: enquiries@basingstokegolfclub.co.uk

A well-maintained parkland course with wide and inviting fairways. You are inclined to expect longer drives than are actually achieved – partly on account of the trees. There are many 200-year-old beech trees, since the course was built on an old deer park.

18 holes, 6350yds, Par 70, SSS 70, Course record 66.

Club membership: 700. **Visitors:** must contact in advance and play Mon-Fri only (ex bank holidays). **Societies:** must contact in advance. **Green Fees:** £40 per day. **Cards:** 💳 💳 💳 **Prof:** Guy Shoesmith **Course Designer:** James Braid **Facilities:** ⓣ ⓞ ⓛ ⓑ ⓦ ⓣ ⓛ ⓔ ⓕ ⓕ **Conf:** facilities available Corporate Hospitality Days available **Location:** 3.5m SW on A30 M3 exit 7

Hotel
★★★★ 70% **Apollo Hotel,**
Aldermaston Roundabout, BASINGSTOKE
☎ 01256 796700 – 125 en suite

Blackmoor
Firgrove Rd, Whitehill GU35 9EH
☎ 01420 472775 📄 01420 487666
e-mail: admin@blackmoorgolf.co.uk

A first-class moorland course with a great variety of holes. Fine greens and wide pine tree-lined fairways are a distinguishing feature. The ground is mainly flat and walking easy.

18 holes, 6164yds, Par 69, SSS 69, Course record 63.

Club membership: 750. **Visitors:** must contact in advance, must have handicap certificate and may not play at weekends. **Societies:** must telephone in advance. **Green Fees:** £49 per 36 holes; £37 per 18 holes (weekdays only). **Cards:** 💳 💳 💳 💳 💳 **Prof:** Stephen Clay **Course Designer:** H S Colt **Facilities:** ⓣ by prior arrangement ⓞ by prior arrangement ⓑ ⓦ ⓣ ⓛ ⓔ ⓕ **Conf:** Corporate Hospitality Days available **Location:** Travelling S on A325, 6m beyond Farnham, pass through Whitehill and turn right at roundabout

Hotel
★★★ 66% **Alton House Hotel,**
Normandy St, ALTON
☎ 01420 80033 – 39 en suite

Brokenhurst Manor
Sway Rd SO42 7SG
☎ 01590 623332 (Secretary) 📄 01590 624140
e-mail: secretary@brokenhurst-manor.org.uk

An attractive forest course set in the New Forest, with the unusual feature of three loops of six holes each to complete the round. Fascinating holes include the short 5th and 12th, and the 4th and 17th, both dog-legged. A stream also features on seven of the holes.

18 holes, 6222yds, Par 70, SSS 70, Course record 63.

Club membership: 700. Visitors: must contact in advance, numbers limited. Must have a handicap certificate & be a current member of recognised club, max handicap 24 men 36 ladies. Societies: Thu only, apply in writing. Green Fees: not confirmed. Cards: 💳 💳 💳 💳 💳 Prof: Bruce Parker Course Designer: H S Colt Facilities: ⑪ ℹ️ 🍴 🍺 🏌️ 🎯 🏡 ⚐ Location: 1m S on B3055

Hotel
★★ 66% **Watersplash Hotel,**
The Rise, BROCKENHURST
☎ 01590 622344 – 23 en suite

North Hants
Minley Rd GU51 1RF
☎ 01252 616443 📄 01252 811627
e-mail: secretary@north-hants-fleetgc.co.uk

Picturesque tree-lined course with much heather and gorse close to the fairways. A comparatively easy par 4 first hole may lull the golfer into a false sense of security, only to be rudely awakened at the testing holes which follow. The ground is rather undulating and, though not tiring, does offer some excellent 'blind' shots, and more than a few surprises in judging distance.

18 holes, 6519yds, Par 70, SSS 72, Course record 66.

Club membership: 600. Visitors: must contact at least 48 hours in advance. Must play with member at weekends. Societies: Tue & Wed only. Subject to pre-booking. Green Fees: terms on application. Prof: Steve Porter Course Designer: James Braid Facilities: ⑪ ℹ️ 🍴 🍺 🏌️ 🎯 🏡 ⚐ Conf: Corporate Hospitality Days available Location: 0.25m N of Fleet station on B3013

Hotel
★★★ 65% **Falcon Hotel,**
68 Farnborough Rd, FARNBOROUGH
☎ 01252 545378 – 30 en suite

Hayling
Links Ln PO11 0BX
☎ 023 92464446 📄 023 92461119
e-mail: hgcltd@aol.com

A delightful links course among the dunes offering fine seascapes and views across to the Isle of Wight. Varying sea breezes and sometimes strong winds ensure that the course seldom plays the same two days running. Testing holes at the 12th and 13th, both par 4. Club selection is important.

18 holes, 6531yds, Par 71, SSS 71, Course record 65.

Club membership: 1000. Visitors: must contact in advance by telephone or in writing and have a handicap certificate, no jeans, denims or collarless shirts allowed. Societies: welcome Tue & Wed, or half days Mon & Thu, apply in writing or telephone. Green Fees: £60 per day; £45 per round (£60 per round weekends). Cards: 💳 💳 💳 💳 💳 Prof: Raymond Gadd Course Designer: Taylor 1905, Simpson 1933 Facilities: ⑪ ℹ️ 🍴 🍺 🏌️ 🎯 🏡 ⛳ ⚐ Conf: facilities available Corporate: Hospitality Days available Location: SW side of island at West Town

Hotel
★★★ 69% **Brookfield Hotel,**
Havant Rd, EMSWORTH
☎ 01243 373363 – 40 en suite

Sandford Springs
Wolverton RG26 5RT
☎ 01635 296800 & 296808 (Pro Shop)
📄 01635 296801
e-mail: garye@sandfordspringsgolf.co.uk

The course has unique variety in beautiful surroundings and offers three distinctive loops of 9 holes. There are water hazards, woodlands and gradients to negotiate, providing a challenge for all playing categories.

The Park: 9 holes, 2963yds, Par 34.
The Lakes: 9 holes, 3042yds, Par 35.
The Wood: 9 holes, 3180yds, Par 36.

Club membership: 700. Visitors: must contact in

advance. Restricted at weekends. **Societies:** must contact in advance. **Green Fees:** £45 per day, £35 per 18 holes (£40 per 18 holes weekends). **Cards:** 🔲🔲 🔲🔲 **Prof:** Rhys ap Iolo **Course Designer:** Hawtree & Son **Facilities:** 🏌️🍴🛒🍺🍽️🎯🏠🟎 🚗🏌️🏳️ **Conf:** facilities available **Location:** On A339 between Basingstoke and Newbury

Hotel
★★★ 63% **The Chequers Hotel,**
6-8 Oxford St, NEWBURY
☎ 01635 38000 – 46 en suite 11 annexe en suite

LIPHOOK

Liphook
Wheatsheaf Enclosure GU30 7EH
☎ 01428 723271 & 723785 📠 01428 724853
e-mail: liphookgolfclub@btconnect.com

Heathland course with easy walking and fine views.

18 holes, 6167yds, Par 70, SSS 69, Course record 67.

Club membership: 800. **Visitors:** must contact in advance; may not play Tue, competition days etc. Handicap certificate required. **Societies:** Wed-Fri only. Must contact in advance. **Green Fees:** £49 per day, £41 per round (£51/£61 Sat, £59 Sun & bank holidays pm only). **Prof:** Ian Mowbray **Course Designer:** A C Croome **Facilities:** 🏌️🛒🍺🍽️🎯🏠🟎 **Location:** 1m S on B2070 (old A3)

Hotel
★★★★ 71% **Lythe Hill Hotel & Spa,**
Petworth Rd, HASLEMERE
☎ 01428 651251 – 41 en suite

Old Thorns Hotel, Golf & Country Club
Griggs Green GU30 7PE
☎ 01428 724555 📠 01428 725036
e-mail: info@oldthorns.com

A challenging 18-hole championship course with rolling hills, undulating greens, demanding water features and magnificent views. A challenge to any level of golfer.

18 holes, 6581yds, Par 72, SSS 71, Course record 66.

Club membership: 250. **Visitors:** subject to availability. **Societies:** must telephone in advance.

Green Fees: not confirmed. **Cards:** 🔲🔲 🔲🔲 🔲🔲 **Prof:** Roger Hyder **Course Designer:** Peter Alliss/Dave Thomas **Facilities:** 🏌️🍴🛒🍺🍽️🎯🏠🟎 🏌️🔷🍽️🏌️ 🍴 🏠 sauna, solarium, gymnasium. **Location:** Leave A3 at Griggs Green, S of Liphook, signposted 'Old Thorns'

Hotel
★★★ 75% **Old Thorns Hotel Golf & Country Club,**
Griggs Green, LIPHOOK
☎ 01428 724555
29 en suite 4 annexe rms (3 en suite)

LYNDHURST

Bramshaw
Brook SO43 7HE
☎ 023 8081 3433 📠 023 8081 3460
e-mail: golf@bramshaw.co.uk

Two 18-hole courses. The Manor Course is landscaped parkland with excellent greens, and features mature trees and streams. The Forest Course is set amid beautiful open forest. Easy walking.

Manor Course:
18 holes, 6517yds, Par 71, SSS 71, Course record 65.
Forest Course:
18 holes, 5774yds, Par 69, SSS 68, Course record 65.

Club membership: 950. **Visitors:** limited availability weekends and bank holidays unless accompanied by member or resident of Bell Inn. Phone in advance. **Societies:** apply in writing or telephone in advance. **Green Fees:** not confirmed. **Prof:** Clive Bonner **Facilities:** 🏌️🍴🛒🍺🍽️🎯🏠🟎🔷🏌️🚗🏌️ **Conf:** Corporate Hospitality Days available **Location:** On B3079 1m W of M27 junct 1

Hotel
★★★ 67% **Bell Inn,** BROOK
☎ 023 8081 2214 – 25 en suite

New Forest
Southampton Rd SO43 7BU
☎ 023 8028 2752 📠 023 8028 4030
e-mail: barbara@nfgc.sagehost.co.uk

This picturesque heathland course is laid out in a typical stretch of the New Forest on high ground a little above the village of Lyndhurst. Natural hazards include the inevitable forest ponies. The first two holes are somewhat teasing, as is the 485-yard (par 5) 9th. Walking is easy.

Continued

18 holes, 5742yds, Par 69, SSS 67.

Club membership: 500. Visitors: must contact in advance, dress code applies. Societies: must contact in advance. Green Fees: £13 per 18 holes (£17 weekends). Cards: 💳 💳 💳 💳 Prof: Colin Murray Facilities: 🏨 🛅 🍴 ⛹ 🏡 🚩 ⛳ Conf: Corporate Hospitality Days available Location: 0.5m NE off A35)

Hotel
★★★ 70% **Crown Hotel**, High St, LYNDHURST
☎ 023 8028 2922 – 39 en suite

ROWLAND'S CASTLE

Rowlands Castle
31 Links Ln PO9 6AE
☎ 023 92412784 📠 023 92413649
e-mail: manager@rowlandscastlegolfclub.co.uk

Reasonably dry in winter, the flat parkland course is a testing one with a number of tricky dog-legs and bunkers much in evidence. The par 4 13th is a signature hole necessitating a drive to a narrow fairway and a second shot to a two-tiered green. The 7th, at 522 yards, is the longest hole on the course and leads to a well-guarded armchair green.

18 holes, 6612yds, Par 72, SSS 72, Course record 68.

Club membership: 800. Visitors: may not play Sat; must contact in advance and hold a handicap certificate. Societies: Tue & Thu only; must contact in writing. Green Fees: terms on application. Cards: 💳 Prof: Peter Klepacz Course Designer: Colt Facilities: 🏨 🍴 🛅 ⛹ 🏡 ⛳ Conf: Corporate Hospitality Days available Location: W side of village off B2149

Hotel
★★★ 69% **Brookfield Hotel**,
Havant Rd, EMSWORTH
☎ 01243 373363 – 40 en suite

SHEDFIELD

Marriott Meon Valley Hotel & Country Club
Sandy Ln SO32 2HQ
☎ 01329 833455 📠 01329 834411

It has been said that a golf course architect is as good as the ground on which he has to work. Here Hamilton Stutt had magnificent terrain at his disposal and a very good and lovely parkland course is the result. There are three holes over water. The hotel provides many sports facilities.

Meon Course: 18 holes, 6520yds, Par 71, SSS 71, Course record 66.
Valley Course: 9 holes, 2721yds, Par 35, SSS 33.

Club membership: 700. Visitors: may book up to seven days in advance. Societies: telephone in advance, written confirmation. Green Fees: not confirmed. Cards: 💳 💳 💳 💳 💳 Prof: Rod

Cameron Course Designer: Hamilton Stutt Facilities: 🏨 🍴 🛅 ⛹ 🍴 ⛹ 🏡 🚩 ◇ ⛳ 🛅 ⛳ 🏌 sauna, solarium, gymnasium. Location: Off A334 between Botley and Wickham. Access via junct 7 M27

Hotel
★★★★ 66% **Marriott Meon Valley Hotel & Country Club**, Sandy Ln, SHEDFIELD
☎ 01329 833455 – 113 en suite

SOUTHAMPTON

Stoneham
Monks Wood Close, Bassett SO16 3TT
☎ 023 8076 9272 📠 023 8076 6320
e-mail: richard.penley-martin@stonehamgolfclub.org.uk

A hilly, heather course with sand or peat sub-soil; the fairways are separated by belts of woodland and heather to present a varied terrain. The interesting 4th is a difficult par 4 and the fine 11th has cross-bunkers about 150 yards from the tee.

18 holes, 6392yds, Par 72, SSS 70, Course record 63.

Club membership: 800. Visitors: advisable to contact in advance, handicap certificate required. Societies: Mon, Thu & Fri only. Must telephone in advance or apply in writing. Green Fees: £45 per day; £40 per round (£60/£50 weekends & bank holidays). Cards: 💳 💳 💳 💳 💳 Prof: Ian Young Course Designer: Willie Park Jnr Facilities: 🏨 🍴 🛅 ⛹ 🍴 ⛹ 🏡 🚩 ⛳ Conf: Corporate Hospitality Days available Location: 4m N of city centre off A27

Hotel
★★★ 70% **Chilworth Manor**, CHILWORTH
☎ 023 8076 7333 – 95 en suite

WINCHESTER

Royal Winchester
Sarum Rd SO22 5QE
☎ 01962 852462 📠 01962 865048
e-mail: manager@royalwinchestergolfclub.com

The Royal Winchester course is a sporting downland course centred on a rolling valley, so the course is hilly in places with fine views over the surrounding countryside. Built on chalk downs, the course drains extremely well and offers an excellent playing surface.

18 holes, 6216yds, Par 71, SSS 70, Course record 65.

Club membership: 800. Visitors: must play with member at weekends. Must contact in advance and have a handicap certificate. Societies: must contact in writing or by telephone. Green Fees: £60 per day, £36 per round. Cards: 💳 💳 💳 💳 💳 💳 💳 Prof: Steven Hunter Course Designer: J H Taylor Facilities: 🏨 🍴 🛅 ⛹ 🍴 ⛹ 🏡 ⛳ Conf: Corporate Hospitality Days available Location: 1.5m W off A3090

Hotel
★★★★★ 🏨 **Lainston House Hotel,**
Sparsholt, WINCHESTER
☎ 01962 863588 – 50 en suite

HEREFORDSHIRE

KINGTON

Kington
Bradnor Hill HR5 3RE
☎ 01544 230340 (club) & 231320 (pro shop) 📄
01544 230340/231320 (pro)

The highest 18-hole course in England, with
magnificent views over seven counties. A natural
heathland course with easy walking on mountain
turf cropped by sheep. There is bracken to catch
any really bad shots but no sand traps. The greens
play true and fast and are generally
acknowledged as some of the best in the West
Midlands.

18 holes, 5980yds, Par 70, SSS 68, Course record 63.

Club membership: 510. Visitors: contact the
professional, particularly at weekends by phoning
01544 231320. Societies: must book in advance
through the Professional. Green Fees: not confirmed.
Prof: Andy Gealy Course Designer: Major C K
Hutchison Facilities: ⑪ 🍴 🛍 ♥ 🍷 ⚑ 🛒 🏷 🏌 🚗 🛺
🏌 🎌 Location: 0.5m N of Kington, off B4355

Hotel
★★★ 66% **Talbot Hotel,** West St, LEOMINSTER
☎ 01568 616347 – 20 en suite

ROSS-ON-WYE

Ross-on-Wye
Two Park, Gorsley HR9 7UT
☎ 01989 720267 📄 01989 720212
e-mail: secretary@therossonwyegolfclub.co.uk

This undulating, parkland course has been cut out
of a silver birch forest. The fairways are well-
screened from each other and tight, the greens
good and the bunkers have been restructured.

18 holes, 6451yds, Par 72, SSS 71, Course record 68.

Club membership: 760. Visitors: must contact
secretary or professional in advance. Societies: apply
in writing/telephone in advance. Green Fees: £50 per
36 holes; £46 per 27 holes; £40 per round.. Cards: 💳
💳 Prof: Jon Moody Course Designer: Mr C K
Cotton Facilities: ⑪ 🍴 🛍 ♥ 🍷 🏌 ⚑ 🛒 🚗 🏌 🛺
Conf: Corporate Hospitality Days available Location:
On B4221 N side of M50 junct 3

Hotel
★★★ 74% **Pengethley Manor,**
Pengethley Park, ROSS-ON-WYE
☎ 01989 730211 – 11 en suite 14 annexe en suite

HERTFORDSHIRE

BERKHAMSTED

Berkhamsted
The Common HP4 2QB
☎ 01442 865832 📄 01442 863730
e-mail: barryh@berkhamstedgc.co.uk

There are no sand bunkers on this Championship
heathland course but this does not make it any
easier to play. The natural hazards will test the
skill of the most able players, with a particularly
testing hole at the 11th, 568 yards, par 5. Fine
greens, long carries and heather and gorse. The
clubhouse is very comfortable.

18 holes, 6605yds, Par 71, SSS 72, Course record 65.

Club membership: 700. Visitors: must contact in
advance and be competent golfer. Societies: must
contact in advance. Green Fees: £50 per day, £37 per
18 holes (£45 per 18 holes weekends after 11am).
Cards: 💳 💳 💳 Prof: John Clarke Course
Designer: Colt/Braid Facilities: ⑪ 🍴 🛍 ♥ 🍷 🏌 🏌
🏠 🏌 Location: 1.5m E

Hotel
★★★★ 68% **Pendley Manor,** Cow Ln, TRING
☎ 01442 891891 – 74 en suite

BROOKMANS PARK

Brookmans Park
Golf Club Rd AL9 7AT
☎ 01707 652487 📄 01707 661851
e-mail: info@bpgc.co.uk

Brookmans Park is an undulating parkland course,
with several cleverly constructed holes. But it is a
fair course, although it can play long. The 11th,
par 3, is a testing hole which plays across a lake.

18 holes, 6473yds, Par 71, SSS 71, Course record 65.

Club membership: 750. Visitors: must contact
professional in advance 01707 652468 and have a
handicap certificate; must play with member at
weekends & bank holidays. Societies: must telephone
or write in advance. Green Fees: not confirmed.
Prof: Ian Jelley Course Designer: Hawtree/Taylor
Facilities: ⑪ 🍴 🛍 ♥ 🍷 🏌 🏠 🏌 🚗 🏌 Location:
N side of village off A1000

Hotel
★★★ 71% **Bush Hall,** Mill Green, HATFIELD
☎ 01707 271251 – 25 en suite

BROXBOURNE

Hertfordshire
Broxbournebury Mansion, White Stubbs Ln
☎ 01992 466666 & 441268 (pro shop)
📄 01992 470326
e-mail: hertfordshire@americangolf.uk.com

18 holes, 6314yds, Par 70, SSS 70, Course record 62.

Championship Course

Marriott Hanbury Manor

Golf & Country Club, SG12 0SD
☎ 01920 487722   📄 01920 487692
e-mail: golf.hanburymanor@marriotthotels.co.uk

There can be few golf venues that combine so successfully the old and the new. The old is the site itself, dominated since the 19th century by Hanbury Manor, a Jacobean-style mansion; the wonderful grounds included a 9-hole parkland course designed by the legendary Harry Vardon. The new is the conversion of the estate into the golf and country club; the manor now offers a five-star country house hotel, while Jack Nicklaus II redesigned the grounds for an 18-hole course. The American-style design took the best of Vardon's original and added meadowland to produce a course that looks beautiful and plays superbly. Hanbury Manor has hosted a number of professional events, including the Women's European Open in 1996 and the Men's European Tour's English Open from 1997 to 1999, won respectively by Per Ulrik Johannson, Lee Westwood and Darren Clarke.

WHERE TO STAY NEARBY

★★★★★71%
Marriott Hanbury Manor Hotel & Country Club, WARE
☎ 01920 487722 & 0870 400 7222
📄 01920 487692
134 en suite 27 annexe en suite

★★★68%
Roebuck Hotel, Baldock St, WARE
☎ 01920 409955 📄 01920 468016
50 en suite

---

18 holes, 7016yds, Par 72, SSS 74, Course record 61

Club Membership
900

Visitors
Handicap certificate; hotel residents and golf day participants only; must contact in advance

Societies
Mon, Tue, Wed, Thu, must book in advance

Green Fees
Terms on application

Cards
💳 💳 💳 💳 💳 💳

Professional
Richard Booth

Course Designer
Jack Nicklaus II

Facilities
🍴 🍽 🛋 ☕ 🍷 🛏 ⛳ 🏠
🏌 ⛳ 🏌 🛒 ⛳ 🔧 🔍 🏊
sauna, solarium, gymnasium

Conference
Facilities available

Corporate
Hospitality Days available

Location
M25 junct 25, 12m N on A10

Course Designer: Jack Nicklaus II Location: on A10 take Broxbourne exit and follow signs for Paradise Wildlife Park. Turn left at Bell Lane and follow road over A10, course on right.
Telephone for further details

LETCHWORTH

Letchworth

Letchworth Ln SG6 3NQ
☎ 01462 683203 📄 01462 484567
e-mail: letchworthgolfclub@uk2.net

Planned more than 50 years ago by Harry Vardon, this adventurous, parkland course is set in a peaceful corner of 'Norman' England. To its variety of natural and artificial hazards is added an unpredictable wind.

18 holes, 6450yds, Par 71, SSS 71, Course record 66.

Club membership: 750. Visitors: may not play Tue and with member only at weekends. Must contact in advance and have a handicap certificate. Societies: Wed, Thu & Fri only, must telephone in advance. Green Fees: terms on application. Prof: Karl Teschner Course Designer: Harry Vardon Facilities: ⑪ ⑩ ⑩ ⒤ ⒢ ⒥ ⒜ ⒟ ⒞ ⒡ 9-hole par 3 course. Conf: Corporate Hospitality Days available Location: S side of town centre off A505

Hotel
★★★ 63% **The Cromwell Hotel,**
High St, Old Town, STEVENAGE
☎ 01438 779954 – 76 en suite

RADLETT

Porters Park

Shenley Hill WD7 7AZ
☎ 01923 854127 📄 01923 855475
e-mail: info@porterspark.fsnet.co.uk

A splendid, undulating parkland course with fine trees and lush grass. The holes are all different and interesting – on many, accuracy of shot to the green is of paramount importance.

18 holes, 6313yds, Par 70, SSS 70, Course record 64.

Club membership: 700. Visitors: must book 24hrs in advance. With member only weekends. Societies: Wed & Thu only, must apply in writing. Green Fees: terms on application. Cards: ⬤ ⬛ ⬛ ⬛ ⬛ Prof: David Gleeson Course Designer: Braid Facilities: ⑪ ⑩ ⑩ ⒤ ⒢ ⒥ ⒜ ⒟ ⒞ ⒡ Location: NE side of village off A5183

Hotel
⌂ **Innkeeper's Lodge Borehamwood,**
Studio Way, BOREHAM WOOD
☎ 020 8905 1455 – 55 en suite

RICKMANSWORTH

Moor Park

WD3 1QN
☎ 01923 773146 📄 01923 777109
e-mail: enquiries@moorparkgc.co.uk

Two parkland courses with rolling fairways – High Course is challenging and will test the best golfer and West Course demands a high degree of accuracy. The clubhouse is a Grade I listed mansion.

High Golf Course:
18 holes, 6713yds, Par 72, SSS 72, Course record 63.
West Golf Course:
18 holes, 5815yds, Par 69, SSS 68, Course record 60.

Club membership: 1700. Visitors: must contact in advance but may not play at weekends, bank holidays or before 1pm on Tue & Thu. Societies: must contact in advance. Green Fees: High: £77.50 per round. West: £47.50 per round. Cards: ⬤ ⬛ ⬛ ⬛ ⬛ Prof: Lawrence Farmer Course Designer: H S Colt Facilities: ⑪ ⑩ ⑩ ⒤ ⒢ ⒥ ⒜ ⒟ ⒞ ⒡ chipping green snooker room. Conf: facilities available Corporate Hospitality Days available Location: Off A404 to Northwood, close to junct 17 & 18 on M25

Hotel
★★★ 71% **The Bedford Arms,** CHENIES
☎ 01923 283301 – 10 en suite

WATFORD

West Herts

Cassiobury Park WD3 3GG
☎ 01923 236484 📄 01923 222300

Set in parkland surroundings, the West Herts course is close to Watford but its tree-lined setting is beautiful and tranquil. Set out on a plateau the course is exceedingly dry. It also has a very severe finish with the 17th, a hole of 378 yards, the toughest on the course. The last hole measures over 480 yards.

18 holes, 6528yds, Par 72, SSS 71, Course record 65.

Club membership: 700. Visitors: must contact in advance. Societies: must telephone in advance and confirm in writing. Green Fees: £38 per 18 holes (£48 weekends). Cards: ⬤ ⬛ ⬛ Prof: Charles Gough Course Designer: Tom Morris Facilities: ⑪ ⑩ ⑩ ⒤ ⒢ ⒥ ⒜ ⒟ ⒞ ⒡ indoor teaching facility. Conf: Corporate Hospitality Days available Location: W side of town centre off A412

Hotel
★★★ 67% **The White House,** Upton Rd, WATFORD
☎ 01923 237316 – 57 en suite

KENT

BROADSTAIRS

North Foreland

Convent Rd, Kingsgate CT10 3PU
☎ 01843 862140 🖹 01843 862663
e-mail: office@northforeland.co.uk

A picturesque cliff-top course situated where the Thames Estuary widens towards the sea. One of the few courses where the sea can be seen from every hole. Walking is easy and the wind is deceptive. The 8th and 17th, both par 4, are testing holes. There is also an 18-hole approach and putting course.

18 holes, 6430yds, Par 71, SSS 71, Course record 63.

Club membership: 1100. **Visitors:** for main course required to book in advance & have handicap certificate. May play afternoons only Mon and Tue, weekends restricted and no visitors Sun morning. Short course has no restrictions. **Societies:** Wed & Fri only, by arrangement. **Green Fees:** £50 per day; £35 per round (£75/50 weekends and bank holidays). **Cards:** 💳 💳 💳 💳 **Prof:** Darren Parris **Course Designer:** Fowler & Simpson **Facilities:** 🏌 🍴 🛍 💼 🍸 🏖 🏠 🍸 🚗 🚗 🏌 ⛳ 18-hole par 3 course. **Location:** 1.5m N off B2052

Hotel
★★★ 68% **Royal Albion Hotel,** Albion St, BROADSTAIRS
☎ 01843 868071 – 19 en suite

DEAL

Royal Cinque Ports

Golf Rd CT14 6RF
☎ 01304 374007 🖹 01304 379530
e-mail: rcpgcsec@aol.com

Famous championship seaside links, windy but with easy walking. Outward nine is generally considered the easier, inward nine is longer and includes the renowned 16th, perhaps the most difficult hole. On a fine day there are wonderful views across the Channel.

18 holes, 6899yds, Par 72, SSS 73.

Club membership: 950. **Visitors:** restricted Wed mornings, weekends & bank holidays. Must contact in advance and have a handicap certificate. Men max 20 handicap; Ladies max 30 handicap. **Societies:** must contact in advance. **Green Fees:** not confirmed. **Cards:** 💳 💳 💳 **Prof:** Andrew Reynolds **Course Designer:** James Braid **Facilities:** 🏌 🍴 by prior arrangement 🛍 💼 🍸 🏖 🏠 🍸 🚗 ⛳ **Conf:** Corporate Hospitality Days available **Location:** Along seafront at N end of Deal

Hotel
★★★ 75% **Wallett's Court Country House Hotel & Spa,** West Cliffe, St Margarets at Cliffe, DOVER
☎ 01304 852424 & 0800 0351628 🖹 01304 853430
3 en suite 13 annexe en suite

FAVERSHAM

Faversham

Belmont Park ME13 0HB
☎ 01795 890561 📠 01795 890760
e-mail: themanager@favershamgolf.co.uk

A beautiful inland course laid out over part of a large estate with pheasants walking the fairways quite tamely. Play follows two heavily wooded valleys but the trees affect only the loose shots going out of bounds. Fine views.

18 holes, 5965yds, Par 70, SSS 69, Course record 62.

Club membership: 800. Visitors: must have handicap certificate. With member only at weekends. Contacting the club in advance is advisable. Societies: must contact in advance. Green Fees: £30 per round. Prof: Stuart Rokes Facilities: ⑪ ⑩ 🏌 🐦 🛒 🐦 ⛳ 🐦 Conf: Corporate Hospitality Days available Location: 3.5m S on road to Belmont

Hotel
★★★★✦🏠 Eastwell Manor,
Eastwell Park, Boughton Lees, ASHFORD
☎ 01233 213000 – 23 en suite 39 annexe en suite

GRAVESEND

Mid Kent

Singlewell Rd DA11 7RB
☎ 01474 568035 📠 01474 564218
e-mail: midkentgolfclub@aol.com

A well-maintained downland course with some easy walking and some excellent greens. The first hole is short, but nonetheless a real challenge. The slightest hook and the ball is out of bounds or lost.

18 holes, 6106yds, Par 70, SSS 69, Course record 60.

Club membership: 900. Visitors: must contact in advance & have handicap certificate. May not play weekends. Societies: Tue only, apply in writing. Green Fees: £35 per day; £25 per round. Prof: Mark Foreman Course Designer: Frank Pennick Facilities: ⑪ ⑩ by prior arrangement 🏌 ⛳🐦 🐦 🐦 Location: S side of town centre off A227

Hotel
⌂ Premier Travel Inn Gravesend,
Wrotham Rd, GRAVESEND
☎ 08701 977118 – 36 en suite

KINGSDOWN

Walmer & Kingsdown

The Leas CT14 8EP
☎ 01304 373256 📠 01304 382336
e-mail: kingsdown.golf@gtwiz.co.uk

18 holes, 6444yds, Par 72, SSS 71, Course record 66.

Course Designer: James Braid Location: 1.5m E of Ringwould off A258 Dover/Deal road
Telephone for further details

Hotel
★★★ 72% Dunkerleys Hotel & Restaurant,
19 Beach St, DEAL
☎ 01304 375016 – 16 en suite

LITTLESTONE

Littlestone

St Andrew's Rd TN28 8RB
☎ 01797 363355 📠 01797 362740
e-mail: secretary@littlestonegolfclub.org.uk

Located in the Romney Marshes, this fairly flat seaside links course calls for every variety of shot. The 8th, 15th, 16th and 17th are regarded as classics by international golfers. Fast running fairways and faster greens.

18 holes, 6486yds, Par 71, SSS 72, Course record 66.

Club membership: 550. Visitors: must contact in advance, no visitors before 11am weekends and bank holidays. Societies: must apply in advance. Green Fees: £60 per day; £40 per round (£75/£60 weekends & bank holidays). Cards: 💳 💳 💳 💳 Prof: Andrew Jones Course Designer: Laidlaw Purves Facilities: ⑪ ⑩ 🏌 🐦 🐦 ⛳ 🐦 🐦 🐦 🐦 Conf: Corporate Hospitality Days available Location: 1m from New Romney off Littlestone road B2070

Hotel
★★★★ 77% The Hythe Imperial,
Princes Pde, HYTHE
☎ 01303 267441 – 100 en suite

RAMSGATE

St Augustine's

Cottington Rd, Cliffsend CT12 5JN
☎ 01843 590333 📠 01843 590444
e-mail: sagc@ic24.net

18 holes, 5254yds, Par 69, SSS 66, Course record 61.

Course Designer: Tom Vardon Location: Off A256 Ramsgate/Sandwich road
Telephone for further details

Hotel
★★★ 68% Royal Albion Hotel,
Albion St, BROADSTAIRS
☎ 01843 868071 – 19 en suite

ROCHESTER

Rochester & Cobham Park

Park Pale ME2 3UL
☎ 01474 823411 📄 01474 824446
e-mail: rcpgc@talk21.com

A first-rate course of challenging dimensions in undulating parkland. All holes differ and each requires accurate drive placing to derive the best advantage.

18 holes, 6597yds, Par 71, SSS 72, Course record 64.

Club membership: 640. **Visitors:** must contact in advance & have handicap certificate. No visitors weekends. **Societies:** apply in advance. **Green Fees:** £45 per day, £35 per round. **Prof:** Iain Higgins **Course Designer:** Donald Steel **Facilities:** ⑪ ⑩ ⓛ 🍺🍴🏌️🛄🏧🏌️ **Conf:** Corporate Hospitality Days available **Location:** 2.5m W on A2

Hotel
★★★★ 74% **Bridgewood Manor,** Bridgewood Roundabout, Walderslade Woods, CHATHAM
☎ 01634 201333 – 100 en suite

SANDWICH

Prince's

Prince's Dr, Sandwich Bay CT13 9QB
☎ 01304 611118 📄 01304 612000
e-mail: office@princesgolfclub.co.uk

With 27 championship holes, Prince's Golf Club enjoys a world wide reputation as a traditional links of the finest quality and is a venue that provides all that is best in modern links golf. One of only 14 courses to be selected to host the Open Championship.

Dunes: 9 holes, 3343yds, Par 36, SSS 36.
Himalayas: 9 holes, 3163yds, Par 35, SSS 35.
Shore: 9 holes, 3347yds, Par 36, SSS 36.

Club membership: 250. **Visitors:** available all week, must contact in advance. **Societies:** welcome all week, please contact in advance in writing, by e-mail or telephone. **Green Fees:** terms on application. **Cards:** 💳 💳 💳 💳 💳 **Prof:** Derek Barbour **Course Designer:** (1951) Sir Guy Campbell and J S F Morrison **Facilities:** ⑪ ⑩ by prior arrangement ⓛ 🍺 🍴🛄🏧🏌️🏧🏌️ private beach area. **Conf:** facilities available **Corporate:** Hospitality Days available **Location:** 2m E via toll road, follow signs from Sandwich

Hotel
★★★ 72% **Dunkerleys Hotel & Restaurant,**
19 Beach St, DEAL
☎ 01304 375016 – 16 en suite

SEVENOAKS

Knole Park

Seal Hollow Rd TN15 0HJ
☎ 01732 452150 📄 01732 463159
e-mail: secretary@knolepark.fsnet.co.uk

The course is laid out within the grounds of the Knole Estate and can rightfully be described as a natural layout. The course designer has used the natural contours of the land to produce a challenging course in all weather conditions and throughout all seasons. While, for most of the year, it may appear benign, in summer, when the bracken is high, Knole Park represents a considerable challenge but always remains a fair test of golf.

18 holes, 6246yds, Par 70, SSS 70, Course record 62.

Club membership: 750. **Visitors:** must have a handicap certificate and contact the Secretary in advance, may not play at weekends or bank holidays. **Societies:** telephone initially. **Green Fees:** £45 per day, £35 per round. **Cards:** 💳 💳 💳 💳 💳 **Prof:** Phil Sykes **Course Designer:** J A Abercromby **Facilities:** ⑪ ⑩ ⓛ 🍺🍴🛄🏧🏌️ squash. **Conf:** Corporate Hospitality Days available **Location:** NE side of town centre off B2019

Hotel
★★★ 71% **Donnington Manor,**
London Rd, Dunton Green, SEVENOAKS
☎ 01732 462681 – 60 en suite

TUNBRIDGE WELLS (ROYAL)

Nevill

Benhall Mill Rd TN2 5JW
☎ 01892 525818 📄 01892 517861
e-mail: manager@nevillgolfclub.co.uk

The county boundaries of Kent and Sussex run along the northern perimeter of the course. Open undulating ground, well-wooded with some heather and gorse for the first half. The second nine holes slope away from the clubhouse to a valley where a narrow stream hazards two holes.

18 holes, 6349yds, Par 71, SSS 70, Course record 64.

Club membership: 800. **Visitors:** must contact 48 hours in advance, handicap certificate required, permission from Secretary for weekends play. **Societies:** must apply in writing one month in advance. **Green Fees:** £45 per day; £30 per round (£50/£40 weekends). **Prof:** Paul Huggett **Course Designer:** Henry Cotton **Facilities:** ⑪ ⑩ ⓛ 🍺🍴🛄🏧🏌️ **Location:** S of Tunbridge Wells, off forest road

Hotel
★★★★ 71% **The Spa Hotel,**
Mount Ephraim, TUNBRIDGE WELLS
☎ 01892 520331 – 69 en suite

Championship Course

SANDWICH

Royal St George's

CT13 9PB

☎ 01304 613090 📄 01304 611245

e-mail: secretary@royalstgeorges.com

Consistently ranked among the leading golf courses in the world, Royal St George's occupies a unique place in the history of golf, playing host in 1894 to the first Open Championship outside Scotland. Set among the dunes of Sandwich Bay, the links provide a severe test for the greatest of golfers. Only two Open winners (Bill Rogers in 1981 and Greg Norman in 1993) have managed to under par after 72 holes. The undulating fairways, the borrows on the greens, the strategically placed bunkers, and the prevailing winds that blow on all but the rarest of occasions, these all soon reveal any weakness in the player; there are few over the years who have mastered all the vagaries in one round. It hosted its thirteenth Open Championship in 2003, dramatically won by outsider Ben Curtis.

WHERE TO STAY NEARBY

★★★72%

Dunkerleys Hotel & Restaurant, 19 Beach St, DEAL

☎ 01304 375016 16 en suite

★★★67%

The Falstaff Hotel,

8–10 St Dunstan's St, CANTERBURY

☎ 0870 609 6102 📄 01227 463525

25 en suite 22 annexe en suite

★★70%

The Bow Window Inn,

50 High St, Littlebourne, CANTERBURY

☎ 01227 721264 📄 01227 721250

11 annexe en suite

---

18 holes, 7102yds, Par 70, SSS 74, Course record 67

Club Membership
750

Visitors
Not weekends; three and four-ball golf Tue only; must contact in advance; handicap certificate of 18 or under

Societies
Mon, Tue, Thu, must apply in writing

Green Fees
£150 per 36 holes, £115 per 18 holes; reduced winter rates

Cards
💳

Professional
A Brooks

Course Designer
Dr Laidlaw Purves

Facilities
🍴 🏌 💼 🍽 🧳 🏠 🏷 ◇ ⛳ 🐾

Corporate
Hospitality Days available

Location
1.5m E of Sandwich. Enter town and follow signs for golf courses

LANCASHIRE

CHORLEY

Chorley

Hall o' th' Hill, Heath Charnock PR6 9HX
☎ 01257 480263 📠 01257 480722
e-mail: secretary@chorleygolfclub.freeserve.co.uk

A splendid moorland course with plenty of fresh air. The well-sited clubhouse affords some good views of the Lancashire coast and of Angelzarke, a local beauty spot. Beware of the short 3rd hole with its menacing out of bounds.

18 holes, 6269yds, Par 71, SSS 70, Course record 62.

Club membership: 550. **Visitors:** must contact in advance, must play from yellow tees and may not play weekends or bank holidays. **Societies:** must contact in advance. Tue-Fri only. **Green Fees:** not confirmed. **Prof:** Mark Bradley **Course Designer:** J A Steer **Facilities:** ⊕ ⬚ ☕ ⬚ ⬚ ⬚ ⬚ ⬚ **Location:** 2.5m SE on A673

Hotel
★★★ 72% **Pines Hotel,**
570 Preston Rd, Clayton-Le-Woods, CHORLEY
☎ 01772 338551 – 37 en suite

Shaw Hill Hotel Golf & Country Club

Preston Rd, Whittle-Le-Woods PR6 7PP
☎ 01257 269221 📠 01257 261223
e-mail: info@shaw-hill.co.uk

18 holes, 6246yds, Par 72, SSS 70, Course record 65.

Course Designer: Harry Vardon **Location:** On A6 1.5m N
Telephone for further details

CLITHEROE

Clitheroe

Whalley Rd, Pendleton BB7 1PP
☎ 01200 422292 📠 01200 422292
e-mail: secretary@clitheroegolfclub.com

One of the best inland courses in the country. Clitheroe is a parkland-type course with water hazards and good scenic views, particularly towards Longridge, and Pendle Hill.

18 holes, 6326yds, Par 71, SSS 71, Course record 63.

Club membership: 750. **Visitors:** must contact in advance. **Societies:** must contact in advance. **Green Fees:** £33-£45. **Prof:** Paul McEvoy **Course Designer:** James Braid **Facilities:** ⊕ ⬚ ⬚ ⬚ ⬚ ⬚ ⬚ ⬚ ⬚ **Conf:** Corporate Hospitality Days available **Location:** 2m S of Clitheroe on Whalley Road

Hotel
★★ 70% **Shireburn Arms Hotel,**
Whalley Rd, Hurst Green, CLITHEROE
☎ 01254 826518 – 18 en suite

FLEETWOOD

Fleetwood

Princes Way FY7 8AF
☎ 01253 873661 & 773573 📠 01253 773573
e-mail: fleetwoodgc@aol.com

Championship length, flat seaside links where the player must always be alert to changes of direction or strength of the wind.

18 holes, 6723yds, Par 72, SSS 72.

Club membership: 600. **Visitors:** may not play on competition days or Tue after 11am. **Societies:** must contact in advance. A deposit of £5 per player is required. **Green Fees:** terms on application. **Prof:** S McLaughlin **Course Designer:** J A Steer **Facilities:** ⊕ ⬚ ⬚ ⬚ ⬚ ⬚ ⬚ ⬚ **Location:** W side of town centre

Hotel
⬚ **Premier Travel Inn Blackpool (Bispham),**
Devonshire Rd, Bispham, BLACKPOOL
☎ 08701 977033 – 39 en suite

LANCASTER

Lancaster Golf Club

Ashton Hall, Ashton-with-Stodday LA2 0AJ
☎ 01524 751247 📠 01524 752742

This course is unusual for parkland golf as it is exposed to the winds coming off the Irish Sea. It is situated on the Lune estuary and has some natural hazards and easy walking. There are several fine holes among woods near the old clubhouse. Fine views over the Fylde estuary and the Lake District.

18 holes, 6282yds, Par 71, SSS 71, Course record 66.

Club membership: 925. **Visitors:** must play with member or resident weekends. Must contact in advance and have a handicap certificate. **Societies:** Mon-Fri only. Must contact in advance. Handicap certificate required. **Green Fees:** £42 per day, £35 per round. **Cards:** 💳 💳 💳 💳 **Prof:** David Sutcliffe **Course Designer:** James Braid **Facilities:** ⊕ ⬚ ⬚ ⬚ ⬚ ⬚ ⬚ ⬚ **Conf:** Corporate Hospitality Days available **Location:** 3m S on A588

Hotel
★★★★ 71% **Lancaster House Hotel,**
Green Ln, Ellel, LANCASTER
☎ 01524 844822 – 80 en suite

Championship Course

Lancashire **LYTHAM ST ANNES**

Royal Lytham & St Annes

Links Gate FY8 3LQ
☎ 01253 724206 📠 01253 780946
e-mail: bookings@royallytham.org

Founded in 1886, this huge links course can be difficult, especially in windy conditions. Unusually for a championship course, it starts with a par 3, the nearby railway line and red-brick houses creating distractions that add to the challenge. The course has hosted 10 Open Championships with some memorable victories: amateur Bobby Jones famously won the first here in 1926; Bobby Charles of New Zealand became the only left-hander to win the title; in 1969 Tony Jacklin helped to revive British golf with his win; and the most recent in 2001 was won by David Duval.

WHERE TO STAY NEARBY

★★★★70%
Clifton Arms Hotel, West
Beach, Lytham, LYTHAM ST ANNES
☎ 01253 739898
48 en suite

★★★69%
Bedford Hotel, 307–311 Clifton
Dr South, LYTHAM ST ANNES
☎ 01253 724636 📠 01253 729244
45 en suite

★★★69%
Chadwick Hotel, South
Promenade, LYTHAM ST ANNES
☎ 01253 720061 📠 01253 714455
75 en suite

★★★64%
**The Best Western
Glendower Hotel,** North
Promenade, LYTHAM ST ANNES
☎ 01253 723241 📠 01253 640069
60 en suite

---

18 holes, 6882yds, Par 71, SSS 74, Course record 64

Club Membership
850

Visitors
Not Tue, Wed, Fri, weekends unless a guest in the Dormy House; handicap certificate (max 21 men, max 30 women)

Societies
Must contact secretary in advance; large groups Thu only

Green Fees
£165 per 36 holes, £110 per 18 holes (limited play Sun £165 per 18 holes)

Cards

Professional
Eddie Birchenough

Course Designer
George Lowe

Facilities
caddies available.

Corporate
Hospitality Days available

Location
0.5m E of St Annes

MORECAMBE

Morecambe

Bare LA4 6AJ

☎ 01524 412841 📄 01524 400088

e-mail: secretary@morecambegolfclub.com

Holiday golf at its most enjoyable. The well-maintained, wind-affected seaside parkland course is not long but full of character. Even so the panoramic views across Morecambe Bay and to the Lake District and Pennines make concentration difficult. The 4th is a testing hole.

18 holes, 5750yds, Par 67, SSS 69, Course record 69.

Club membership: 850. Visitors: may play from yellow tees, must contact in advance. Societies: must contact in advance. Green Fees: terms on application. Cards: 💳 💳 💳 💳 💳 Prof: Simon Fletcher Course Designer: Dr Alister Mackenzie Facilities: ⑨ 🍴 🛒 🍺 🍴 🏌 🏠 ✐ Location: N side of town centre on A5105

Hotel

★★★ 63% Elms Hotel, Bare Village, MORECAMBE

☎ 01524 411501 – 39 en suite

ORMSKIRK

Ormskirk

Cranes Ln, Lathom L40 5UJ

☎ 01695 572227 📄 01695 572227

e-mail: ormskirk@ukgolfer.org

A pleasantly secluded, fairly flat, parkland course with much heath and silver birch. Accuracy from the tees will provide an interesting variety of second shots.

18 holes, 6358yds, Par 70, SSS 71, Course record 63.

Club membership: 300. Visitors: restricted Sat. Societies: must telephone or contact in writing. Green Fees: terms on application. Prof: Jack Hammond Course Designer: Harold Hilton Facilities: ⑨ 🍴 🛒 🍺 🍴 🏌 🏠 ✐ Conf: Corporate Hospitality Days available Location: 1.5m NE

Hotel

★★★ 66% Beaufort Hotel,

High Ln, Burscough, ORMSKIRK

☎ 01704 892655 – 20 en suite

PLEASINGTON

Pleasington

BB2 5JF

☎ 01254 202177 📄 01254 201028

e-mail: secretary.manager@pleasington-golf.co.uk

Plunging and rising across lovely parkland and heathland turf, this course tests judgement of distance through the air to greens of widely differing levels. The 11th and 4th are testing holes.

18 holes, 6417yds, Par 70, SSS 70.

Club membership: 700. Visitors: may play Mon & Wed-Fri only. Societies: must contact in advance. Green Fees: £55 per day, £44 per round. Prof: Ged Furey Course Designer: George Lowe Facilities: ⑨ 🍴 🛒 🍺 🍴 🏌 🏠 ✐ 🏌 Conf: facilities available Location: M65 junct 3, follow sign for Blackburn

Hotel

★★ 78% The Millstone at Mellor,

Church Ln, Mellor, BLACKBURN

☎ 01254 813333 – 18 en suite 6 annexe en suite

PRESTON

Penwortham

Blundell Ln, Penwortham PR1 0AX

☎ 01772 744630 📄 01772 740172

e-mail: penworthamgolfclub@supanet.com

A progressive golf club set close to the banks of the River Ribble. The course has tree-lined fairways, excellent greens, and provides easy walking. Testing holes include the 175yd, par 3 3rd, the 483yd, par 5 6th, and the 385yd par 4 16th.

18 holes, 5877yds, Par 69, SSS 69, Course record 65.

Club membership: 1100. Visitors: must contact in advance, restricted Tue & weekends. Societies: must apply in writing/telephone in advance. Green Fees: not confirmed. Prof: Darren Hopwood Facilities: ⑨ 🍴 🛒 🍺 🍴 🏌 🏠 ✐ Conf: Corporate Hospitality Days available Location: 1.5m W of town centre off A59

Hotel

★★★ 67% Tickled Trout,

Preston New Rd, Samlesbury, PRESTON

☎ 01772 877671 – 102 en suite

UPHOLLAND

Dean Wood

Lafford Ln WN8 0QZ

☎ 01695 622219 📄 01695 622245

e-mail: dwgc1922secretary@freenet.co.uk

This parkland course has a varied terrain – flat front nine, undulating back nine. Beware the par 4 11th and 17th holes, which have ruined many a card. If there were a prize for the best maintained course in Lancashire, Dean Wood would be a strong contender.

18 holes, 6148yds, Par 71, SSS 70, Course record 65.

Club membership: 730. Visitors: must play with member Tue, Wed. Societies: must contact in advance. Green Fees: £30 per day. Prof: Stuart Danchin Course Designer: James Braid Facilities: ⑨ 🍴 🛒 🍺 🍴 🏌 🏠 🍴 ✐ Conf: Corporate Hospitality Days available Location: 1m from junct 26 of M6 on A577

Hotel

★★★ 60% Lancashire Manor Hotel,

Prescott Rd, UPHOLLAND

☎ 01695 720401 – 55 en suite

Championship Course

Lincolnshire

WOODHALL SPA

Woodhall Spa

The Broadway LN10 6PU
☎ 01526 352511 📠 01526 351817
e-mail: booking@englishgolfunion.org

The Championship Course at Woodhall Spa, now known as the Hotchkin, is arguably the best inland course in Britain. This classic course has cavernous bunkers and heather-lined fairways. Golf has been played here for over a century and the Hotchkin has hosted most of the top national and international amateur events. The English Golf Union acquired Woodhall Spa in 1995 to create a centre of excellence. A second course, the Bracken, has been built, along with extensive practice facilities including one of Europe's finest short-game practice areas. The English Golf Union actively encourages visits to the National Golf Centre throughout the year, to experience the facilities and to enjoy the unique ambience.

WHERE TO STAY NEARBY

★★★68%
Petwood Hotel,
Stixwould Rd, WOODHALL SPA
☎ 01526 352411 53 en suite

★★★63%
Golf Hotel, The Broadway,
WOODHALL SPA
☎ 01526 353535 📠 01526 353096
50 en suite

★★65%
Eagle Lodge Hotel,
The Broadway, WOODHALL SPA
☎ 01526 353231 📠 01526 352797
23 en suite

The Hotchkin
18 holes, 7080yds, Par 73, SSS 75, Course record 66

The Bracken
18 holes, 6735yds, Par 72, SSS 74, Course record 68

Club Membership
520

Visitors
Must contact in advance; handicap certificate

Societies
Apply by phone initially

Green Fees
Hotchkin £100 per day, £65 per round; Bracken £75 per day, £50 per round. £90 per day playing both courses

Cards

Professional
A Hare

Course Designer
Col S V Hotchkin

Facilities

Conferences
Facilities available

Corporate
Hospitality Days available

Location
NE of village off B1191

LEICESTERSHIRE

LOUGHBOROUGH

Longcliffe

Snell's Nook Ln, Nanpantan LE11 3YA
☎ 01509 239129 📠 01509 231286
e-mail: longcliffegolf@btconnect.com

Course of natural heathland, tree lined fairways with water in play on the 14th and 15th holes. This course is recognised by the English Golf Championship.

18 holes, 6625yds, Par 72, SSS 72, Course record 65.

Club membership: 660. **Visitors:** must contact in advance. Handicap certificate required. **Societies:** telephone in advance for availability, handicap certificate required. **Green Fees:** terms on application. **Cards:** 💳 💳 🗠 **Prof:** David Mee **Course Designer:** Williamson **Facilities:** ⊕ ⚑ ⛳ ⛳ ⛳ ⛳ 🏠 ✦ **Conf:** Corporate Hospitality Days available **Location:** 1.5m from M1 junct 23 off A512

Hotel
★★★ 65% **Quality Hotel & Suites Loughborough,** New Ashby Rd, LOUGHBOROUGH
☎ 01509 211800 – 94 en suite

LINCOLNSHIRE

SKEGNESS

Seacroft

Drummond Rd, Seacroft PE25 3AU
☎ 01754 763020 📠 01754 763020
e-mail: richard@seacroft-golfclub.co.uk

A championship seaside links traditionally laid out with tight undulations and hogsback fairways. Adjacent to Gibraltar Point Nature Reserve.

18 holes, 6479yds, Par 71, SSS 71, Course record 65.

Club membership: 590. **Visitors:** must be a member of an affiliated golf club/society. **Societies:** contact in advance. **Green Fees:** terms on application. **Cards:** 💳 💳 🗠 **Prof:** Robin Lawie **Course Designer:** Tom Dunn/Willie Fernie **Facilities:** ⊕ ⚑ ⛳ 🏠 ⛳ ✦ **Conf:** Corporate Hospitality Days available **Location:** S side of town centre, towards Gibraltar Point Nature Reserve

Hotel
★★★ 65% **Crown Hotel,** Drummond Rd, Seacroft, SKEGNESS
☎ 01754 610760 – 30 en suite

LONDON

N20 WHETSTONE

South Herts

Links Dr, Totteridge N20 8QU
☎ 020 8445 2035 📠 020 8445 7569
e-mail: secretary@southhertsgolfclub.co.uk

An open undulating parkland course perhaps most famous for the fact that two of the greatest of all British professionals, Harry Vardon and Dai Rees, CBE were professionals at the club. The course is testing, over rolling fairways, especially in the prevailing south-west wind.

18 holes, 6432yds, Par 72, SSS 71, Course record 63.

Club membership: 850. **Visitors:** must be members of recognised golf club & have handicap certificate of 24 or less. May not play at weekends. **Societies:** Wed-Fri only, must apply in writing. **Green Fees:** terms on application. **Prof:** Bobby Mitchell **Course Designer:** Harry Vardon **Facilities:** ⊕ ⚑ ⛳ ⛳ ⛳ 🏠 ⛳ ✦ **Conf:** Corporate Hospitality Days available **Location:** 2m E of A1 at Apex Corner

Hotel
⌂ **Innkeeper's Lodge Southgate,** 22 The Green, Southgate, LONDON
☎ 020 8447 8022 – 19 en suite

SE9 ELTHAM

Royal Blackheath

Court Rd SE9 5AF
☎ 020 8850 1795 📠 020 8859 0150
e-mail: info@rbgc.com

A pleasant, parkland course of great character as befits the antiquity of the club; the clubhouse dates from the 17th century. Many great trees survive and there are two ponds. The 18th requires a pitch to the green over a thick clipped hedge, which also crosses the front of the 1st tee. You may wish to visit the club's fine museum of golf.

18 holes, 6219yds, Par 70, SSS 70, Course record 66.

Club membership: 720. **Visitors:** must contact in advance but may play mid-week only, handicap certificate is required. **Societies:** must apply in writing. **Green Fees:** £60 per day; £45 per round. **Cards:** 💳 💳 💳 **Prof:** Richard Harrison **Course Designer:** James Braid **Facilities:** ⊕ 🍴 🏌 ☕ 🍴 ⚐ 🥤 golf museum. **Conf:** facilities available Corporate Hospitality Days available **Location:** M25 junct 3 take A20 towards London. Turn right at 2nd traffic lights to club 500yds on right

Hotel
★★★ 71% **Bromley Court Hotel,**
Bromley Hill, BROMLEY
☎ 020 8461 8600 – 114 en suite

SW15 PUTNEY

Richmond Park
Roehampton Gate, Priory Ln SW15 5JR
☎ 020 8876 1795 📠 020 8878 1354
e-mail: richmondpark@glendale-services.co.uk
Two public parkland courses.

Princes Course: 18 holes, 5868yds, Par 69, SSS 67.
Dukes Course: 18 holes, 6036yds, Par 69, SSS 68.

Visitors: must contact in advance for weekends. **Societies:** must contact in advance. **Green Fees:** £19 per 18 holes; (£22 weekends). **Cards:** 💳 💳 💳 💳 💳 **Prof:** Stuart Hill & David Bown **Course Designer:** Fred Hawtree **Facilities:** ⊕ 🏌 ☕ 🥤 🍴 ⚐ 🥤 **Conf:** Corporate Hospitality Days available **Location:** Inside Richmond Park Roehampton gate

Hotel
★★★ 69% **The Richmond Hill Hotel,**
Richmond Hill, RICHMOND UPON THAMES
☎ 020 8940 2247 – 138 en suite

SW19 WIMBLEDON

Royal Wimbledon
29 Camp Rd SW19 4UW
☎ 020 8946 2125 📠 020 8944 8652
e-mail: secretary@rwgc.co.uk

Third oldest club in England, established in 1865 and steeped in the history and traditions of the game. Mainly heathland with trees and heather, a good test of golf with many fine holes, the 12th being rated as the best.

18 holes, 6350yds, Par 70, SSS 71, Course record 66.

Club membership: 1050. **Visitors:** must be guests of current club member or contact club in advance, weekdays only. Maximum handicap 18 and must be member of recognised club. **Societies:** welcome Wed-Thu. Must apply in writing. **Green Fees:** £85 per day, £60 per round. **Prof:** David Jones **Course Designer:** H Colt **Facilities:** ⊕ 🍴 🏌 ☕ 🍴 🥤 🏌 ⚐ 🍴 **Conf:** Corporate Hospitality Days available **Location:**

1m from Tibbalt's Corner roundabout on Wimbledon Rd

Hotel
Ⓤ **Premier Travel Inn London Wimbledon South,**
Merantum Way, Merton
☎ 0870 990 6342

MERSEYSIDE

BLUNDELLSANDS

West Lancashire
Hall Rd West L23 8SZ
☎ 0151 924 1076 📠 0151 931 4448
e-mail: golf@westlancashiregolf.co.uk

Challenging, traditional links with sandy subsoil overlooking the Mersey estuary. The course provides excellent golf throughout the year. The four short holes are very fine.

18 holes, 6763yds, Par 72, SSS 73, Course record 66.

Club membership: 650. **Visitors:** May not play before 9.30am Mon-Fri. No play Tue. **Societies:** must contact in advance. **Green Fees:** £75 per day; £60 per round (£85/£70 weekends). **Cards:** 💳 💳 💳 💳 💳 **Prof:** Gary Eoge **Course Designer:** C K Cotton **Facilities:** ⊕ 🍴 🏌 ☕ 🍴 🥤 🏌 🍴 ⚐ 🍴 **Conf:** Corporate Hospitality Days available **Location:** N side of village, adjacent to Hall Rd station

CALDY

Caldy
Links Hey Rd CH48 1NB
☎ 0151 625 5660 📠 0151 6257394
e-mail: secretarycaldygc@btconnect.com

A heathland/cliff top links course situated on the estuary of the River Dee with many of the fairways running parallel to the river. Of championship length, the course offers excellent golf all year, but is subject to variable winds that noticeably alter the day-to-day playing of each hole. There are excellent views of North Wales and Snowdonia.

18 holes, 6651yds, Par 72, SSS 72, Course record 65.

Club membership: 800. **Visitors:** may play on weekdays only by prior arrangement. Not before 3.30pm Tue or after 12.30pm Wed. **Societies:** must telephone in advance. **Green Fees:** £80 per day, £70 per round. **Prof:** A Gibbons **Course Designer:** J Braid **Facilities:** ⊕ 🍴 🏌 ☕ 🍴 🥤 🏌 ⚐ 🍴 **Conf:** Corporate Hospitality Days available **Location:** SE side of village, from Caldy rdbt on A540 follow signs to Caldy and golf club

Hotel
★★★★ 70% **Thornton Hall Hotel,**
Neston Rd, THORNTON HOUGH
☎ 0151 336 3938 – 63 en suite

Merseyside   **HOYLAKE**

Royal Liverpool

Meols Dr CH47 4AL
☎ 0151 632 3101 & 632 3102   🖨 0151 632 6737
e-mail: sec@royal-liverpool-golf.com

Built in 1869 on the site of a former racecourse, this world-famous championship course was one of the first seaside courses to be established in England. In 1921 Hoylake was the scene of the first international match between the US and Britain, now known as the Walker Cup. Over the years, golfing enthusiasts have come to Hoylake to witness 18 amateur championships and 10 Open Championships, which the club is set to host again in 2006. Visitors playing on this historic course can expect a challenging match, with crosswinds, deep bunkers and hollows, all set against the backdrop of stunning Welsh hills. Watch out for the 8th hole, which saw the great Bobby Jones take an 8 on this par 5 on the way to his famous Grand Slam in 1930.

WHERE TO STAY NEARBY

★★★66%
Kings Gap Court Hotel,
HOYLAKE
☎ 0151 632 2073
30 en suite

★★★69%
Leasowe Castle Hotel,
Leasowe Rd, MORETON
☎ 0151 606 9191 🖨 0151 678 5551
47 en suite

★★★68%
Riverhill Hotel, Talbot Rd,
Prenton, BIRKENHEAD
☎ 0151 653 3773 🖨 0151 653 7162
15 en suite

---

18 holes, 6240yds, Par 72, SSS 71

Club Membership
650

Visitors
Not Thu am (Ladies Day); restricted before 9.30am, 1–2pm and pm weekends; must contact in advance; handicap certificate

Societies
Must contact in advance

Green Fees
£150 per day,
£100 per round

Cards
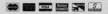

Professional
John Heggarty

Course Designers
R Chambers, G Morris

Facilities
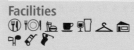

Corporate
Hospitality Days available

Location
SW of town centre on A540

FORMBY

Formby
Golf Rd L37 1LQ
☎ 01704 872164 📠 01704 833028
e-mail: info@formbygolfclub.co.uk

Championship seaside links through sandhills and pine trees. Partly sheltered from the wind by high dunes it features firm, springy turf, fast seaside greens and natural sandy bunkers. Well drained it plays well throughout the year.

18 holes, 6701yds, Par 72, SSS 72, Course record 65.

Club membership: 700. **Visitors:** must contact in advance, weekends after 3.30pm **Societies:** must contact well in advance. **Green Fees:** not confirmed. **Cards:** 💳 **Prof:** Gary Butler **Course Designer:** Park/Colt **Facilities:** 🏵🍴🛏♨🎯⚑🏌⚲🛖◇⚘ **Conf:** facilities available **Corporate:** Hospitality Days available **Location:** N side of town, next to Freshfield Railway Station

HESWALL

Heswall
Cottage Ln CH60 8PB
☎ 0151 342 1237 📠 0151 342 6140
e-mail: dawn@heswellgolfclub.com

A pleasant parkland course in soft undulating country overlooking the estuary of the River Dee. There are excellent views of the Welsh hills and coastline, and a good test of golf. The clubhouse is modern and well-appointed with good facilities.

18 holes, 6492yds, Par 72, SSS 72, Course record 62.

Club membership: 940. **Visitors:** must contact in advance. **Societies:** must apply in advance. **Green Fees:** not confirmed. **Prof:** Alan Thompson **Facilities:** 🏵🍴🛏♨🎯⚑🏌⚲🛖◇⚘ **Location:** 1m S off A540

Hotel
★★★★ 70% **Thornton Hall Hotel,**
Neston Rd, THORNTON HOUGH
☎ 0151 336 3938 – 63 en suite

LIVERPOOL

The Childwall
Naylors Rd, Gateacre L27 2YB
☎ 0151 487 0654 📠 0151 487 0882
e-mail: office@childwallgolfclub.co.uk

Parkland golf is played here over a testing course, where accuracy from the tee is well-rewarded. The course is very popular with visiting societies for the clubhouse has many amenities. Course designed by James Braid.

18 holes, 6425yds, Par 72, SSS 71, Course record 66.

Club membership: 650. **Visitors:** must contact in advance, no societies Tue, weekends and bank holidays. **Societies:** must apply in writing. **Green Fees:** £35 (£40 weekends & bank holidays). **Prof:** Nigel M Parr **Course Designer:** James Braid **Facilities:** 🏵🍴🛏♨🎯⚑🏌⚲🛖◇⚘ **Conf:** facilities available **Corporate:** Hospitality Days available **Location:** 7m E of city centre off B5178

Hotel
⌂ **Premier Travel Inn Liverpool (Roby),**
Roby Rd, Huyton, LIVERPOOL
☎ 0870 9906596 – 53 en suite

West Derby
Yew Tree Ln, West Derby L12 9HQ
☎ 0151 254 1034 📠 0151 259 0505
e-mail: pmilne@westderbygc.freeserve.co.uk

A parkland course always in first-class condition, and so giving easy walking. The fairways are well-wooded. Care must be taken on the first nine holes to avoid the brook which guards many of the greens. A modern well-designed clubhouse with many amenities overlooks the course.

18 holes, 6277yds, Par 72, SSS 70, Course record 65.

Club membership: 550. **Visitors:** may not play before 9.30am. May play weekends by arrangement. **Societies:** may not play on Sat, Sun & bank holidays; must contact in advance. **Green Fees:** £29.50 per day/round (£37 weekends) **Prof:** Andrew Witherup **Facilities:** 🏵🍴🛏♨🎯⚑🏌⚲🛖◇⚘ **Conf:** facilities available **Corporate:** Hospitality Days available **Location:** 4.5m E of city centre off A57

Hotel
★★★ 68% **The Royal Hotel,**
Marine Ter, Waterloo, LIVERPOOL
☎ 0151 928 2332 – 25 en suite

NEWTON-LE-WILLOWS

Haydock Park
Newton Ln WA12 0HX
☎ 01925 228525 📠 01925 224984

A well-wooded parkland course, close to the well-known racecourse, and always in excellent condition. The pleasant undulating fairways offer some very interesting golf and the 6th, 9th, 11th

Continued **49**

and 13th holes are particularly testing. The clubhouse is very comfortable.

18 holes, 6058yds, Par 70, SSS 69, Course record 65.

Club membership: 560. Visitors: welcome weekdays except Tue, with member only weekends & bank holidays. Must contact in advance. Societies: must contact in advance. Green Fees: not confirmed. Prof: Peter Kenwright Course Designer: James Braid Facilities: ⑪ ⑧ ⅃ ☞ ☏▯ ⚲ ⌂ ✍ Location: 0.75m NE off A49

Hotel
★★ 65% **Kirkfield Hotel,**
2/4 Church St, NEWTON-LE-WILLOWS
☎ 01925 228196 – 20 en suite

ST HELENS
Grange Park
Prescot Rd WA10 3AD
☎ 01744 26318 📠 01744 26318
e-mail: gpgc@ic24.net

A course of championship length set in pleasant country surroundings – playing the course it is hard to believe that industrial St Helens lies so close to hand. The course is a fine test of golf and there are many attractive holes liable to challenge all grades.

18 holes, 6446yds, Par 72, SSS 71, Course record 65.

Club membership: 730. Visitors: welcome except Tue, may not play weekends. Advisable to contact professional in advance (01744 28785) Societies: apply in writing Green Fees: not confirmed. Prof: Paul Roberts Course Designer: James Braid Facilities: ⑪ ⑧ ⅃ ☞ ☏▯ ⚲ ⌂ ✍ Location: 1.5m SW on A58

Hotel
★★ 65% **Kirkfield Hotel,**
2/4 Church St, NEWTON-LE-WILLOWS
☎ 01925 228196 – 20 en suite

SOUTHPORT
The Hesketh
Cockle Dick's Ln, off Cambridge Rd PR9 9QQ
☎ 01704 536897 📠 01704 539250
e-mail: secretary@heskethgolfclub.co.uk

The Hesketh is the oldest of the six clubs in Southport, founded in 1885. Set at the northern end of south-west Lancashire's sand dune system, the course sets a unique challenge with half of the holes threaded through tall sand dunes whilst the other holes border the Ribble estuary. The course is next to a renowned bird reserve and across the estuary are fine views of the mountains of Lancashire, Cumbria and Yorkshire. Used as a final qualifying course for the Open Championship.

18 holes, 6655yds, Par 72, SSS 72, Course record 67.

Club membership: 600. Visitors: welcome, with

handicap certificate, at all times except Tue am (Ladies), 12.30-2pm daily, after 2.30pm Sat & 10.30am Sun. Must contact in advance. Societies: please contact Martyn G Senior in advance. Green Fees: £60 per day; £50 per round (£60 per round weekends & bank holidays). Cards: 💳 📧 VISA 📧 📧 📧 Prof: Scott Astin Course Designer: J F Morris Facilities: ⑪ ⑧ ⅃ ☞ ☏▯ ⚲ ⌂ ☂ ✍ Conf: Corporate Hospitality Days available Location: 1m NE of town centre off A565

Hotel
★★★ 69% **Stutelea Hotel & Leisure Club,**
Alexandra Rd, SOUTHPORT
☎ 01704 544220 – 20 en suite

Hillside
Hastings Rd, Hillside PR8 2LU
☎ 01704 567169 📠 01704 563192
e-mail: secretary@hillside-golfclub.co.uk

Championship links course with natural hazards open to strong wind.

18 holes, 6850yds, Par 72, SSS 74, Course record 65.

Club membership: 700. Visitors: welcome except Sat, restricted on Sun & Tue (Ladies Day), must contact in advance through Secretary. Societies: must apply to Secretary in advance. Green Fees: £85 per day; £65 per round (£85 per round Sun). Cards: VISA 📧 Prof: Brian Seddon Course Designer: Hawtree/Steel Facilities: ⑪ ⑧ ⅃ ☞ ☏▯ ⚲ ⌂ ⚒ Conf: Corporate Hospitality Days available Location: 3m S of town centre on A565

Hotel
★★★ 65% **Royal Clifton Hotel,**
Promenade, SOUTHPORT
☎ 01704 533771 – 111 en suite

SOUTHPORT
Southport & Ainsdale
Bradshaws Ln, Ainsdale PR8 3LG
☎ 01704 578000 📠 01704 570896
e-mail: secretary@sandagolfclub.co.uk

'S and A', as it is known in the North, is another of the fine Championship courses for which this part of the country is famed. This Club has staged many important events and offers golf of the highest order.

18 holes, 6705yds, Par 72, SSS 73, Course record 62.

Club membership: 815. Visitors: welcome except Thu after 1pm, Sat after 3pm & Sun after 12 noon & bank holidays. Must contact club in advance & have handicap certificate. Societies: must apply in advance. Green Fees: £60 per 18 holes; £75 per 36 holes (£75 per 18 holes weekends). Cards: 💳 VISA 📧 Prof: J Payne Course Designer: James Braid Facilities: ⑪ ⑧ ⅃ ☞ ☏▯ ⚲ ⌂ ☂ ✍ Location: 3m S off A565

Continued

Championship Course

Royal Birkdale

Waterloo Rd, Birkdale PR8 2LX
☎ 01704 567920 📄 01704 562327
e-mail: secretary@royalbirkdale.com

Founded in 1889, the Royal Birkdale is considered by many to be the ultimate championship venue, having hosted every major event in the game including eight Open Championships, two Ryder Cup matches, the Walker Cup, the Curtis Cup and many amateur events. The 1st hole provides an immediate taste of what is to come, requiring a well-placed drive to avoid a bunker, water hazard and out of bounds to leave a reasonably clear view of the green. The 10th, the first of the inward nine is unique in that it is the only hole to display the significant fairway undulations one expects from the classic links course. The 12th is the most spectacular of the short holes on the course, and is considered by Tom Watson to be one of the best par 3s in the world; tucked away in the sand hills it continues to claim its fair share of disasters. The approach on the final hole is arguably the most recognisable in golf with the distinctive clubhouse designed to appear like an ocean cruise liner rising out of the sand hills. It's a par 5 for mere mortals, and played as a par 4 in the Open, but it will provide a memorable finish to any round of golf.

WHERE TO STAY NEARBY

★★★71%
Scarisbrick Hotel,
Lord St, SOUTHPORT
☎ 01704 543000
88 en suite

★★★69%
Stutelea Hotel & Leisure Club, Alexandra Rd, SOUTHPORT
☎ 01704 544220 📄 01704 500232
20 en suite

★★★65%
Royal Clifton Hotel,
Promenade, SOUTHPORT
☎ 01704 533771 📄 01704 500657
111 en suite

★★71%
Balmoral Lodge Hotel,
41 Queens Rd, SOUTHPORT
☎ 01704 544298 & 530751
📄 01704 501224
15 en suite

---

18 holes, 6726yds, Par 72, SSS 73

Club Membership
800

Visitors
Not Sat; restricted Tue, Fri, Sun; must contact in advance; handicap certificate

Societies
Must apply in advance; handicap certificates

Green Fees
May–Sep £165 per day, £130 per round (£155 per round Sun); Mar, Apr, Oct–Nov £90 per round including soup and sandwiches (£115 Sun); Dec–Feb £70 per round soup and sandwiches (£95 Sun)

Cards
💳 💳 💳 💳 💳 💳

Professional
Brian Hodgkinson

Course Designer
Hawtree

Facilities
🍴 🍽 by arrangement.
🛋 🍺 🍸 🧗 🏠 ⛳ ✏ 🏌

Corporate
Hospitality Days available

Location
1.75m S of town centre on A565

Hotel
★★★ 65% **Royal Clifton Hotel,**
Promenade, SOUTHPORT
☎ 01704 533771 – 111 en suite

Wallasey
Bayswater Rd CH45 8LA
☎ 0151 691 1024 🗎 0151 638 8988
e-mail: wallaseygc@aol.com

A well-established sporting links, adjacent to the Irish Sea, with huge sandhills and many classic holes where the player's skills are often combined with good fortune. Large, firm greens and fine views but not for the faint-hearted.

18 holes, 6503yds, Par 72, SSS 72, Course record 65.

Club membership: 650. **Visitors:** must contact one month in advance. **Societies:** must apply in writing or telephone. **Green Fees:** not confirmed. **Cards:** 🖃 **Prof:** Mike Adams **Course Designer:** Tom Morris **Facilities:** ⑪ ⑩ ⓛ ⓦ ⑨⓵ ⌂ 🏠 ⑨ 🏌 **Location:** N side of town centre off A554

Hotel
★★★ 71% **Grove House Hotel,** Grove Rd, WALLASEY
☎ 0151 639 3947 & 0151 630 4558 🗎 0151 639 0028
14 en suite

NORFOLK

Barnham Broom Hotel, Golf, Conference, Leisure
Honingham Rd NR9 4DD
☎ 01603 759552 & 759393 🗎 01603 758224
e-mail: golfmanager@barnham-broom.co.uk

Valley Course meanders through the River Yare Valley, parkland and mature trees. Hill Course has wide fairways, heavily guarded greens and spectacular views.

Valley Course: 18 holes, 6483yds, Par 72, SSS 71.
Hill Course: 18 holes, 6495yds, Par 71, SSS 71.

Club membership: 500. **Visitors:** must contact in advance on 01603 759552. **Societies:** must contact in advance on 01603 759393 or 759552 **Green Fees:** £30 for 18 holes (£40 weekends). **Cards:** 🖃 **Prof:** Ian Rollett **Course Designer:** Frank Pennink **Facilities:** ⑪ ⑩ ⓛ ⓦ ⑨⓵ ⌂ 🏠 ⑨ 🏌 🏌 🏌 squash, sauna, solarium, gymnasium, 3 academy holes. Golf school. Squash tuition. **Conf:** facilities available **Corporate:** Hospitality Days available **Location:** 10m SW of Norwich, off A47 at Honingham or A11 at Wymondham

Hotel
★★★ 75% **Barnham Broom Hotel,**
Golf & Country Club, BARNHAM BROOM

☎ 01603 759393 759522 🗎 01603 758224
52 en suite

Royal West Norfolk
PE31 8AX
☎ 01485 210223 🗎 01485 210087

A fine links laid out in a grand manner characterised by sleepered greens, superb cross bunkers and salt marshes. The varied and tranquil surrounds include a harbour, the sea, farmland; and marshland inhabited by many rare species of birds. A great part of the year the club is cut off by tidal flooding which restricts the amount of play possible.

18 holes, 6428yds, Par 71, SSS 71, Course record 66.

Club membership: 865. **Visitors:** must contact well in advance. Restrictions at weekends and in Aug. **Societies:** must contact Secretary in advance. **Green Fees:** terms on application. **Cards:** 🖃 🖃 🖃 🖃 **Prof:** S Rayner **Course Designer:** Holcombe-Ingleby **Facilities:** ⑪ ⑩ ⓛ ⓦ ⑨⓵ ⌂ 🏠 ⑨ 🏌 **Location:** 7m E of Hunstanton. In Brancaster village turn N at the beach/Broad Lane junct with A149 for 1m

Hotel
★★ 76% **The White Horse,** BRANCASTER STAITHE
☎ 01485 210262 – 7 en suite 8 annexe en suite

Royal Cromer
145 Overstrand Rd NR27 0JH
☎ 01263 512884 🗎 01263 512430
e-mail: general.manager@royal-cromer.com

Seaside course set out on cliff edge, hilly and subject to wind. Challenging upland course with spectacular views out to sea and overlooking town. Strong sea breezes affect the clifftop holes, the most famous being the 14th (the Lighthouse) which has a green in the shadow of the lighthouse.

18 holes, 6508yds, Par 72, SSS 72, Course record 67.

Club membership: 700. **Visitors:** must contact in advance, handicap certificate preferred. **Societies:** must contact in advance. **Green Fees:** £45 per day (£55 weekends & bank holidays). **Cards:** 🖃 🖃 🖃 🖃 🖃 🖃 **Prof:** Lee Patterson **Course Designer:** J H Taylor **Facilities:** ⑪ ⑩ ⓛ ⓦ ⑨⓵ ⌂ 🏠 ⑨ 🏌 🏌 **Conf:** Corporate Hospitality Days available **Location:** 1m E on B1159

Hotel
★★ 73% **Red Lion,** Brook St, CROMER
☎ 01263 514964 – 12 en suite

Great Yarmouth & Caister
Beach House, Caister-on-Sea NR30 5TD
☎ 01493 728699 🗎 01493 728831

e-mail: office@caistergolf.co.uk

A traditional links style course played over tight and undulating fairways. A great deal of gorse and marram grass. The 468 yard 8th (par 4) is a testing hole and the 7th is an extremely fine short hole. A feature of the course is a number of sleepered bunkers, a line of four bisecting the 4th.

18 holes, 6330yds, Par 70, SSS 70, Course record 65.

Club membership: 720. Visitors: must contact in advance. Restricted weekends. Societies: must apply in writing or telephone. Green Fees: £35 per day; £20 after 4pm (£45/£30 weekends & bank holidays). Cards: 💳 💳 💳 💳 Prof: Martyn Clarke Course Designer: H Colt Facilities: 🏌 🍴 🛏 🍺 🍴 🎿 📷 ✦ snooker. Location: 0.5m N off A149, at southern end of Caister-on-Sea

Hotel
★★★ 71% Imperial Hotel,
North Dr, GREAT YARMOUTH
☎ 01493 842000 – 39 en suite

HUNSTANTON

Hunstanton
Golf Course Rd PE36 6JQ
☎ 01485 532811 📠 01485 532319
e-mail: hunstanton.golf@eidosnet.co.uk

A championship links course set among some of the most natural golfing country in East Anglia. Keep out of the numerous bunkers and master the fast greens to play to your handicap – then you only have the wind to contend with! Good playing conditions all year round.

18 holes, 6759yds, Par 72, SSS 73.

Club membership: 675. Visitors: must contact in advance and be a club member with current handicap certificate. Restricted at weekends & may not play bank holiday weekends. Play in two ball format ie singles or foursomes. Societies: apply in advance. Green Fees: £65 per day; £40 after 3pm (£75/£50 weekends). Cards: 💳 💳 💳 💳 Prof: James Dodds Course Designer: James Braid Facilities: 🏌 🍴 by prior arrangement 🛏 🍺 🍴 🎿 📷 ✦ ✦ Location: Off A149 in Old Hunstanton village, signposted

Hotel
★★★ 69% Le Strange Arms Hotel,
Golf Course Rd, Old Hunstanton, HUNSTANTON
☎ 01485 534411 – 36 en suite

SHERINGHAM

Sheringham
Weybourne Rd NR26 8HG
☎ 01263 823488 📠 01263 825189
e-mail: info@sheringhamgolfclub.co.uk

The course is laid out along the rolling, gorse-clad cliff top from where the sea is visible on every hole. The par 4 holes are outstanding with a fine

along the cliffs from the 5th tee.

18 holes, 6456yds, Par 70, SSS 71, Course record 64.

Club membership: 760. Visitors: must contact in advance & have handicap certificate. Restricted weekends. Societies: bookings may be made in writing or by telephone. Green Fees: terms on application. Prof: M W Jubb Course Designer: Tom Dunn Facilities: 🏌 🍴 🛏 🍺 🍴 🎿 📷 🚜 ✦ Location: W side of town centre on A149

Hotel
★★ 71% Beaumaris Hotel, South St, SHERINGHAM
☎ 01263 822370 – 21 en suite

THETFORD

Thetford
Brandon Rd IP24 3NE
☎ 01842 752169 📠 01842 766212
e-mail: sally@thetfordgolfclub.co.uk

This is a course with a good pedigree. It was laid out by a fine golfer, C H Mayo, later altered by James Braid and then again altered by another famous course designer, Mackenzie Ross. It is a testing heathland course with a particularly stiff finish.

18 holes, 6849yds, Par 72, SSS 73, Course record 66.

Club membership: 750. Visitors: pre booking advisable, may not play weekends or bank holidays except with member. Handicap certificate required. Societies: must contact in advance, Wed-Fri only. Green Fees: £40 per day, £30 per round. Cards: 💳 💳 💳 💳 💳 Prof: Gary Kitley Course Designer: James Braid Facilities: 🏌 🍴 🛏 🍺 🍴 🎿 📷 ✦ ✦ short game area. Location: 2m W of Thetford on B1107

Hotel
★★ 65% The Thomas Paine Hotel,
White Hart St, THETFORD
☎ 01842 755631 – 13 en suite

NORTHAMPTONSHIRE

COLLINGTREE

Collingtree Park
Windingbrook Ln NN4 0XN
☎ 01604 700000 & 701202 📠 01604 702600
e-mail: info@collingtreeparkgolf.com

An 18-hole resort course designed by former US and British Open champion Johnny Miller. The American style course has water hazards on ten holes with a spectacular par 5 18th Island Green. The Golf Academy includes a driving range, practice holes and indoor video teaching room.

18 holes, 6776yds, Par 72, SSS 72, Course record 66.

Club membership: 660. Visitors: must contact in advance & have handicap certificate. Societies: contact in advance. Green Fees: terms on application.. Cards: 💳 💳 💳 💳 💳 💳 Prof: G Pook/A Carter Course Designer: Johnny Miller Facilities: 🍴 🍽 🛒 🛍 🏌 🏵 🏪 🅿 🚗 🏌 3-hole Academy. indoor teaching room. Conf: facilities available Corporate: Hospitality Days available Location: M1 junct 15 on A508 to Northampton

Hotel
★★★★ 70% **Northampton Marriott Hotel**, Eagle Dr, NORTHAMPTON
☎ 01604 768700 – 120 en suite

NORTHUMBERLAND

BAMBURGH

Bamburgh Castle
The Club House, 40 The Wynding NE69 7DE
☎ 01668 214378 (club) & 214321 (sec)
📠 01668 214607
e-mail: bamburghcastlegolfclub@hotmail.com

Superb coastal course with excellent greens that are both fast and true, natural hazards of heather and whin bushes abound. Magnificent views of the Farne Islands, Holy Island, Lindisfarne Castle, Bamburgh Castle and Cheviot Hills.

18 holes, 5621yds, Par 68, SSS 67, Course record 64.

Club membership: 785. Visitors: must contact in advance. Restricted weekends, bank holidays and competition days. Societies: apply in writing. Weekdays & Sun only. Green Fees: £45 per day, £32 per round (£50/£37 weekends). Cards: 💳 💳 💳 💳 💳 Course Designer: George Rochester Facilities: 🍴 🍽 🛒 🛍 🏌 🏵 🏪 🅿 Conf: Corporate Hospitality Days available Location: 6m E of A1 via B1341 or B1342

Hotel
★★ 69% **The Lord Crewe**, Front St, BAMBURGH
☎ 01668 214243 – 18 rms (17 en suite)

BERWICK-UPON-TWEED

Berwick-upon-Tweed (Goswick)
Goswick TD15 2RW
☎ 01289 387256 📠 01289 387334
e-mail: goswickgc@btconnect.com

18 holes, 6686yds, Par 72, SSS 72, Course record 69.

Course Designer: James Braid Location: 6m S of Berwick off A1 Telephone for further details

Hotel
★★★ 70% **Marshall Meadows Country House Hotel**, BERWICK-UPON-TWEED
☎ 01289 331133 – 19 en suite

HEXHAM

Hexham
Spital Park NE46 3RZ
☎ 01434 603072 📠 01434 601865
e-mail: info@hexhamgolf.co.uk

A very pretty well-drained parkland course with interesting natural contours. Exquisite views from parts of the course of the Tyne Valley below. As good a parkland course as any in the North of England.

18 holes, 6294yds, Par 70, SSS 68, Course record 64.

Club membership: 700. Visitors: advance booking advisable. Societies: welcome weekdays, contact in advance. Green Fees: £30 per round (£40 weekends & bank holidays). Cards: 💳 💳 💳 💳 💳 💳 Prof: Martin Forster Course Designer: Vardon/Caird Facilities: 🍴 🍽 🛒 🛍 🏌 🏵 🏪 🅿 🚗 squash, squash courts. Conf: facilities available Corporate

Hospitality Days available **Location:** 1m NW on B6531

Hotel
★★★ 68% **Beaumont Hotel,** Beaumont St, HEXHAM
☎ 01434 602331 – 25 en suite

NOTTINGHAMSHIRE

KIRKBY IN ASHFIELD

Notts
Derby Rd NG17 7QR
☎ 01623 753225 📄 01623 753655
e-mail: nottsgolfclub@hollinwell.fsnet.co.uk
Undulating heathland championship course.

18 holes, 7103yds, Par 72, SSS 75, Course record 64.

Club membership: 450. **Visitors:** must contact in advance & have handicap certificate. With member only weekends & bank holidays. **Societies:** must apply in advance. **Green Fees:** £90 per day; £60 per round.. **Cards:** 💳 📇 💳 📇 🦺 💳 **Prof:** Mike Bradley **Course Designer:** Willie Park **Facilities:** 🏉 🍴 🛒 ☕ 🏌 ⚖ 🏠 ☂ ⚡ 🏌 🏌 ✈ **Conf:** facilities available **Location:** 2m SE of Mansfield off A611

Hotel
★★★★ 70% **Renaissance Derby/Nottingham Hotel,** Carter Ln East, SOUTH NORMANTON
☎ 01773 812000 – 158 en suite

MANSFIELD

Sherwood Forest
Eakring Rd NG18 3EW
☎ 01623 627403 & 627403 📄 01623 420412
e-mail: sherwood@forest43.freeserve.co.uk

As the name suggests, the Forest is the main feature of this natural heathland course with its heather, silver birch and pine trees. The homeward nine holes are particularly testing. The 11th to the 14th are notable par 4 holes on this well-bunkered course designed by the great James Braid.

18 holes, 6853yds, Par 71, SSS 74, Course record 67.

Club membership: 750. **Visitors:** weekdays only by prior arrangement with the golf manager. **Societies:** by arrangement with the golf manager. **Green Fees:** £70 per day, £50 per round (weekdays only). **Cards:** 💳 📇 💳 📇 🦺 💳 **Prof:** Ken Hall **Course Designer:** W S Colt/James Braid **Facilities:** 🏉 🍴 🛒 ☕ 🏌 ⚖ 🏠 ⚡ 🛒 ✈ snooker. **Conf:** facilities available Corporate Hospitality Days available **Location:** E of Mansfield

Hotel
★★ 68% **Pine Lodge Hotel,**
281-283 Nottingham Rd, MANSFIELD
☎ 01623 622308 – 20 en suite

NOTTINGHAM

Wollaton Park
Limetree Av, Wollaton Park NG8 1BT
☎ 0115 978 7574 📄 0115 970 0736
e-mail: wollatonparkgc@aol.com

A traditional parkland course on slightly undulating land, winding its way through historic woodland and set in a historic deer park. Fine views of 16th-century Wollaton Hall.

18 holes, 6445yds, Par 71, SSS 71, Course record 64.

Club membership: 700. **Visitors:** may not play Wed or competition days. **Societies:** must apply in advance. **Green Fees:** £48 per day; £35 per round (£55/£40 weekends & bank holidays). **Cards:** 💳 📇 💳 🦺 💳 **Prof:** John Lower **Course Designer:** T Williamson **Facilities:** 🏉 🍴 🛒 ☕ 🏌 ⚖ 🏠 ☂ ⚡ **Conf:** Corporate Hospitality Days available **Location:** 2.5m W of city centre off Nottingham ring road at junct with A52

Hotel
★★★ 62% **Swans Hotel & Restaurant,** 84-90 Radcliffe Rd, West Bridgford, NOTTINGHAM
☎ 0115 981 4042 – 30 en suite

SUTTON IN ASHFIELD

Coxmoor
Coxmoor Rd NG17 5LF
☎ 01623 557359 📄 01623 557359
e-mail: coxmoor@freeuk.com

Undulating moorland/heathland course with easy walking and excellent views. The clubhouse is traditional with a well-equipped games room. The course lies adjacent to Forestry Commission land over which there are several footpaths and extensive views.

18 holes, 6577yds, Par 73, SSS 72, Course record 65.

Club membership: 700. **Visitors:** must play with member weekends & bank holidays. Must contact in advance. **Societies:** must apply in advance. **Green Fees:** £55 per day; £40 per round. **Cards:** 💳 📇 💳 🦺 **Prof:** David Ridley **Facilities:** 🏉 🍴 🛒 ☕ 🏌 ⚖ 🏠 ⚡ snooker. **Conf:** Corporate Hospitality Days available **Location:** 2m SE off A611; 4m from junct 27 on M1

Hotel
★★★★ 70% **Renaissance Derby/Nottingham Hotel,** Carter Ln East, SOUTH NORMANTON
☎ 01773 812000 – 158 en suite

WORKSOP

Lindrick
Lindrick Common S81 8BH
☎ 01909 475282 📄 01909 488685
e-mail: lgc@ansbronze.com

Heathland course with some trees and masses of gorse.

18 holes, 6486yds, Par 71, SSS 71, Course record 63.

Club membership: 510. **Visitors:** must contact in advance. Restricted Tue & weekends. Handicap certificate required. **Societies:** welcome except Tue (am) & weekends by prior arrangement with the Secretary. **Green Fees:** £60 per day, £50 per 18 holes. Reduced winter rate. **Cards:** 💳 🏧 VISA ⬛ Barclays CONNECT 🏧 **Prof:** John R King **Facilities:** 🏮 🍴 ⬛ 🍺 ♥ 🏌 ⚲ 🏠 ✦ buggies for disabled only. **Conf:** Corporate Hospitality Days available **Location:** M1 junct 31, 4m NW of Worksop on A57

Hotel
★★★ 68% **Lion Hotel,** 112 Bridge St, WORKSOP
☎ 01909 477925 – 45 en suite

OXFORDSHIRE

FRILFORD

Frilford Heath
OX13 5NW
☎ 01865 390864 📄 01865 390823
e-mail: secretary@frilfordheath.co.uk

Has 54 holes in three distinctive layouts of significantly differing character. The Green Course is a fully mature heathland course of some 6000 yards. The Red Course is of championship length at 6800 yards with a parkland flavour and a marked degree of challenge. The Blue Course is of modern design, and at 6728 yards, it incorporates water hazards and large shallow sand traps.

Red Course:
18 holes, 6884yds, Par 73, SSS 73, Course record 66.
Green Course:
18 holes, 6006yds, Par 69, SSS 69, Course record 67.
Blue Course:
18 holes, 6728yds, Par 72, SSS 72, Course record 63.

Club membership: 1300. **Visitors:** contact in advance. Handicap certificates required. **Societies:** apply in advance. **Green Fees:** £55 per day (£70 weekends). **Cards:** 💳 VISA 🏧 🟨 **Prof:** Derek Craik **Course Designer:** J Taylor/D Cotton/S Gidman **Facilities:** 🏮 🍴 ⬛ 🍺 ♥ 🏌 ⚲ 🏠 🍴 ✦ 🚗 ✦ **Conf:** facilities available Corporate Hospitality Days available **Location:** 3m W of Abingdon off A338 Oxford-Wantage road

Hotel
★★★ 66% **Abingdon Four Pillars Hotel,** Marcham Rd, ABINGDON
☎ 0800 374 692 – 62 en suite

MILTON COMMON

The Oxfordshire
Rycote Ln OX9 2PU
☎ 01844 278300 📄 01844 278003
e-mail: info@theoxfordshiregolfclub.com

Designed by Rees Jones, The Oxfordshire is considered to be one of the most exciting courses in the country. The strategically contoured holes blend naturally into the surrounding countryside to provide a challenging game of golf. With 4 lakes and 135 bunkers, the course makes full use of the terrain and the natural elements to provide characteristics similar to those of a links course.

18 holes, 7192yds, Par 72, SSS 75, Course record 64.

Club membership: 376. **Visitors:** After 11am weekends and bank holidays, contact in advance, handicap certificates must be provided **Societies:** Apply in writing/telephone in advance. **Green Fees:** not confirmed. **Cards:** 💳 🏧 VISA Barclays CONNECT 🏧 🟨 **Prof:** Stephen Gibson **Course Designer:** Rees Jones **Facilities:** 🏮 🍴 ⬛ 🍺 ♥ 🏌 ⚲ 🏠 🍴 ✦ 🚗 ✦ 🏌 Japanese ofuro baths. **Conf:** facilities available Corporate Hospitality Days available **Location:** 1.5m from junct 7, M40 on A329

Hotel
★★★ 74% **Spread Eagle Hotel,** Cornmarket, THAME
☎ 01844 213661 – 33 en suite

NUFFIELD

Huntercombe
RG9 5SL
☎ 01491 641207 📄 01491 642060
e-mail: office@huntercombegolfclub.co.uk

This heathland/woodland course overlooks the Oxfordshire plain and has many attractive and interesting fairways and greens. Walking is easy after the 3rd which is a notable hole. The course is subject to wind and grass pot bunkers are interesting hazards.

18 holes, 6271yds, Par 70, SSS 70, Course record 63.

Club membership: 800. **Visitors:** must contact in advance and have a handicap certificate. **Societies:** must contact in advance. **Green Fees:** £60 per day; £40 per round (£75/£60 per round weekends and bank holidays). **Cards:** 💳💳💳 **Prof:** Ian Roberts **Course Designer:** Willie Park jnr **Facilities:** ⊕🎯🍴🏌 🍽🍴👤🏠⛳🏌🚗🏌🏌 **Location:** 6m W of Henley-on-Thames off A4130 at Nuffield

Hotel
★★★ 68% **Shillingford Bridge Hotel,** Shillingford, WALLINGFORD
☎ 01865 858567 – 34 en suite 8 annexe en suite

OXFORD
Southfield
Hill Top Rd OX4 1PF
☎ 01865 242158 📠 01865 728544
e-mail: sgcltd@btopenworld.com

Home of the City, University and Ladies Clubs, and well-known to graduates throughout the world. A challenging course, in a varied parkland setting, providing a real test for players.

18 holes, 6325yds, Par 70, SSS 70, Course record 64.

Club membership: 740. **Visitors:** visitors welcome. **Societies:** must apply in writing. **Green Fees:** £35 per day; £25 per round. **Cards:** 💳💳💳💳 **Prof:** Tony Rees **Course Designer:** H S Colt **Facilities:** ⊕🎯🍴🍽🍴👤🏠⛳🏌🚗🏌 **Conf:** Corporate Hospitality Days available **Location:** 1.5m SE of city centre off B480

Hotel
★★★ 67% **Eastgate Hotel,** 73 High St, OXFORD
☎ 0870 400 8201 – 64 en suite

TADMARTON
Tadmarton Heath
OX15 5HL
☎ 01608 737278 📠 01608 730548
e-mail: thgc@btinternet.com

A mixture of heath and sandy land, on a high plateau in the Cotswolds. The course opens gently before reaching the scenic 7th hole across a trout stream close to the clubhouse. The course then progressively tightens through the gorse before a

challenging 430 yard dog-leg completes the round.

18 holes, 5917yds, Par 69, SSS 69, Course record 63.

Club membership: 650. **Visitors:** weekday by appointment, with member only at weekends. No visitors Thu mornings **Societies:** by arrangement with club office. **Green Fees:** £45 per day, £35 after 2.30pm, (weekends £50, £40 after noon). **Prof:** Tom Jones **Course Designer:** Col C K Hutchinson **Facilities:** ⊕🍴🍽🍴👤🏠⛳🏌🚗🏌 **Conf:** Corporate Hospitality Days available **Location:** 1m SW of Lower Tadmarton off B4035, 4m from Banbury

Hotel
★★★ 71% **Banbury House,** Oxford Rd, BANBURY
☎ 01295 259361 – 63 en suite

RUTLAND

KETTON
Luffenham Heath
PE9 3UU
☎ 01780 720205 📠 01780 722146
e-mail: jringleby@theluffenhamheathgc.co.uk

This undulating heathland course with low bushes, much gorse and many trees, lies in a conservation area for flora and fauna. From the higher part of the course there is a magnificent view across the Chater Valley. The course places a premium on accuracy with many demanding driving holes, challenging bunkers and well-guarded greens. The course is not long but there are several outstanding holes.

18 holes, 6315yds, Par 70, SSS 70, Course record 64.

Club membership: 550. **Visitors:** must contact in advance. Weekends with member only before 2.30pm. **Societies:** write or telephone in advance. **Green Fees:** not confirmed. **Cards:** 💳💳💳 **Prof:** Ian Burnett **Course Designer:** James Braid **Facilities:** ⊕🍴🍽🍴👤🏠⛳🏌 **Conf:** Corporate Hospitality Days available **Location:** 1.5m SW of Ketton by Fosters Railway Bridge on A6121

Hotel
★★★ 80% **The George of Stamford,** 71 St Martins, STAMFORD
☎ 01780 750750 & 750700 (Res) 📠 01780 750701
47 en suite

SHROPSHIRE

WESTON-UNDER-REDCASTLE

Hawkstone Park Hotel
SY4 5UY
☎ 01939 200611 📄 01939 200335
e-mail: info@hawkstone.co.uk

The Hawkstone Course plays through the English Heritage designated Grade I landscape of the historic park and follies providing a beautiful, tranquil yet dramatic back drop to a round of golf. The Windmill Course utilises many American- style features and extensive water hazards and is a challenging alternative.

Hawkstone Course:
18 holes, 6491yds, Par 72, SSS 71, Course record 65.
Windmill Course:
18 holes, 6476yds, Par 72, SSS 72, Course record 64.
Academy Course: 6 holes, 741yds, Par 18, SSS 18.

Club membership: 650. Visitors: advance bookings recommended. Societies: must contact in advance by telephone. Green Fees: £34 per round (£44 weekends). Cards: 💳 💳 💳 💳 💳 Prof: Stuart Leech Course Designer: J Braid Facilities: ⊕ 🍴 🏌 🍺 🍽 🏌 🏌 🏌 🏌 🏌 🏌 6-hole, par 3 course, snooker. Conf: facilities available Corporate: Hospitality Days available Location: Located between Whitchurch and Shrewsbury off the A49/A442

WHITCHURCH

Hill Valley
Terrick Rd SY13 4JZ
☎ 01948 663584 & 667788 📄 01948 665927
e-mail: info@hillvalley.co.uk

Emerald:
18 holes, 6628yds, Par 73, SSS 72, Course record 64.
Sapphire: 18 holes, 4800yds, Par 66, SSS 64.

Course Designer: Peter Alliss/Dave Thomas Location: 1m N. Follow signs from Bypass
Telephone for further details

Hotel
★★ 70% **Crown Hotel & Restaurant,**
High St, NANTWICH
☎ 01270 625283 – 18 en suite

SOMERSET

BATH

Bath
Sham Castle, North Rd BA2 6JG
☎ 01225 463834 📄 01225 331027
e-mail: enquiries@bathgolfclub.org.uk

Considered to be one of the finest courses in the west, this is the site of Bath's oldest golf club. Situated on high ground overlooking the city there are splendid views over the surrounding countryside. The rocky ground supports good quality turf and there are many good holes. The 17th is a dog-leg right past, or over the corner of an out-of-bounds wall, and then on to an undulating green.

18 holes, 6442yds, Par 71, SSS 71, Course record 66.

Club membership: 750. Visitors: advisable to contact in advance. Handicap certificates required. Societies: Wed & Fri by prior arrangement. Green Fees: not confirmed. Prof: Peter J Hancox Course Designer: Colt & others Facilities: ⊕ 🍴 🏌 🍺 🍽 🏌 🏡 🏌 🏌 Location: 1.5m SE city centre off A36

Hotel
★★★ 72% **The Francis,** Queen Square, BATH
☎ 0870 400 8223 – 95 en suite

BURNHAM-ON-SEA

Burnham & Berrow
St Christopher's Way TA8 2PE
☎ 01278 785760 📄 01278 795440
e-mail: secretary@BurnhamandBerrow.golfclub.co.uk

Natural championship links course with panoramic views of the Somerset hills sweeping across the famed reed beds and the Bristol Channel, with the islands of Steepholm and Flatholm against the background of the Welsh coast line.

Championship Course: 18 holes, 6606yds, Par 71, SSS 73, Course record 66.
Channel Course: 9 holes, 6120yds, Par 70, SSS 69.

Club membership: 900. Visitors: must contact in advance & have handicap certificate (gentlemen 22 or under, ladies 30 or under) to play on the Championship course. Societies: telephone in advance. Green Fees: not confirmed. Cards: 💳 💳 💳 💳 Prof: Mark Crowther-Smith Facilities: ⊕ 🍴 🏌 🍺 🍽 🏌 🏡 🏌 🏌 🏌 Location: 1m N of town on B3140

Hotel
★★ 72% **Woodlands Country House Hotel,**
Hill Ln, BRENT KNOLL
☎ 01278 760232 – 9 en suite

CLEVEDON

Clevedon

Castle Rd, Walton St Mary BS21 7AA
☎ 01275 874057 📠 01275 341228
e-mail: secretary@clevedongolfclub.co.uk

Situated on the clifftop overlooking the Severn estuary and with distant views of the Welsh coast. Excellent parkland course in first-class condition. Magnificent scenery and some tremendous 'drop' holes.

18 holes, 6557yds, Par 72, SSS 72, Course record 68.

Club membership: 750. **Visitors:** must contact in advance. No play Wed morning. **Societies:** not bank holidays; telephone or apply in writing. **Green Fees:** £30 per day (£40 weekends). **Prof:** Robert Scanlan **Course Designer:** S Herd **Facilities:** ⑪ ⑩ ⓛ 🍺 ☕ ⏍ 🏌 🏠 ⛳ 🚩 ⚑ **Conf:** facilities available Corporate Hospitality Days available **Location:** M5 junct 20, 1m NE of town centre

Hotel
★★★ 67% **Walton Park Hotel,**
Wellington Ter, CLEVEDON
☎ 01275 874253 – 40 en suite

MINEHEAD

Minehead & West Somerset

The Warren TA24 5SJ
☎ 01643 702057 📠 01643 705095
e-mail: secretary@mineheadgolf.co.uk

Flat seaside links, very exposed to wind, with good turf set on a shingle bank. The last five holes adjacent to the beach are testing. The 215-yard 18th is wedged between the beach and the club buildings and provides a good finish.

18 holes, 6228yds, Par 71, SSS 70, Course record 65.

Club membership: 620. **Visitors:** must contact Secretary in advance. **Societies:** telephone in advance. **Green Fees:** not confirmed. **Cards:** 💳 🔲 🔲 💳 🔲 🔲 **Prof:** Ian Read **Facilities:** ⑪ ⑩ ⓛ 🍺 ☕ ⏍ 🏌 🏠 🚩 ⛳ **Conf:** Corporate Hospitality Days available **Location:** E end of esplanade

Hotel
★★★ 64% **Northfield Hotel,**
Northfield Rd, MINEHEAD
☎ 01643 705155 – 28 en suite

WESTON-SUPER-MARE

Weston-Super-Mare

Uphill Rd North BS23 4NQ
☎ 01934 626968 & 633360(pro) 📠 01934 621360
e-mail: wsmgolfclub@eurotelbroadband.com

A compact and interesting layout with the opening hole adjacent to the beach. The sandy, links-type course is slightly undulating and has beautifully maintained turf and greens. The 15th

is a testing 455-yard par 4. Superb views across the Bristol Channel to Cardiff.

18 holes, 6245yds, Par 70, SSS 70, Course record 65.

Club membership: 750. **Visitors:** must have handicap certificate to play. **Societies:** apply in writing or telephone. **Green Fees:** £36 per round (£56 weekends). **Cards:** 💳 🔲 🔲 💳 🔲 🔲 **Prof:** Mike Laband **Course Designer:** T Dunne/Dr Mackenzie **Facilities:** ⑪ ⑩ ⓛ 🍺 ☕ ⏍ 🏌 🏠 ⛳ 🚩 **Location:** S side of town centre off A370

Hotel
★★★ 65% **Beachlands Hotel,**
17 Uphill Rd North, WESTON-SUPER-MARE
☎ 01934 621401 – 23 en suite

YEOVIL

Yeovil

Sherborne Rd BA21 5BW
☎ 01935 422965 📠 01935 411283
e-mail: yeovilgolfclub@yeovilgc.fsnet.co.uk

On the Old Course the opener lies by the River Yeo before the gentle climb to high downs with good views. The outstanding 14th and 15th holes present a challenge, being below the player with a deep railway cutting on the left of the green. The 1st on the Newton Course is played over the river which then leads to a challenging but scenic golf course.

Old Course: 18 holes, 6150yds, Par 72, SSS 70, Course record 64.
Newton Course: 9 holes, 4905yds, Par 68, SSS 65, Course record 63.

Club membership: 1000. **Visitors:** must contact in advance. Members only before 9.30am and 12.30-2pm. Handicap certificate required for Old Course. **Societies:** telephone in advance. **Green Fees:** Old Course Apr-Oct: £30 (£40 weekends & bank holidays); Nov-Mar: £25 (£30). Newton Course: £18 (£20). **Cards:** 💳 💳 🔲 🔲 **Prof:** Geoff Kite **Course Designer:** Fowler & Allison **Facilities:** ⑪ ⑩ ⓛ 🍺 ☕ ⏍ 🏌 🏠 🚩 ⛳ 🚩 **Location:** 1m E on A30

Hotel
★★★ 74% **The Yeovil Court Hotel Limited,**
West Coker Rd, YEOVIL
☎ 01935 863746 – 18 en suite 12 annexe en suite

STAFFORDSHIRE

LICHFIELD

Whittington Heath
Tamworth Rd WS14 9PW
☎ 01543 432317 📠 01543 433962
e-mail: info@whgcgolf.freeserve.co.uk

Eighteen magnificent holes wind their way through heathland and trees, presenting a good test for the serious golfer. Leaving the fairway can be severely punished. The dog-legs are most tempting, inviting the golfer to chance his arm. Local knowledge is a definite advantage. Clear views of the famous three spires of Lichfield Cathedral.

18 holes, 6490yds, Par 70, SSS 71, Course record 64.

Club membership: 660. Visitors: must contact in advance. May not play at weekends. Handicap certificate required. Societies: welcome Wed & Thu, must apply in writing. Green Fees: £50 per 36 holes; £42 per 27 holes; £35 per 18 holes. Cards: 💳 💳 💳 Prof: Adrian Sadler Course Designer: Colt Facilities: 🏌 🍴 🛒 🍺 🏌 🧳 🏧 Conf: Corporate Hospitality Days available Location: 2.5m SE on A51 Lichfield-Tamworth road

Hotel
★★★ 68% Little Barrow Hotel,
62 Beacon St, LICHFIELD
☎ 01543 414500 – 24 en suite

SUFFOLK

ALDEBURGH

Aldeburgh
Saxmundham Rd IP15 5PE
☎ 01728 452890 📠 01728 452937
e-mail: info@aldeburghgolfclub.co.uk

Good natural drainage provides year round golf in links type conditions. Accuracy is the first challenge on well-bunkered, gorse lined holes. Fine views over an Area of Outstanding Natural Beauty.

18 holes, 6349yds, Par 68, SSS 71, Course record 65. River Course: 9 holes, 4228yds, Par 64, SSS 61, Course record 62.

Club membership: 900. Visitors: must contact in advance and have a handicap certificate. 2 ball/foursomes only. Societies: must contact in advance. Green Fees: £50 per day; £40 after 12 noon (weekends £60/£50). Cards: 💳 💳 💳 Prof: Keith Preston Course Designer: Thompson, Fernie, Taylor, Park. Facilities: 🏌 🛒 🍺 🏌 🧳 🏧 🏧 Location: 1m W of Aldeburgh on A1094

Hotel
★★★ 78% Wentworth Hotel,
Wentworth Rd, ALDEBURGH
☎ 01728 452312 – 28 en suite 7 annexe en suite

HINTLESHAM

Hintlesham
IP8 3JG
☎ 01473 652761 📠 01473 652750
e-mail: office@hintleshamgolfclub.com

Magnificent championship length course blending harmoniously with the ancient parkland surrounding the hotel. Originally opened in 1991 but seeded two years beforehand, this parkland course has reached a level maturity that allows it to be rivalled in the area only by a few ancient courses. The signature holes are the 4th and 17th, both featuring water at very inconvenient interludes.

18 holes, 6638yds, Par 72, SSS 72, Course record 63.

Club membership: 470. Visitors: must contact 24 hours in advance. Societies: must telephone in advance. Green Fees: £36 per round (£44 weekends & bank holidays). Cards: 💳 💳 💳 💳 Prof: Alastair Spink Course Designer: Hawtree & Sons Facilities: 🏌 🍴 🛒 🍺 🏌 🧳 🏧 🏧 🏧 sauna, gymnasium. Conf: Corporate Hospitality Days available Location: In village on A1071

Hotel
★★★★ 80% Hintlesham Hall Hotel,
George St, HINTLESHAM
☎ 01473 652334 – 33 en suite

IPSWICH

Ipswich
Purdis Heath IP3 8UQ
☎ 01473 728941 📠 01473 715236
e-mail: mail@ipswichgolfclub.com

Many golfers are surprised when they hear that Ipswich has, at Purdis Heath, a first-class golf course. In some ways it resembles some of Surrey's better courses; a beautiful heathland course with two lakes and easy walking.

Purdis Heath: 18 holes, 6439yds, Par 71, SSS 71, Course record 64 or 9 holes, 1930yds, Par 31.

Club membership: 865. Visitors: must contact in advance & have a handicap certificate for 18-hole course. Societies: must contact in advance. Green

Fees: 18-hole course: £45 per day; £35 per round pm (£50/£40 weekends & bank holidays). 9-hole course: £10 per day (£15). **Cards:** 💳 💳 *VISA* 💳 💳 💳 **Prof:** Stephen Whymark **Course Designer:** James Braid **Facilities:** 🏤 🍴 🛏 💼 🍽 🧘 🏠 ⛳ **Location:** 3 miles E of town centre off A1156, 1m from St Augustine's Church on Bucklesham road

Hotel
★★★ 71% **Courtyard by Marriott Ipswich,** The Havens, Ransomes Europark, IPSWICH
☎ 01473 272244 – 60 en suite

RAYDON

Brett Vale
Noakes Rd IP7 5LR
☎ 01473 310718
e-mail: info@brettvalegolf.com

Brett Vale Course takes you through a nature reserve and on lakeside walks, affording views over Dedham Vale. The excellent fairways demand an accurate tee and good approach shots. Holes 1, 2, 3, 8, 10 and 15 are all affected by crosswinds, but once in the valley it is much more sheltered. Although only 5813 yards the course is testing and interesting at all levels of golf.

18 holes, 5813yds, Par 70, SSS 69, Course record 65.

Club membership: 600. **Visitors:** must book tee times and wear appropriate clothing, soft spikes only. **Societies:** apply in writing or telephone. **Green Fees:** £22.50 per 18 holes (£28 weekends and bank holidays). **Cards:** 💳 💳 *VISA* 💳 💳 💳 **Course Designer:** Howard Swan **Facilities:** 🏤 🍴 🛏 💼 🍽 🧘 🏠 ⛳ 🏌 🍳 🍽 🔨 ⛳ gymnasium. **Conf:** facilities available **Corporate:** Hospitality Days available **Location:** From A12 take B1070 towards Hadleigh. Turn left at Raydon. Water tower marks spot

Hotel
★★★★🏰 **Maison Talbooth,** Stratford Rd, DEDHAM
☎ 01206 322367 – 10 en suite

THORPENESS

Thorpeness Golf Club & Hotel
Lakeside Av IP16 4NH
☎ 01728 452176 📠 01728 453868
e-mail: info@thorpeness.co.uk

Thorpeness Golf Club provides a 6271-yard coastal heathland course, designed in 1923 by James Braid. The quality of his design combined with modern green keeping techniques has resulted in an extremely challenging course for golfers at all levels. It is also one of the driest courses in the region.

18 holes, 6271yds, Par 69, SSS 71, Course record 66.

Club membership: 500. **Visitors:** contact in advance, handicap certificate required. **Societies:** telephone in advance, handicap certificate and deposit required. **Green Fees:** £33 per day, £22 after 3pm. **Cards:** 💳 💳 *VISA* 💳 💳 💳 **Prof:** Frank Hill **Course Designer:** James Braid **Facilities:** 🏤 🍴 🛏 💼 🍽 🧘 🏠 ⛳ 🍳 🧘 🐾 🛎 snooker room. **Conf:** facilities available **Corporate:** Hospitality Days available **Location:** Take A12 heading N of Ipswich, turn onto A1094 then turn off to Aldeburgh and follow local signposting

Hotel
★★★ 77% **White Lion Hotel,** Market Cross Place, ALDEBURGH
☎ 01728 452720 – 38 en suite

WOODBRIDGE

Woodbridge
Bromeswell Heath IP12 2PF
☎ 01394 382038 📠 01394 382392
e-mail: woodbridgegc@anglianet.co.uk

A beautiful course, one of the best in East Anglia. It is situated on high ground and in different seasons presents golfers with a great variety of colour. Some say that of the many good holes the 16th is the best.

Main Course: 18 holes, 6299yds, Par 70, SSS 70, Course record 64.
Forest Course: 9 holes, 3191yds, Par 70, SSS 70.

Club membership: 700. **Visitors:** Main Course: must contact in advance, handicap certificate required, with member only weekends. Forest Course: open all days and no handicap certificate required. **Societies:** by prior telephone call or in writing. **Green Fees:** Main Course: £42 per day. Forest Course: £18 per day. **Prof:** Campbell Elliot **Course Designer:** Davie Grant **Facilities:** 🏤 🍴 by prior arrangement 🛏 💼 🍽 🧘 🏠 ⛳ **Location:** 2.5m NE off A1152

Continued 61

Hotel
★★★★♣🏰 76% **Seckford Hall Hotel,** WOODBRIDGE
☎ 01394 385678 – 22 en suite 10 annexe en suite

Royal Worlington & Newmarket
IP28 8SD
☎ 01638 712216 & 717787 📄 01638 717787

Inland 'links' course, renowned as one of the best 9-hole courses in the world. Well drained, giving excellent winter playing conditions.

9 holes, 3105yds, Par 35, SSS 70, Course record 65.

Club membership: 325. **Visitors:** with member only at weekends. Must contact in advance and have a handicap certificate. **Societies:** must apply in writing. **Green Fees:** £55 per day (reductions after 2 pm). **Prof:** Steve Barker **Course Designer:** Tom Dunn **Facilities:** ⑪ 🛏 ☕🍴 🏊 🏠 ⛳ ✐ **Location:** 0.5m SE of Worlington village near Mildenhall

Hotel
★★★ 73% **Riverside Hotel,** Mill St, MILDENHALL
☎ 01638 717274 – 17 en suite 6 annexe en suite

SURREY

New Zealand
Woodham Ln KT15 3QD
☎ 01932 345049 📄 01932 342891
e-mail: roger.marrett@nzgc.org

18 holes, 6073yds, Par 68, SSS 69, Course record 66.

Course Designer: Muir Fergusson/Simpson **Location:** 1.5m E of Woking Telephone for further details

Hotel
★★★ 67% **The Ship Hotel,**
Monument Green, WEYBRIDGE
☎ 01932 848364 – 39 en suite

West Hill
Bagshot Rd GU24 0BH
☎ 01483 474365 📄 01483 474252
e-mail: secretary@westhill-golfclub.co.uk

A challenging course with fairways lined with heather and tall pines, one of Surrey's finest courses. Demands every club in the bag to be played.

18 holes, 6343yds, Par 69, SSS 70, Course record 62.

Club membership: 500. **Visitors:** must contact in advance & have handicap certificate, may not play weekends & bank holidays. **Societies:** weekdays only. Telephone in advance. **Green Fees:** £75 per day; £55 per round. Reduced winter rates. **Cards:** 💳💳 💳 **Prof:** John A Clements **Course Designer:** C Butchart/W Parke **Facilities:** ⑪ 🍴 by prior

arrangement 🛏 ☕🍴 🏊 🏠 ⛳ ✐ **Conf:** facilities available **Corporate:** Hospitality Days available **Location:** E side of village on A322

Hotel
★★★★★ **Pennyhill Park Hotel & The Spa,**
London Rd, BAGSHOT
☎ 01276 471774 – 26 en suite 97 annexe en suite

Camberley Heath
Golf Dr GU15 1JG
☎ 01276 23258 📄 01276 692505
e-mail: info@camberleyheathgolfclub.co.uk

One of the great 'heath and heather' courses so frequently associated with Surrey. Several very good short holes – especially the 8th. The 10th is a difficult and interesting par 4, as is the 17th, where the drive must be held well to the left as trouble lies to the right. A fairway irrigation system has been installed.

18 holes, 6147yds, Par 72, SSS 70, Course record 65.

Club membership: 600. **Visitors:** may not play at weekends. Must contact in advance. **Societies:** must apply in advance. **Green Fees:** not confirmed. **Cards:** 💳💳 💳 💳 💳 💳 **Prof:** Glenn Ralph **Course Designer:** Harry S Colt **Facilities:** ⑪ 🛏 ☕🍴 🏊 🏠 ⛳ ✐🚐✐ **Conf:** facilities available **Corporate:** Hospitality Days available **Location:** 1.25m SE of town centre off A325

Hotel
★★★★★ **Pennyhill Park Hotel & The Spa,**
London Rd, BAGSHOT
☎ 01276 471774 – 26 en suite 97 annexe en suite

Effingham
Guildford Rd KT24 5PZ
☎ 01372 452203 📄 01372 459959
e-mail: secretary@effinghamgolfclub.com

Easy-walking downland course laid out on 270 acres with tree-lined fairways. It is one of the longest of the Surrey courses with wide subtle greens that provide a provocative but by no means exhausting challenge. Fine views over the London skyline.

18 holes, 6524yds, Par 71, SSS 71, Course record 64.

Club membership: 800. **Visitors:** contact in advance. With member only weekends & bank holidays. **Societies:** Wed, Thu & Fri only and must book in advance. **Green Fees:** terms on application. **Prof:** Steve Hoatson **Course Designer:** H S Colt **Facilities:** ⑪ ⑩ by prior arrangement ⮽ ⮽⮽⮽ ⮽ ⮽ ⮽ ⮽ ⮽ ⮽ ⮽ **Conf:** facilities available **Corporate:** Hospitality Days available **Location:** W side of village on A246

Hotel
★★ 66% **Bookham Grange Hotel,**
Little Bookham Common, Bookham, LEATHERHEAD
☎ 01372 452742 – 27 en suite

ENTON GREEN

West Surrey
GU8 5AF
☎ 01483 421275 📄 01483 41519
e-mail: westsurreygolfclub@btinternet.com

18 holes, 6520yds, Par 71, SSS 71, Course record 65.

Course Designer: Herbert Fowler **Location:** S side of village Telephone for further details

Hotel
★★★ 68% **The Bush Hotel,** The Borough, FARNHAM
☎ 0870 400 8225 01252 715237 📄 01252 733530
83 en suite

FARNHAM

Farnham
The Sands GU10 1PX
☎ 01252 782109 📄 01252 781185
e-mail: info@farnhamgolfclub.com

A mixture of meadowland and heath with quick drying sandy subsoil. Several of the earlier holes have interesting features.

18 holes, 6447yds, Par 72, SSS 71, Course record 66.

Club membership: 700. **Visitors:** must contact in advance. Must be member of recognised club & have handicap certificate. With member only weekends. **Societies:** must apply in writing. **Green Fees:** £50 per day; £45 per round. **Cards:** 📇 📇 📇 📇 **Prof:** Grahame Cowlishaw **Course Designer:** Donald Steel **Facilities:** ⑪ ⑩ by prior arrangement ⮽ ⮽⮽⮽ ⮽ ⮽ **Conf:** Corporate Hospitality Days available **Location:** 3m E off A31

Hotel
★★★ 68% **The Bush Hotel,** The Borough, FARNHAM
☎ 0870 400 8225/01252 715237 📄 01252 733530
83 en suite

GUILDFORD

Guildford
High Path Rd, Merrow GU1 2HL

☎ 01483 563941 📄 01483 453228
e-mail: secretary@guildfordgolfclub.co.uk

The course is on typical Surrey downland bordered by attractive woodlands. Situated on chalk, it is acknowledged to be one of the best all-weather courses in the area, and the oldest course in Surrey. Although not a long course, the prevailing winds across the open downs make low scoring difficult. It is possible to see four counties on a clear day.

18 holes, 6090yds, Par 69, SSS 70, Course record 64.

Club membership: 700. **Visitors:** must contact in advance. With member only weekends & bank holidays. **Societies:** welcome Mon-Fri. Must apply in advance. **Green Fees:** £48 per day; £38 per round. **Prof:** P G Hollington **Course Designer:** J H Taylor/Hawtree **Facilities:** ⑪ ⑩ ⮽ ⮽ ⮽⮽ ⮽ ⮽ ⮽ ⮽ **Conf:** facilities available **Corporate:** Hospitality Days available **Location:** E side of town centre off A246

Hotel
★★★ 69% **The Manor,** Newlands Corner, GUILDFORD
☎ 01483 222624 – 50 en suite

HINDHEAD

Hindhead
Churt Rd GU26 6HX
☎ 01428 604614 📄 01428 608508
e-mail: secretary@the-hindhead-golf-club.co.uk

A picturesque example of a Surrey heath-and-heather course. Players must be prepared for some hard walking. The first 9 fairways follow narrow valleys requiring straight hitting; the second 9 are much less restricted. The Open Championship pre-qualifying round is played in July.

18 holes, 6356yds, Par 70, SSS 70, Course record 63.

Club membership: 610. **Visitors:** must contact in advance and have a handicap certificate. **Societies:** Wed & Thu only, contact in advance **Green Fees:** £52 per day; £42 per round. **Prof:** Ian Benson **Course Designer:** J H Taylor **Facilities:** ⑪ ⮽ ⮽ ⮽⮽ ⮽ ⮽ ⮽ ⮽ **Conf:** Corporate Hospitality Days available **Location:** 1.5m NW of Hindhead on A287

Hotel
★★★★ 71% **Lythe Hill Hotel & Spa,**
Petworth Rd, HASLEMERE
☎ 01428 651251 – 41 en suite

OTTERSHAW

Foxhills Club and Resort
Stonehill Rd KT16 0EL
☎ 01932 872050 📄 01932 875200
e-mail: events@foxhills.co.uk

A pair of parkland courses designed in the grand manner with three championship courses. One course is tree-lined, the other, as well as trees, has massive bunkers and artificial lakes which contribute to the interest. Both courses offer testing golf and they finish on the same long 'double green'. Par 3 'Manor' course also available.

The Bernard Hunt Course: 18 holes, 6770yds, Par 73, SSS 72, Course record 65.
Longcross Course: 18 holes, 6453yds, Par 72, SSS 71, Course record 70.

Visitors: tee times bookable through events office Mon-Fri. Only after midday at weekends **Societies:** welcome Mon-Fri, must apply in advance. **Green Fees:** not confirmed. **Cards:** 💳 💳 💳 💳 **Prof:** B Hunt/R Summerscales **Course Designer:** F W Hawtree **Facilities:** ⛳🏌🍴🛒🏨🥂 ⚽ squash, sauna, solarium, gymnasium, par 3 course. **Conf:** facilities available **Corporate:** Hospitality Days available **Location:** M25 junct 11 follow signs to Woking, 2nd rdbt, 3rd exit into Foxhills road, left at T-junct, 100yds on right

Hotel
★★★★ 71% **Foxhills,**
Stonehill Rd, OTTERSHAW, Surrey
☎ 01932 872050 – 38 en suite

Tandridge

RH8 9NQ
☎ 01883 712274 📠 01883 730537
e-mail: secretary@tandridgegolfclub.com

A parkland course with two loops of 9 holes from the clubhouse. The first 9 is relatively flat. The second 9 undulates and reveals several outstanding views of the North Downs and the South.

18 holes, 6250yds, Par 70, SSS 70, Course record 66.

Club membership: 750. **Visitors:** must contact in advance. May play Mon, Wed, Thu **Societies:** Mon, Wed & Thu, apply in advance. **Green Fees:** £65 per day, £45 after noon. Winter:£35 per round. **Cards:** 💳 💳 💳 **Prof:** Chris Evans **Course Designer:** H S Colt **Facilities:** ⛳🍴🛒🥂🏨 ✏ **Conf:** Corporate Hospitality Days available **Location:** 2m SE junc 6 M25, 1.5m E of Godstone on A25

Hotel
★★★★ 73% **Nutfield Priory,** Nutfield, REDHILL
☎ 01737 824400 – 60 en suite

Hankley Common

The Club House GU10 2DD
☎ 01252 792493 📠 01252 795699

A natural heathland course subject to wind. Greens are first rate. The 18th, a long par 4, is most challenging, the green being beyond a deep chasm which traps any but the perfect second shot. The 7th is a spectacular one-shotter.

18 holes, 6702yds, Par 72, SSS 72, Course record 62.

Club membership: 700. **Visitors:** handicap certificate required, restricted to afternoons at weekends. **Societies:** apply in writing. **Green Fees:** £60 per round/£75 per day (£75 per round weekends). **Cards:** 💳 💳 💳 💳 💳 **Prof:** Peter Stow **Course Designer:** James Braid **Facilities:** ⛳🏌🍴🛒🥂🏨 🏨🚃✏ **Location:** 0.75m SE of Tilford

Hotel
★★★ 68% **The Bush Hotel,** The Borough, FARNHAM
☎ 0870 400 8225 01252 715237 📠 01252 733530
83 en suite

Burhill

Burwood Rd KT12 4BL
☎ 01932 227345 📠 01932 267159
e-mail: info@burhillgolf-club.co.uk

The Old Course is a mature tree-lined parkland course with some of the finest greens in Surrey. The New Course, opened in 2001, is a modern course built to USGA specifications and has many bunkers and water hazards, including the River Mole.

Old Course:
18 holes, 6479yds, Par 70, SSS 71, Course record 65.
New Course: 18 holes, 6597yds, Par 72, SSS 71.

Club membership: 1100. **Visitors:** no visitors weekends or bank holidays unless introduced by member. Must contact in advance. **Societies:** apply in writing. **Green Fees:** £85 per day, £62.50 per 18 holes. **Cards:** 💳 💳 💳 **Prof:** Ian Partington **Course Designer:** Willie Park/Simon Gidman **Facilities:** ⛳🏌🍴🛒🥂🏨🏨✏ 🚃✏ **Conf:** facilities available **Corporate** Hospitality Days available **Location:** M25 junct 10 on to A3 towards London, 1st exit (Painshill junct)

Hotel
★★★ 67% **The Ship Hotel,**
Monument Green, WEYBRIDGE
☎ 01932 848364 – 39 en suite

West Byfleet

Sheerwater Rd KT14 6AA
☎ 01932 343433 📠 01932 340667
e-mail: secretary@wbgc.co.uk

An attractive course set against a background of woodland and gorse. The 13th is the famous 'pond' shot with a water hazard and two bunkers fronting the green. No less than six holes of 420 yards or more.

18 holes, 6211yds, Par 70, SSS 70.

Club membership: 622. **Visitors:** must contact professional in advance, only with member at weekends. Restricted Thu (Ladies Day). **Societies:** must apply in writing/telephone. **Green Fees:** £70 per day, £50 per round. **Cards:** 💳 💳 💳 💳 💳 **Prof:** David

Continued

Championship Course

Surrey **VIRGINIA WATER**

Wentworth

Wentworth Dr GU25 4LS
☎ 01344 842201 🖶 01344 842804
e-mail: reception@wentworthclub.com

Wentworth Club, the home of the Volvo PGA and Cisco World Match Play championships, is a very special venue for any sporting, business or social occasion. The West Course (7047 yards) is familiar to millions of television viewers who have followed the championships here. There are two other 18-hole courses, the East Course (6201 yards) and the Edinburgh Course (7004 yards), as well as a 9-hole par 3 executive course. The courses cross Surrey heathland with woods of pine, oak and birch. The Club is renowned for its fine English food, and the superb tennis and health facilities include a holistic spa. The centre opened in January 1999 and has 13 outdoor tennis courts with four different playing surfaces, a 25-metre indoor pool and further extensive leisure facilities.

WHERE TO STAY NEARBY

★★72%
The Wheatsheaf,
London Rd, VIRGINIA WATER
☎ 01344 842057
17 en suite

★★★★66%
The Berystede, Bagshot Rd,
Sunninghill, ASCOT
☎ 0870 400 8111 🖶 01344 872301
90 en suite

★★★★73%
Runnymede Hotel & Spa,
Windsor Rd, EGHAM
☎ 01784 436171 🖶 01784 436340
180 en suite

★★★★71%
**The Royal Berkshire
Ramada Plaza,** London Rd,
Sunninghill, ASCOT
☎ 01344 623322 🖶 01344 627100
63 en suite

West Course
18 holes, 7047yds, Par 73, SSS 74, Course record 63

East Course
18 holes, 6201yds, Par 68, SSS 70, Course record 62

Edinburgh Course
18 holes, 7004yds, Par 72, SSS 74, Course record 67

Visitors
Not weekends; handicap certificate (men max 24, women max 32); must contact in advance

Societies
Must contact in advance in writing

Green Fees
West Course £95–£260; Edinburgh Course £80–£155; East Course £75–£125

Cards
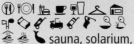

Professional
David Rennie

Course Designers
Jacobs, Gallacher, Player

Facilities
🍴🏌️🛏️☕🍷🛅🏡
🏐🔷🗑️🛒🎣🔧🔍🏌️
🏊🏊🔔 sauna, solarium, gymnasium

Conferences
Facilities available

Corporate
Hospitality Days available

Location
On A30, main gate opp turning for A329

Championship Course

Walton Heath

Deans Ln, Walton on the Hill KT20 7TP
☎ 01737 812380   📠 01737 814225
e-mail: secretary@whgc.co.uk

Walton Heath, a traditional member club, has two extremely challenging courses. Enjoying an enviable international reputation, the club was founded in 1903. It has played host to over 60 major amateur and professional championships, including the 1981 Ryder Cup and five European Open Tournaments (1977, 1980, 1987, 1991 and 1989); among the many prestigious amateur events, Walton Heath hosted the English Amateur in 2002. The Old Course is popular with visitors, while the New Course is very challenging, requiring subtle shots to get the ball near the hole. Straying from the fairway brings gorse, bracken and heather to test the most patient golfer.

WHERE TO STAY NEARBY

★★66%
Bookham Grange Hotel,
Little Bookham Common,
Bookham, LEATHERHEAD
☎ 01372 452742
27 en suite

★★★73%
Chalk Lane Hotel, Chalk Ln,
Woodcote End, EPSOM
☎ 01372 721179 📠 01372 727878
22 en suite

★★★67%
Reigate Manor Hotel,
Reigate Hill, REIGATE
☎ 01737 240125 📠 01737 223883
50 en suite

★★★★66%
The Burford Bridge,
Burford Bridge, Box Hill, DORKING
☎ 0870 400 8283 📠 01306 880386
57 en suite

★★★68%
The White Horse, High St,
DORKING
☎ 0870 400 8282 📠 01306 887241
37 en suite   41 annexe en suite

Old Course
18 holes, 6836yds, Par 72,
SSS 73, Course record 65

New Course
18 holes, 6613yds, Par 72,
SSS 72, Course record 67

Club Membership
1000

Visitors
Restricted weekends;
must contact in advance;
handicap certificate or
letter of introduction

Societies
Must contact in advance

Green Fees
£90 before 11.30am,
£80 after 11.30am
(£100 weekends)

Cards
💳 💳 💳 💳 💳 💳

Professional
Ken Macpherson

Course Designer
Herbert Fowler

Facilities
🍴 🛏 🍺 🏌 🏊 🏠 ⛳ 🏌

Corporate
Hospitality Days available

Location
SE of village off B2032

Regan **Course Designer:** C S Butchart **Facilities:** ⑨
⑪⑥ 🍴 ♨ ☎ 🅿 ⚑ ⚙ 🏌 ⛳ 🚃 ⚙ 🏆 **Conf:** Corporate
Hospitality Days available **Location:** W side of village
on A245, from A3 take A245 towards Byfleet and West
Byfleet, after going over M25 pass through 2 sets lights,
mini rdbt turn right into Sheerwater Road, club on left

Hotel
★★★ 69% **The Manor,** Newlands Corner, GUILDFORD
☎ 01483 222624 – 50 en suite

WEYBRIDGE

St George's Hill
Golf Club Rd, St George's Hill KT13 0NL
☎ 01932 847758 🖥 01932 821564
e-mail: admin@stgeorgeshillgolfclub.co.uk

**Comparable and similar to Wentworth, a feature
of this course is the number of long and difficult
par 4s. To score well it is necessary to place the
drive – and long driving pays handsomely. Walking
is hard on this undulating, heavily wooded course
with plentiful heather and rhododendrons.**

Red & Blue:
18 holes, 6513yds, Par 70, SSS 71, Course record 64.
Green: 9 holes, 2897yds, Par 35.

Club membership: 600. **Visitors:** must contact in
advance and have a handicap certificate. Visitors may
only play Wed-Fri. **Societies:** apply in writing/
telephone. **Green Fees:** £120 per day; £90 per round.
Prof: A C Rattue **Course Designer:** H S Colt
Facilities: ⑨⑥ 🍴 ♨ ☎ 🅿 ⚑ 🏌 ⚙ **Conf:** Corporate
Hospitality Days available **Location:** 2m S off B374

Hotel
★★★ 67% **The Ship Hotel,**
Monument Green, WEYBRIDGE
☎ 01932 848364 – 39 en suite

WOKING

Woking
Pond Rd, Hook Heath GU22 0JZ
☎ 01483 760053 🖥 01483 772441
e-mail: woking.golf@btconnect.com

**An 18-hole course on Surrey heathland with few
changes from the original course designed in
1892 by Tom Dunn. Bernard Darwin, a past
Captain and President, has written 'the beauty of
Woking is that there is something distinctive
about every hole.'**

18 holes, 6340yds, Par 70, SSS 70, Course record 65.

Club membership: 600. **Visitors:** must contact
Secretary at least 7 days prior to playing. No visitors
weekends & bank holidays. **Societies:** telephone
intially then confirm in writing, normally 12 months
notice. **Green Fees:** not confirmed. **Cards:** 💳 💳
📇 **Prof:** Carl Bianco **Course Designer:** Tom
Dunn **Facilities:** ⑨⑪⑥ 🍴 ♨ ☎ 🅿 ⚑ ⚙ 🚃 ⚙
Conf: Corporate Hospitality Days available **Location:**

W of town centre in area of St Johns/Hook Heath

Hotel
★★★★★ **Pennyhill Park Hotel & The Spa,**
London Rd, BAGSHOT
☎ 01276 471774 – 26 en suite 97 annexe en suite

Worplesdon
Heath House Rd GU22 0RA
☎ 01483 472277
e-mail: office@worplesdongc.co.uk

**The scene of the celebrated mixed-foursomes
competition. Accurate driving is essential on this
heathland course. The short 10th across a lake
from tee to green is a notable hole, and the 18th
provides a wonderfully challenging par 4 finish.**

18 holes, 6431yds, Par 71, SSS 71, Course record 64.

Club membership: 610. **Visitors:** must play with
member at weekends & bank holidays. Must contact in
advance and have a handicap certificate. **Societies:**
must contact in writing. **Green Fees:** £80 per day; £60
per round (Winter £35). **Cards:** 💳 💳 💳 📇 📇
Prof: J Christine **Course Designer:** J F Abercromby
Facilities: ⑨⑥ 🍴 ♨ ☎ 🅿 ⚑ ⚙ **Location:** 6m N
of Guildford, off A322

Hotel
★★★★★ **Pennyhill Park Hotel & The Spa,**
London Rd, BAGSHOT
☎ 01276 471774 – 26 en suite 97 annexe en suite

SUSSEX, EAST

BEXHILL

Cooden Beach
Cooden Sea Rd TN39 4TR
☎ 01424 842040 & 843938 (Pro Shop)
🖥 01424 842040
e-mail: enquiries@coodenbeachgc.com

**The course is close by the sea, but is not real links
in character. Despite that, it is dry and plays well
throughout the year. There are some excellent
holes such as the 4th, played to a built-up green,
the short 12th, and three good holes to finish.
There are added ponds which make the player
think more about tee shots and shots to the green.**

Continued **67**

18 holes, 6504yds, Par 72, SSS 71, Course record 67.

Club membership: 850. **Visitors:** must have a handicap certificate. Restricted at weekends. Book in advance with professional 01424 843938. **Societies:** must contact in advance by telephoning Secretary. **Green Fees:** £40 per day, £35 per round (£45/£40 weekends). **Cards:** 💳 **Prof:** Jeffrey Sim **Course Designer:** W Herbert Fowler **Facilities:** ⑪ 🍽 🛍 🍺 🎱 ⚒ 🏠 ⛳ ⚒ 🚡 ⚒ 🏌 indoor practice facility. **Conf:** facilities available **Corporate:** Hospitality Days available **Location:** 2m W of Bexhill on A259

Hotel
★★★⚜️ 76% **Powder Mills Hotel,**
Powdermill Ln, BATTLE
☎ 01424 775511 – 30 en suite 10 annexe en suite

BRIGHTON & HOVE

Dyke
Devils Dyke, Dyke Rd BN1 8YJ
☎ 01273 857296 (office) & 857260 (pro shop)
🖨 01273 857078
e-mail: secretary@dykegolfclub.org.uk

This downland course has some glorious views both towards the sea and inland. The signature hole on the course is probably the 17th; it is one of those tough par 3s of just over 200 yards, and is played across a gully to a high green.

18 holes, 6627yds, Par 72, SSS 72, Course record 66.

Club membership: 800. **Visitors:** advisable to contact in advance. May not play before noon on Sun. **Societies:** apply by telephone or in writing. **Green Fees:** not confirmed. **Cards:** 💳 **Prof:** Richard Arnold **Course Designer:** Fred Hawtree **Facilities:** ⑪ 🍽 🛍 🍺 🎱 🏠 ⛳ ⚒ 🚡 ⚒ **Conf:** Corporate Hospitality Days available **Location:** 4m N of Brighton, between A23 & A27

Hotel
★★★ 69% **The Old Tollgate Restaurant & Hotel,**
The Street, BRAMBER
☎ 01903 879494 – 11 en suite 20 annexe en suite

CROWBOROUGH

Crowborough Beacon
Beacon Rd TN6 1UJ
☎ 01892 661511 🖨 01892 611988
e-mail: secretary@cbgc.co.uk

Standing some 800 feet above sea level, this is a testing heathland course where accuracy off the tee rather than distance is paramount. Panoramic views of the South Downs, Eastbourne and even the sea on a clear day.

18 holes, 6279yds, Par 71, SSS 70, Course record 66.

Club membership: 700. **Visitors:** must contact in advance & have handicap certificate but may only play at weekends & bank holidays after 2.30pm. **Societies:** telephone or apply in writing to Secretary. **Green Fees:** £50 per round, £60 per day (£60 per round weekends after 2.30pm). **Cards:** 💳 **Prof:** Mr D C Newnham **Facilities:** ⑪ 🛍 🍺 🎱 🏠 ⛳ ⚒ **Location:** 9m S of Tunbridge Wells on A26

Hotel
★★★★ 71% **The Spa Hotel,**
Mount Ephraim, TUNBRIDGE WELLS
☎ 01892 520331 – 69 en suite

EASTBOURNE

Royal Eastbourne
Paradise Dr BN20 8BP
☎ 01323 729738 🖨 01323 744048
e-mail: sec@regc.co.uk

A famous club which celebrated its centenary in 1987. The course plays longer than it measures. Testing holes are the 8th, a par 3 played to a high green and the 16th, a par 5 right-hand dog-leg.

Devonshire Course:
18 holes, 6077yds, Par 70, SSS 69, Course record 62.
Hartington Course: 9 holes, 2147yds, Par 64, SSS 61.

Club membership: 800. **Visitors:** must contact in advance, may not play weekends except by arrangement. Handicap certificate required for Devonshire course. **Societies:** must apply in advance. **Green Fees:** Devonshire: £46 per day, £29 per round (£58/£35 weekends & bank holidays); Hartington: £17 per day. **Cards:** 💳 **Prof:** Alan Harrison **Course Designer:** Arthur Mayhewe **Facilities:** ⑪ 🍽 by prior arrangement 🛍 🍺 🎱 🏠 ⛳ 🛒 ⚒ 🚡 ⚒ snooker table. **Conf:** Corporate Hospitality Days available **Location:** 0.5m W of town centre

Hotel
★★★ 74% **Lansdowne Hotel,**
King Edward's Pde, EASTBOURNE
☎ 01323 725174 – 101 en suite

FOREST ROW

Royal Ashdown Forest
Chapel Ln RH18 5LR
☎ 01342 822018 🖨 01342 825211
e-mail: office@royalashdown.co.uk

Old Course is on undulating heathland with no bunkers. Long carries off the tees and magnificent views over the Forest. Not a course for the high handicapper. **West Course on natural heathland with no bunkers. Less demanding than Old Course although accuracy is at a premium.**

Old Course:
18 holes, 6477yds, Par 72, SSS 71, Course record 67.
West Course: 18 holes, 5606yds, Par 68, SSS 67.

Club membership: 450. **Visitors:** Old Course: some restrictions at weekends & Tue. Must have a handicap certificate. No restrictions on West Course. **Societies:** must contact in advance. **Green Fees:** Old Course: £50 per round (£70 weekends). West Course: £25 per round (£29 weekends). **Cards:** 💳 💳 VISA 💳 💳 **Prof:** Martyn Landsborough **Facilities:** ⑪ ⑪ ⬚ ⬛ ⬛ ⬛ ⬚ ⬛ ⬛ ⬛ ⬛ **Location:** 4m S of East Grinstead off A22 on B2110 in Forest Row

Hotel
★★★★ **Ashdown Park Hotel and Country Club,** Wych Cross, FOREST ROW
☎ 01342 824988 – 106 en suite

RYE

Rye
New Lydd Rd, Camber TN31 7QS
☎ 01797 225241 📠 01797 225460
e-mail: ryelinks@btconnect.com

Unique links course with superb undulating greens set among ridges of sand dunes alongside Rye Harbour. Fine views over Romney Marsh and towards Fairlight and Dungeness.

Old Course:
18 holes, 6317yds, Par 68, SSS 71, Course record 64.
Jubilee Course: 9 holes, 3109yds, Par 71, SSS 70.

Club membership: 1100. **Visitors:** must be invited/introduced by a member. **Green Fees:** terms on application. **Prof:** Michael Lee **Course Designer:** H S Colt **Facilities:** ⑪ ⬛ ⬛ ⬚ ⬛ ⬛ ⬚ ⬛ **Location:** 2.75m SE off A259

Hotel
★★★ 61% **The George,** High St, RYE
☎ 01797 222114 – 22 en suite

SEAFORD

Seaford
Firle Rd, East Blatchington BN25 2JD
☎ 01323 892442 📠 01323 894113
e-mail: secretary@seafordgolfclub.co.uk

The great J H Taylor did not perhaps design as many courses as his friend and rival, James Braid, but Seaford's original design was Taylor's. It is a splendid downland course with magnificent views and some fine holes.

18 holes, 6551yds, Par 69, SSS 71.

Club membership: 600. **Visitors:** must contact in advance. **Societies:** must contact in advance. **Green Fees:** terms on application. **Cards:** 💳 💳 VISA 💳 💳

Prof: David Mills/Clay Morris **Course Designer:** J H Taylor **Facilities:** ⑪ ⑪ ⬛ ⬛ ⬛ ⬛ ⬚ ⬛ ⬛ ⬛ ⬛ ⬛ ⬛ **Conf:** Corporate Hospitality Days available **Location:** Turn inland at war memorial off A259

Hotel
★★★ 69% **The Star Inn,** ALFRISTON
☎ 01323 870495 – 37 en suite

TICEHURST

Dale Hill Hotel & Golf Club
TN5 7DQ
☎ 01580 200112 📠 01580 201249
e-mail: info@dalehill.co.uk

Dale Hill is set in over 350 acres, high on the Kentish Weald in an Area of Outstanding Natural Beauty. Offering two 18-hole golf courses, one of which has been designed by Ian Woosnam to USGA specifications.

Dale Hill: 18 holes, 6106yds, Par 70, SSS 69.
Ian Woosnam: 18 holes, 6512yds, Par 71, SSS 71, Course record 64.

Club membership: 850. **Visitors:** booking only 7 days in advance **Societies:** must contact in advance. **Green Fees:** Dale Hill: £30 (£40 weekends). Ian Woosnam £55 (£65 weekends). **Cards:** 💳 💳 VISA 💳 💳 **Prof:** Mark Wood **Course Designer:** Ian Woosnam **Facilities:** ⑪ ⑪ ⬛ ⬛ ⬛ ⬛ ⬚ ⬛ ⬛ ⬛ ⬛ ⬛ ⬛ sauna, gymnasium. **Conf:** facilities available **Corporate:** Hospitality Days available **Location:** M25 junct 5, A21, B2087 left after 1 mile

Hotel
★★★★ 75% **Dale Hill Hotel & Golf Club,** TICEHURST
☎ 01580 200112 – 35 en suite

Championship Course

Sussex, East   **UCKFIELD**

East Sussex National

Little Horsted TN22 5ES
☎ 01825 880088 📄 01825 880066
e-mail: golf@eastsussexnational.co.uk

East Sussex National offers two huge courses ideal for big-hitting professionals. The European Open has been staged here and it is home to the European Headquarters of the David Leadbetter Golf Academy, with indoor and outdoor video analysis. Bob Cupp designed the courses using 'bent' grass from tee to green, resulting in an American-style course to test everyone. The greens on both the East and West courses are immaculately maintained. The West Course, with stadium design and chosen for major events, is reserved for members and their guests; visitors are welcome on the East Course, also with stadium design, and which was the venue for the 1993 and 1994 European Open. The entrance seems daunting for first-time visitors, unprepared for the vast car park, huge red-brick clubhouse, and the suspended corridor from the reception through to the well-stocked professional shop.

WHERE TO STAY NEARBY

★★★★★76%
Buxted Park Country House Hotel,
Buxted, UCKFIELD
☎ 01825 733333
44 en suite

★★★
Newick Park Hotel & Country Estate, NEWICK
☎ 01825 723633 📄 01825 723969
13 en suite 3 annexe en suite

★★★
Horsted Place,
Little Horsted, UCKFIELD
☎ 01825 750581 📄 01825 750459
17 en suite 3 annexe en suite

East Course
18 holes, 7138yds, Par 72, SSS 74, Course record 63

West Course
18 holes, 7154yds, Par 72, SSS 74

Club Membership
650

Visitors
Phone Advance Reservations
01825 880231

Societies
Phone Advance Reservations
01825 880228

Green Fees
£45 per 18 holes
(£50 weekends)

Cards
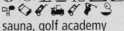

Professionals
Sarah Maclennan, Mike Clark

Course Designer
Bob Cupp

Facilities
sauna, golf academy

Conferences
Facilities available

Corporate
Hospitality Days available

Location
2m S of Uckfield on A22

SUSSEX, WEST

ANGMERING

Ham Manor

BN16 4JE

☎ 01903 783288 📄 01903 850886

e-mail: secretary.ham.manor@tinyonline.co.uk

Two miles from the sea, this parkland course has fine springy turf and provides an interesting test in two loops of nine holes each.

18 holes, 6267yds, Par 70, SSS 70, Course record 64.

Club membership: 780. **Visitors:** must have a handicap certificate. Telephone pro shop in advance 01903 783732. **Societies:** telephone for details **Green Fees:** terms on application. **Prof:** Simon Buckley **Course Designer:** Harry Colt **Facilities:** ⑪ by prior arrangement ⑩ by prior arrangement ⓛ ☕ ▾ ⚲ 🏠 𝒢 **Location:** Off A259

Guesthouse

◆◆◆◆ **Kenmore Guest House,** Claigmar Rd, RUSTINGTON

☎ 01903 784634 – 7 rms (6 en suite)

BOGNOR REGIS

Bognor Regis

Downview Rd, Felpham PO22 8JD

☎ 01243 821929 (Secretary) 📄 01243 860719

e-mail: sec@bognorgolfclub.co.uk

This flattish, well tree-lined, parkland course has more variety than is to be found on some other South Coast courses. The club is also known far and wide for its enterprise in creating a social atmosphere. The course is open to the prevailing wind and the River Rife and many water ditches need negotiation.

18 holes, 6238yds, Par 70, SSS 70, Course record 64.

Club membership: 700. **Visitors:** handicap certificate required. Must contact in advance (pro shop 01243 865209). **Societies:** phone initially. **Green Fees:** not confirmed. **Prof:** Stephen Bassil **Course Designer:** James Braid **Facilities:** ⑪ ⑩ ⓛ ☕ ▾ ⚲ 🏠 𝒢 🛒 𝒢 Conf: facilities available **Location:** 0.5m N at Felpham traffic lights on A259

Hotel

★★ 71% **Beachcroft Hotel,**

Clyde Rd, Felpham Village, BOGNOR REGIS

☎ 01243 827142 – 34 en suite

COPTHORNE

Copthorne

Borers Arms Rd RH10 3LL

☎ 01342 712033 & 712508 📄 01342 717682

e-mail: info@copthornegolfclub.co.uk

Despite having been in existence since 1892, this club remains one of the lesser known Sussex

courses. It is hard to know why because it is most attractive with plenty of trees and much variety.

18 holes, 6435yds, Par 71, SSS 71, Course record 66.

Club membership: 550. **Visitors:** advised to contact in advance, may not play weekends. **Societies:** must contact in advance. **Green Fees:** £34 weekdays. **Cards:** 💳 💳 💳 **Prof:** Joe Burrell **Course Designer:** James Braid **Facilities:** ⑪ ⓛ ☕ ▾ ⚲ 🏠 𝒢 **Location:** E side of village junct 10 of M23 off A264

Hotel

★★★★ 70% **Copthorne Hotel London Gatwick,** Copthorne Way, COPTHORNE

☎ 01342 348800 & 348888 📄 01342 348833

227 en suite

LITTLEHAMPTON

Littlehampton

170 Rope Walk, Riverside West BN17 5DL

☎ 01903 717170 📄 01903 726629

e-mail: lgc@talk21.com

A delightful seaside links in an equally delightful setting – and the only links course in the area.

18 holes, 6226yds, Par 70, SSS 70, Course record 64.

Club membership: 600. **Visitors:** may not book tee times, contact Pro Shop for availability on 01903 717170 (ext 225). **Societies:** welcome weekdays; weekends some restrictions apply **Green Fees:** terms on application. **Prof:** Guy McQuitty **Course Designer:** Hawtree **Facilities:** ⑪ ⑩ ⓛ ☕ ▾ ⚲ 🏠 🛒 𝒢 **Conf:** facilities available Corporate Hospitality Days available **Location:** 1m W of Littlehampton off A259

Hotel

⬦ **Travelodge Littlehampton,**

Worthing Rd, RUSTINGTON

☎ 08700 850 950 – 36 en suite

MANNINGS HEATH

Mannings Heath

Fullers, Hammerpond Rd RH13 6PG

☎ 01403 210228 📄 01403 270974

e-mail: enquiries@manningsheath.com

The Waterfall is a downhill, parkland, part heathland, championship course with streams and trees in abundance. It boasts three spectacular par 3s but all the holes are memorably unique. The Kingfisher Course is a modern design with a lake which comes into play.

Waterfall:

18 holes, 6483yds, Par 72, SSS 71, Course record 63.

Kingfisher:

18 holes, 6217yds, Par 70, SSS 70, Course record 66.

Club membership: 700. **Visitors:** must book in advance. **Societies:** must contact in advance. **Green Fees:** terms on application. **Cards:** 💳 💳 💳 💳 💳 💳 💳 **Prof:** Clive Tucker **Course Designer:** David

Williams **Facilities:** ⑪ †◎ ⑂ ☞ ☜⑪ 丄 ☖ ☏ ⌥ ⚒
⚒ ✦ ☎ sauna, chipping practice area. **Conf:** facilities
available **Corporate:** Hospitality Days available
Location: M23 junct 11, take A281 from Horsham or
Brighton. Club on N side of village

Hotel
★★★★⚑🏠 **South Lodge Hotel,**
Brighton Rd, LOWER BEEDING
☎ 01403 891711 – 45 en suite

PULBOROUGH
West Sussex
Golf Club Ln, Wiggonholt RH20 2EN
☎ 01798 872563 📄 01798 872033
e-mail: secretary@westsussexgolf.co.uk

**An outstanding beautiful heathland course
occupying an oasis of sand, heather and pine in
the middle of attractive countryside which is
predominately clay and marsh. The 6th and 13th
holes are particularly notable.**

18 holes, 6264yds, Par 68, SSS 70, Course record 61.

Club membership: 850. **Visitors:** must contact in
advance, may not play weekends except by prior
agreement of the Secretary, and on Fri except with a
member. **Societies:** Wed & Thu only, apply in writing.
Green Fees: £80 per 36 holes, £65 per 18 holes
(£85/£70 weekends). **Prof:** Tim Packham **Course
Designer:** Campbell/Hutcheson **Facilities:** ⑪ ⑂ ☞⑪
丄 ☖ ⌥ ☎ ✦ ☞ **Location:** 1.5m E of Pulborough
off A283

Hotel
★★★ 69% **Best Western Roundabout Hotel,**
Monkmead Ln, WEST CHILTINGTON
☎ 01798 813838 – 23 en suite

WORTHING
Worthing
Links Rd BN14 9QZ
☎ 01903 260801 📄 01903 694664
e-mail: worthinggolf@easynet.co.uk

**The Upper Course, short and tricky with
entrancing views, will provide good
entertainment. Lower Course is considered to be
one of the best downland courses in the country.**

Lower Course:
18 holes, 6505yds, Par 71, SSS 71, Course record 62.
Upper Course: 18 holes, 5211yds, Par 66, SSS 65.

Club membership: 1200. **Visitors:** advisable to
contact in advance, not weekends during GMT.
Societies: contact in advance. **Green Fees:** terms on
application. **Prof:** Stephen Rolley **Course Designer:**
H S Colt **Facilities:** ⑪ †◎ ⑂ ☞⑪ 丄 ☖ ☏ ⌥ ☎ ✦ ☞
Location: N side of town centre off A27

Hotel
★★★ 72% **Ardington Hotel,**

Steyne Gardens, WORTHING
☎ 01903 230451 – 45 en suite

TYNE & WEAR

NEWCASTLE UPON TYNE
Northumberland
High Gosforth Park NE3 5HT
☎ 0191 236 2498 📄 0191 236 2036
e-mail: gun2446@aol.com

**Predominantly a level heathland style course, the
firm, fast greens are a particular feature.**

18 holes, 6683yds, Par 72, SSS 72, Course record 65.

Club membership: 580. **Visitors:** Limited play
weekends. Must contact in advance. **Societies:** must
apply in writing or telephone. **Green Fees:** £50 per
day; £40 per round (£50 per round weekends). **Course
Designer:** Colt/Braid **Facilities:** ⑪ †◎ ⑂ ☞⑪ 丄
✦ **Conf:** Corporate Hospitality Days available
Location: 4m N of city centre off A1

Hotel
★★★★ 74% **Newcastle Marriott Hotel Gosforth Park,**
High Gosforth Park, Gosforth, NEWCASTLE UPON TYNE
☎ 0191 236 4111 – 178 en suite

SUNDERLAND
Wearside
Coxgreen SR4 9JT
☎ 0191 534 2518 📄 0191 5346186

**Open, undulating parkland course rolling down to
the River Wear and beneath the shadow of the
famous Penshaw Monument. Built on the lines of
an Athenian temple it is a well-known landmark.
Two ravines cross the course presenting a variety
of challenging holes.**

18 holes, 6373yds, Par 71, SSS 74, Course record 63.

Club membership: 648. **Visitors:** may not play
before 9.30am, between 12.30-1.30 or after 4pm.
Societies: must apply in writing. **Green Fees:** not
confirmed. **Prof:** Doug Brolls **Facilities:** ⑪ †◎ ⑂ ☞
☞⑪ 丄 ☖ ✦ **Location:** 3.5m W off A183

Hotel
★★★★ 69% **Sunderland Marriott Hotel,**
Queen's Pde, Seaburn, SUNDERLAND
☎ 0191 529 2041 – 82 en suite

WEST MIDLANDS

BIRMINGHAM
Edgbaston
Church Rd, Edgbaston B15 3TB
☎ 0121 454 1736 📄 0121 454 2395
e-mail: secretary@edgbastongc.co.uk

**Set in 144 acres of woodland, lake and parkland,
two miles from the centre of Birmingham, this**

Continued

Championship Course

Warwickshire   **WISHAW**

The Belfry

Wishaw B76 9PR
☎ 01675 470301   📄 01675 470178
e-mail: enquiries@thebelfry.com

The Belfry is unique as the only venue to have staged the biggest golf event in the world, the Ryder Cup matches, an unprecedented four times, most recently in 2002. The Brabazon is regarded throughout the world as a great championship course with some of the most demanding holes in golf; the 10th (Ballesteros's Hole) and the 18th, with its dangerous lakes and its amphitheatre around the final green, are world famous. These remained intact during the £2.4 million redevelopment in 1998, which made the course even more testing. Alternatively, you can pit your wits against a new legend in the making, the PGA National Course, which has won plaudits from near and far. The Dave Thomas and Peter Alliss designed course has been used for professional competition and is already established as one of Britain's leading courses. For those who like their golf a little easier or like to get back into the swing gently, the Derby is ideal and can be played by golfers of any standard. The Bel Air nightclub, the De Vere Club leisure centre, and the Aqua-Spa with its fire and ice bio-thermal treatments offer unique experiences away from the course.

WHERE TO STAY NEARBY

★★★★75%
De Vere Belfry, WISHAW
☎ 0870 900 0066
324 en suite

★★★★67%
Lea Marston Hotel & Leisure Complex,
Haunch Ln, LEA MARSTON
☎ 01675 470468 📄 01675 470871
80 en suite

★★★★68%
Moor Hall Hotel, Moor Hall Dr, Four Oaks, SUTTON COLDFIELD
☎ 0121 308 3751 📄 0121 308 8974 82 en suite

The Brabazon
18 holes, 6724yds, Par 72, SSS 71

PGA National
18 holes, 6639yds, Par 71, SSS 70

The Derby
18 holes, 6057yds, Par 69, SSS 69

Club Membership
450

Visitors
Handicap certificate required for Brabazon course and PGA National (men 24 or better, women and juniors 32 or better); reservations 24 hours in advance for non-residents

Societies
Must phone in advance

Green Fees
Brabazon £140; PGA £75; Derby: £40; reduced winter rates

Cards

Professional
Simon Wordsworth

Course Designers
Dave Thomas, Peter Alliss

Facilities

squash, sauna, solarium, gymnasium, PGA National Golf Academy

Conferences
Facilities available

Corporate
Hospitality Days available

Location
M42 junct 9, 4m E on A446

Championship Course

MERIDEN

Marriott Forest of Arden

Golf & Country Club, Maxstoke Ln CV7 7HR

☎ 0870 400 7272   📄 0870 400 7372

This is one of the finest golf destinations in the UK, with a range of facilities to impress every golfer. The jewel in the crown is the Arden championship parkland course, set in 10,000 acres of the Packington Estate. Designed by Donald Steele, it presents one of the country's most spectacular challenges and has hosted a succession of international tournaments, including the British Masters and English Open. Beware the 18th hole, which is enough to stretch the nerves of any golfer. The shorter Aylesford Course offers a varied and enjoyable challenge, which golfers of all abilities will find rewarding. Golf events are a speciality, and there is a golf academy and extensive leisure facilities.

WHERE TO STAY NEARBY

★★★★73%
Marriott Forest of Arden Hotel & Country Club,
Maxstoke Ln, MERIDEN
☎ 0870 400 7272; 214 en suite

★★★71%
Manor Hotel,
Main Rd, MERIDEN
☎ 01676 522735 📄 01676 522186
110 en suite

★★★64%
Strawberry Bank Hotel, Main Rd, MERIDEN
☎ 01676 522117 📄 01676 523804
47 en suite

Arden Course
18 holes, 6707yds, Par 72, SSS 73, Course record 63

Aylesford Course
18 holes, 5801yds, Par 69, SSS 68

Club Membership
800

Visitors
Phone to book in advance

Societies
By arrangement

Green Fees
Terms on application

Cards

Professional
Philip Hoye

Course Designer
Donald Steele

Facilities
sauna, solarium, gymnasium, health and beauty salon, steam room, Jacuzzi, aerobics studio

Conferences
Facilities available

Corporate
Hospitality Days available

Location
1m SW on B4102

delightful course utilises the wealth of natural features to provide a series of testing and adventurous holes set in the traditional double loop that starts directly in front of the clubhouse, an imposing Georgian mansion.

18 holes, 6106yds, Par 69, SSS 69, Course record 63.

Club membership: 970. **Visitors:** recommended to contact in advance through golf reservations, must have handicap certificate. Most weekends pm. **Societies:** must apply in writing. **Green Fees:** terms on application. **Cards:** 💳 💳 **Prof:** Jamie Cundy **Course Designer:** H S Colt **Facilities:** 🏌 🍴 🛍 🍺 🍽 ⛳ 🏪 🏴 ⛳ 🚬 🚕 ⛳ **Conf:** facilities available Corporate Hospitality Days available **Location:** 2m S of city centre on B4217 off A38

Hotel
★★★ 63% **The Plough & Harrow Hotel,** 135 Hagley Rd, EDGBASTON
☎ 0870 609 6118 – 44 en suite

COVENTRY

Coventry
St Martins Rd, Finham Park CV3 6RJ
☎ 024 76414152 📠 024 76690131
e-mail: coventrygolfclub@hotmail.com

The scene of several major professional events, this undulating parkland course has a great deal of quality. More than that, it usually plays its length, and thus scoring is never easy, as many professionals have found to their cost.

18 holes, 6601yds, Par 73, SSS 73, Course record 66.

Club membership: 500. **Visitors:** must contact in advance. May not play at weekends and bank holidays. **Societies:** must apply in writing/telephone. **Green Fees:** £35 per day. **Cards:** 💳 💳 💳 💳 💳 **Prof:** Philip Weaver **Course Designer:** Vardon Bros/Hawtree **Facilities:** 🏌 🍴 🛍 🍺 🍽 🏪 🏴 🍽 ⛳ **Conf:** Corporate Hospitality Days available **Location:** 3m S of city centre on B4113, 2m from junct of A45/A46

Hotel
★★★ 66% **Best Western Hylands Hotel,** Warwick Rd, COVENTRY
☎ 024 7650 1600 – 61 en suite

WEST BROMWICH

Sandwell Park
Birmingham Rd B71 4JJ
☎ 0121 553 4637 📠 0121 525 1651
e-mail: secretary@sandwellparkgolfclub.co.uk

A picturesque golf course wandering over wooded heathland and utilising natural features. Each hole is entirely separate, shielded from the others by either natural banks or lines of trees. A course that demands careful placing of shots that have been given a great deal of thought. Natural undulating fairways create difficult and testing approach shots to the greens.

18 holes, 6204yds, Par 71, SSS 71, Course record 65.

Club membership: 550. **Visitors:** must contact in advance. May not play at weekends. **Societies:** must contact in advance. **Green Fees:** £42 per 27/36 holes; £36 per 18 holes. **Prof:** Nigel Wylie **Course Designer:** H S Colt **Facilities:** 🏌 🍴 🛍 🍺 🍽 🏪 🏴 ⛳ practice chipping area. **Conf:** facilities available **Corporate:** Hospitality Days available **Location:** On A41, 200yds from junct 1 of the M5

Hotel
★★★ 63% **The Plough & Harrow Hotel,** 135 Hagley Rd, EDGBASTON
☎ 0870 609 6118   44 en suite

WILTSHIRE

CASTLE COMBE

Manor House

SN14 7JW

☎ 01249 782206 📠 01249 782992

e-mail: enquiries@manorhousegolfclub.com

Set in a wonderful location within the wooded estate of the 14th-century Manor House, this course includes five par 5s and some spectacular par 3s. A special feature is the River Bybrook, which meanders its way through many holes, the most memorable being the 17th with a breathtaking drop to the green.

The Manor House Golf Club at Castle Combe: 18 holes, 6286yds, Par 72, SSS 71, Course record 67.

Club membership: 450. Visitors: must have a handicap certificate and must contact in advance. May only play after noon on Wed and weekends.
Societies: contact in advance. Green Fees: Summer rates £70 (£85 Fri-Sun). Spring/Autumn £60/£75. Winter £40 all week. Cards: 💳 💳 💳 💳 💳 Prof: Peter Green Course Designer: Peter Alliss/Clive Clark
Facilities: ⛳🍴🏌️🛒🏪🏇♦🏌️💪🏌️🎣 sauna, snooker, croquet. Conf: facilities available
Corporate: Hospitality Days available Location: On B4039, 5m NW of Chippenham

Hotel

★★★★★🏨 Manor House Hotel and Golf Club, CASTLE COMBE
☎ 01249 782206 – 22 en suite 26 annexe en suite

GREAT DURNFORD

High Post

SP4 6AT

☎ 01722 782356 📠 01722 782674

e-mail: highpostgolfclub@lineone.net

An interesting downland course on Wiltshire chalk with good turf and splendid views over the southern area of Salisbury Plain. The opening 3 holes are often played with the prevailing wind to the round, however, turning back into the wind on the 2nd and requiring good concentration. The closing three holes are as tough a finish as you will find anywhere.

18 holes, 6305yds, Par 70, SSS 70, Course record 64.

Club membership: 625. Visitors: a handicap certificate is required at weekends & bank holidays. Telephone professional in advance 01722 782219.
Societies: apply by telephone to manager. Green Fees: £40 per day; £32 per round (£50/£42 weekends). Prof: Tony Isaacs Course Designer: Hawtree & Ptrs
Facilities: ⛳🍴🏌️🛒🏪🏇🏪💪♦🏌️ Conf: facilities available Location: Midway between Sailsbury and Amesbury on A345

Hotel

★★★ 60% The Rose & Crown Hotel, Harnham Rd, Harnham, SALISBURY
☎ 0870 6096163 – 28 en suite

TIDWORTH

Tidworth Garrison

Bulford Rd SP9 7AF

☎ 01980 842301 📠 01980 842301

e-mail: tidworth@garrison-golfclub.fsnet.co.uk

A breezy, dry downland course with lovely turf, fine trees and views over Salisbury Plain and the surrounding area. The 4th and 12th holes are notable. The 565-yard 14th, going down towards the clubhouse, gives the big hitter a chance to let fly.

18 holes, 6320yds, Par 70, SSS 70, Course record 63.

Club membership: 800. Visitors: must contact in advance, weekend & bank holiday bookings may not be made until Thu prior, handicap certificate required. Societies: Tue & Thu, bookings required 12-18 months in advance. Green Fees: £34 per round/day. Prof:

Terry Gosden **Course Designer:** Donald Steel
Facilities: ⓉⓄ 🏌 ♨ ▤ ☕ 🅿 🍽 ✍ **Location:**
W side of village off A338

Hotel
★★★ 62% **Quality Hotel Andover,**
Micheldever Rd, ANDOVER
☎ 01264 369111 – 13 en suite 36 annexe en suite

WARMINSTER
West Wilts
Elm Hill BA12 0AU
☎ 01985 213133 📠 01985 219809
e-mail: sec@westwiltsgolfclub.co.uk

A hilltop course among the Wiltshire downs on
downland turf. Free draining, short, but a very
good test of accurate iron play. Excellent greens
and clubhouse facilities.

18 holes, 5754yds, Par 70, SSS 68, Course record 60.

Club membership: 570. **Visitors:** may not play Sat.
must contact in advance. Handicap certificate required.
Societies: Wed and Fri only. Apply by letter or phone
Green Fees: £30 per day; £25 per round (£40/£30 Sun
& bank holidays). **Cards:** 💳 **Prof:** Rob Morris **Course
Designer:** J H Taylor **Facilities:** ⓉⓄ 🏌 ♨ ▤ ☕ 🅿 ▲ 🏠
🅿 ✍ **Location:** N side of town centre off A350

Hotel
★★★★ 74% **Bishopstrow House,** WARMINSTER
☎ 01985 212312 – 32 en suite

WORCESTERSHIRE
ALVECHURCH
Kings Norton
Brockhill Ln, Weatheroak B48 7ED
☎ 01564 826706 & 826789 📠 01564 826955
e-mail: info@kingsnortongolfclub.co.uk

Parkland course with water hazards. A 27-hole
Championship venue playing as three
combinations of 9 holes.

Weatheroak:
18 holes, 6748yds, Par 72, SSS 72, Course record 65.
Brockhill: 18 holes, 6648yds, Par 72, SSS 72.
Wythall: 18 holes, 6612yds, Par 72, SSS 72.

Club membership: 1000. **Visitors:** must contact in
advance. No visitors at weekends. **Societies:** must
telephone in advance. **Green Fees:** terms on
application. **Cards:** 💳 **Prof:** Kevin
Hayward **Course Designer:** F Hawtree **Facilities:** Ⓣ
Ⓞ 🏌 ♨ ▤ ☕ 🅿 ▲ 🏠 🅿 🍽 ✍ par 3 course. **Conf:**
facilities available **Corporate:** Hospitality Days
available **Location:** M42 junct 3, off A435

Hotel
★★★★ 66% **The Bromsgrove Hotel,**
Kidderminster Rd, BROMSGROVE
☎ 01527 576600 – 114 en suite

YORKSHIRE, NORTH
GANTON
Ganton
YO12 4PA
☎ 01944 710329 📠 01944 710922
e-mail: secretary@gantongolfclub.com

Championship course, heathland, gorse-lined
fairways and heavily bunkered; variable winds.
The opening holes make full use of the contours
of the land and the approach to the 2nd demands
the finest touch. The 4th is considered one of the
best holes on the outward half with its shot
across a valley to a plateau green, the
surrounding gorse punishing anything less than a
perfect shot. The finest hole is possibly the 18th,
requiring an accurately placed drive to give a
clear shot to the sloping, well-bunkered green.

18 holes, 6734yds, Par 72, SSS 73, Course record 65.

Club membership: 500. **Visitors:** by prior
arrangement. Restricted play at weekends. **Societies:**
prior arrangement in writing. **Green Fees:** £68 per
day/round (£78 weekends and bank holidays). **Cards:**
💳 💳 💳 💳 💳 **Prof:** Gary Brown **Course
Designer:** Dunn/Vardon/Braid/Colt **Facilities:** ⓉⓄ
🏌 ♨ ▤ ☕ 🅿 🍽 ✍ **Conf:** Corporate
Hospitality Days available **Location:** 11m SW of
Scarborough on A64

Hotel
★★★ 65% **East Ayton Lodge Country House,**
Moor Ln, Forge Valley, EAST AYTON
☎ 01723 864227 – 10 en suite 20 annexe en suite

HARROGATE
Harrogate
Forest Ln Head, Starbeck HG2 7TF
☎ 01423 862999 📠 01423 860073
e-mail: hon.secretary@harrogate-gc.co.uk

Course on fairly flat terrain with Mackenzie-style
greens and tree-lined fairways. Whilst not a long
course, the layout penalises the golfer who strays
off the fairway. Subtly placed bunkers and copses
of trees require the golfer to adopt careful
thought and accuracy if par is be bettered. The
last six holes include five par 4s, of which four
exceed 400 yards.

18 holes, 6241yds, Par 69, SSS 70, Course record 63.

Club membership: 700. **Visitors:** advisable to
contact professional in advance, weekend play limited.
Societies: must contact in writing or intially by
telephone. **Green Fees:** £36 per day, £30 per round
(weekends £40). **Cards:** 💳 💳 💳 💳 💳 **Prof:**
Paul Johnson **Course Designer:** Sandy Herd
Facilities: ⓉⓄ 🏌 ♨ ▤ ☕ 🅿 ▲ 🏠 🅿 🍽 ✍ snooker.
Conf: Corporate Hospitality Days available **Location:**
2.25m N on A59

Continued

Hotel
★★★ 74% **Grants Hotel,** 3-13 Swan Rd, HARROGATE
☎ 01423 560666 – 42 en suite

Oakdale

Oakdale Glen HG1 2LN
☎ 01423 567162 📄 01423 536030
e-mail: sec@oakdale-golfclub.com

A pleasant, undulating parkland course which provides a good test of golf for the low handicap player without intimidating the less proficient. A special feature is an attractive stream which comes in to play on four holes. Excellent views from the clubhouse which has good facilities.

18 holes, 6456yds, Par 71, SSS 71, Course record 61.

Club membership: 1034. **Visitors:** no party bookings weekends. **Societies:** telephone followed by letter. **Green Fees:** £40 for 27 holes, £33 per round (£45 per round weekends and bank holidays). **Prof:** Clive Dell **Course Designer:** Dr McKenzie **Facilities:** ⑪ ⑩ ⒧ ☞ ☜ ☜ ⤴ ⌂ ⋔ ☞ ⌁ **Conf:** Corporate Hospitality Days available **Location:** N side of town centre off A61

Hotel
★★★ 74% **Grants Hotel,** 3-13 Swan Rd, HARROGATE
☎ 01423 560666 – 42 en suite

PANNAL

Pannal

Follifoot Rd HG3 1ES
☎ 01423 872628 📄 01423 870043
e-mail: secretary@pannalgc.co.uk

Fine championship course. Moorland turf but well-wooded with trees closely involved with play. Excellent views enhance the course.

18 holes, 6622yds, Par 72, SSS 72, Course record 62.

Club membership: 780. **Visitors:** preferable to contact in advance, weekends limited. Not Tue am **Societies:** apply in advance. **Green Fees:** £60 per day, £45 per round (£60 per round weekends).. **Cards:** ⬤ VISA ⬤ ☜ ☜ **Prof:** David Padgett **Course Designer:** Sandy Herd **Facilities:** ⑪ ⑩ ⒧ ☞ ☜ ⤴ ⌂ ⋔ ☜ ⌁ ☜ snooker. **Conf:** Corporate Hospitality Days available **Location:** E side of village off A61

Hotel
★★★ 70% **The Yorkshire,**
Prospect Place, HARROGATE
☎ 01423 565071 – 80 en suite

YORK

Fulford

Heslington Ln YO10 5DY
☎ 01904 413579 📄 01904 416918
e-mail: info@fulfordgolfclub.co.uk

A flat, parkland/heathland course well-known for the superb quality of its turf, particularly the

greens, and now famous as the venue for some of the best golf tournaments in the British Isles in past years. In particular, 19 years of hosting the Benson & Hedges Trophy.

18 holes, 6775yds, Par 72, SSS 72, Course record 62.

Club membership: 775. **Visitors:** must contact in advance. Not Tue am. Limited weekends **Societies:** not Tue am, book with the manager. **Green Fees:** £65 per day, £50 per round. **Prof:** Martin Brown **Course Designer:** C MacKenzie **Facilities:** ⑪ ⑩ ⒧ ☞ ☜ ⤴ ⌂ ☜ ⌁ **Conf:** Corporate Hospitality Days available **Location:** 2m S of York off A19

Hotel
★★★★ 69% **York Marriott Hotel,**
Tadcaster Rd, YORK
☎ 01904 701000 – 108 en suite

★★★ 71% **York Pavilion Hotel,**
45 Main St, Fulford, YORK
☎ 01904 622099 📄 01904 626939 – 57 en suite

YORKSHIRE, SOUTH

SHEFFIELD

Hallamshire Golf Club Ltd

Sandygate S10 4LA
☎ 0114 230 2153 📄 0114 230 5413
e-mail: secretary@hallamshiregolfclub.co.uk

Situated on a shelf of land at a height of 850 feet. Magnificent views to the west. Moorland turf, long carries over ravine and small and quick greens.

18 holes, 6346yds, Par 71, SSS 71, Course record 65.

Club membership: 600. **Visitors:** contact professional or secretary in advance. Tees reserved for members 8-10am and noon-2pm. May not play Sat. **Societies:** parties should book in advance with Secretary. May not play Sat. **Green Fees:** £45 per day/round (£60 weekends & bank holidays). **Cards:** ⬤ VISA ⬤ ☜ ☜ **Prof:** G R Tickell **Course Designer:** Various **Facilities:** ⑪ ⑩ ⒧ ☞ ☜ ⤴ ⌂ ⋔ ☜ ⌁ **Conf:** Corporate Hospitality Days available **Location:** Off A57 at Crosspool onto Sandygate Rd, clubhouse 0.75m on right

Hotel
★★★★ 70% **Marriott Sheffield,**
Kenwood Rd, SHEFFIELD
☎ 0870 400 7261 – 114 en suite

YORKSHIRE, WEST

ALWOODLEY

Alwoodley

Wigton Ln LS17 8SA
☎ 0113 268 1680 📄 0113 293 9458

Natural moorland course with heather, whins and shrubs. Plentifully and cunningly bunkered with undulating and interesting greens.

18 holes, 6666yds, Par 72, SSS 72.

Club membership: 460. Visitors: must contact Secretary in advance. Societies: must apply in advance. Green Fees: £65 per day/round (£80 weekends). Cards: 💳 VISA 📇 ⑤ Prof: John R Green Course Designer: Dr Alistair MacKenzie Facilities: ⑪ 🍴 🏌 🍺 🐴 🏹 🏠 ⛽ 🎯 Conf: Corporate Hospitality Days available Location: 5m N off A61

Hotel
★★★ 70% **The Merrion Hotel,** Wade Ln, LEEDS
☎ 0113 243 9191 – 109 en suite

Ilkley
Nesfield Rd, Myddleton LS29 0BE
☎ 01943 600214 📠 01943 816130
e-mail: honsec@ilkleygolfclub.co.uk

This beautiful parkland course is situated in Wharfedale and the Wharfe is a hazard on each of the first 7 holes. In fact, the 3rd is laid out entirely on an island in the middle of the river.

18 holes, 5953yds, Par 69, SSS 70, Course record 64.

Club membership: 450. Visitors: advisable to contact in advance. Societies: apply in writing/telephone in advance. Green Fees: £42 (£50 weekends). Cards: 💳 📇 VISA 💳 Barclays 📇 ⑤ Prof: John L Hammond Course Designer: Mackenzie Facilities: ⑪ 🍴 🏌 🍺 🐴 🏹 🏠 🎯 🎣 🔔 Conf: Corporate Hospitality Days available Location: W side of town centre off A65

Hotel
★★★ 76% **Rombalds Hotel & Restaurant,** 11 West View, Wells Rd, ILKLEY
☎ 01943 603201 – 18 en suite

Moor Allerton
Coal Rd, Wike LS17 9NH
☎ 0113 266 1154 📠 0113 237 1124
e-mail: info@magc.co.uk

The Moor Allerton Club, established in 1923, has 27 holes set in 220 acres of undulating parkland, with testing water hazards and magnificent views extending across the Vale of York. The Championship Course was designed by Robert Trent Jones, the famous American course architect, and provides a challenge to both high and low handicapped golfers.

Lakes Course: 18 holes, 6470yds, Par 71, SSS 72.
Blackmoor Course: 18 holes, 6673yds, Par 71, SSS 73.
High Course: 18 holes, 6841yds, Par 72, SSS 74.

Club membership: 500. Visitors: contact professional (0113 266 5209). Societies: must apply in advance. Green Fees: £70 per day; £49 per round (£65 weekends). Cards: 💳 VISA ⑤ Prof: Richard Lane Course Designer: Robert Trent Jones Facilities: ⑪ 🍴 🏌 🍺 🐴 🏹 🏠 ⛽ 🎯 sauna. Conf: facilities available Corporate: Hospitality Days available Location: 5.5m N of city centre on A61

Hotel
★★★ 70% **The Merrion Hotel,** Wade Ln, LEEDS
☎ 0113 243 9191 – 109 en suite

Moortown
Harrogate Rd, Alwoodley LS17 7DB
☎ 0113 268 6521 📠 0113 268 0986
e-mail: secretary@moortown-gc.co.uk

Championship Course, tough but fair. Springy moorland turf, natural hazards of heather, gorse and streams, cunningly placed bunkers and immaculate greens. Original home of Ryder Cup in 1929.

18 holes, 6757yds, Par 72, SSS 73, Course record 64.

Club membership: 568. Visitors: contact in advance. Societies: apply in writing in advance. Green Fees: £65 per day/round (£75 weekends & bank holidays). Reduced winter rates. Prof: Martin Heggie Course Designer: Alistair Mackenzie Facilities: ⑪ 🍴 🏌 🍺 🐴 🏹 🏠 🎯 🎣 🎯 Conf: Corporate Hospitality Days available Location: 6m N of city centre on A61

Hotel
★★★ 70% **The Merrion Hotel,** Wade Ln, LEEDS
☎ 0113 243 9191 – 109 en suite

Sand Moor
Alwoodley Ln LS17 7DJ
☎ 0113 268 5180 📠 0113 266 1105
e-mail: sandmoorgolf@btclick.com

A beautiful, inland course situated next to Eccup reservoir on the north side of Leeds. It has been described as the finest example of golfing paradise being created out of a barren moor. With magnificent views of the surrounding countryside, the course has sandy soil and drains exceptionally well.

18 holes, 6414yds, Par 71, SSS 71, Course record 63.

Club membership: 600. **Visitors:** restricted weekends & bank holidays. **Societies:** must apply in advance. **Green Fees:** not confirmed. **Cards:** 💳 💳 💳 **Prof:** Frank Houlgate **Course Designer:** Dr A Mackenzie **Facilities:** 🏌 🍴 🏌 💺 🏌 🛄 🏌 🏌 **Conf:** Corporate Hospitality Days available **Location:** 5m N of city centre off A61

Hotel
★★★★ 64% **Cedar Court Hotel,**
Denby Dale Rd, WAKEFIELD
☎ 01924 276310 – 151 en suite

OTLEY

Otley
Off West Busk Ln LS21 3NG
☎ 01943 465329 📄 01943 850387
e-mail: office@otley-golfclub.co.uk

An expansive course with magnificent views across Wharfedale. It is well-wooded with streams crossing the fairway. The 4th is a fine hole which generally needs two woods to reach the plateau green. The 17th is a good short hole. A test of golf as opposed to stamina.

18 holes, 6237yds, Par 70, SSS 70, Course record 62.

Club membership: 700. **Visitors:** telephone to check tee time. May not play Tue morning or Sat. **Societies:** telephone enquiries welcome, bookings in writing. **Green Fees:** £38 per day, £32 per 18/27 holes (£45/£38 weekends & bank holidays). **Cards:** 💳 💳 💳 💳 💳 💳 **Prof:** Steven Tomkinson **Facilities:** 🏌 🍴 🏌 💺 🏌 🛄 🏌 🏌 practice bunker. **Conf:** facilities available Corporate Hospitality Days available **Location:** 1m W of Otley off A6038

Hotel
⌂ **Premier Travel Inn Leeds/Bradford Airport,**
Victoria Av, Yeadon, LEEDS
☎ 08701 977153 – 40 en suite

CHANNEL ISLANDS
GUERNSEY

L'ANCRESSE VALE

Royal Guernsey
GY3 5BY
☎ 01481 246523 📄 01481 243960
e-mail: bobby@rggc.fsnet.co.uk

Not quite as old as its neighbour Royal Jersey, Royal Guernsey is a sporting course which was re-designed after World War II by Mackenzie Ross, who has many fine courses to his credit. It is a

pleasant links, well-maintained, and administered by the States of Guernsey in the form of the States Tourist Committee. The 8th hole, a good par 4, requires an accurate second shot to the green set amongst the gorse and thick rough. The 18th, with lively views, needs a strong shot to reach the green well down below. The course is windy, with hard walking. There is a junior section.

18 holes, 6215yds, Par 70, SSS 70, Course record 64.

Club membership: 934. **Visitors:** must have a handicap certificate; may not play on Thu, Sat afternoons & Sun. **Green Fees:** £44 per day/round (with member £30). **Prof:** Norman Wood **Course Designer:** Mackenzie Ross **Facilities:** 🏌 🍴 🏌 💺 🏌 🛄 🏌 🏌 **Location:** 3m N of St Peter Port

Hotel
★★★★ 67% **St Pierre Park Hotel,**
Rohais, ST PETER PORT
☎ 01481 728282 – 131 en suite

CASTEL

La Grande Mare Golf & Country Club
Vazon Bay GY5 7LL
☎ 01481 253544 📄 01481 255197
e-mail: golf@lagrandemare.com

This hotel and golf complex is set in over 120 acres of land. The Hawtree designed parkland course opened in 1994 and was originally designed around 14 holes with four double greens. The course was extended to a full 18 holes in 2001. Water hazards on 15 holes.

La Grande Mare Golf Course: 18 holes, 4755yards, Par 64, SSS 64, Course record 65.

Club membership: 800. **Visitors:** may book a tee time up to 2 days in advance. **Societies:** must book in advance, **Green Fees:** £32 per 18 holes (£36 weekends). **Cards:** 💳 💳 💳 💳 💳 💳 **Prof:** Matt Groves **Course Designer:** Hawtree **Facilities:** 🏌 🍴 🏌 💺 🏌 🛄 🏌 🏌 🏌 🏌 🏌 🏌 sauna, gymnasium, sports massage. **Conf:** Corporate Hospitality Days available

Hotel
★★★ 70% **Hotel Hougue du Pommier,**
Hougue du Pommier Rd, CASTEL
☎ 01481 256531 – 37 en suite 6 annexe en suite

JERSEY

GROUVILLE

Royal Jersey
Le Chemin au Greves JE3 9BD
☎ 01534 854416 📄 01534 854684
e-mail: thesecretary@royaljersey.com

A seaside links, historic because of its age: its centenary was celebrated in 1978. It is also famous for the fact that Britain's greatest golfer,

Harry Vardon, was born in a little cottage on the edge of the course and learned his golf here.

18 holes, 6100yds, Par 70, SSS 70, Course record 63.

Club membership: 1234. **Visitors:** restricted to 10am-noon & 2pm-4pm Mon-Fri & after 2.30pm weekends & bank holidays. **Societies:** welcome Mon-Fri. Must apply in writing. **Green Fees:** not confirmed. **Cards:** 💳 💳 💳 💳 💳 **Prof:** David Morgan **Facilities:** 🏦 🍴 🛍 🍺 🍽 ⚒ 🏠 ⛳ 🏌 🛳 **Location:** 4m E of St Helier off coast rd

Hotel
★★★ 69% **Old Court House Hotel,** GOREY
☎ 01534 854444 – 58 en suite

LA MOYE

La Moye
La Route Orange JE3 8GQ
☎ 01534 743401 📄 01534 747289

Seaside championship links course (venue for the Jersey Seniors Open) situated in an exposed position on the south-western corner of the island overlooking St Ouens Bay. Offers spectacular views, two start points, full course all year – no temporary greens.

18 holes, 6664yds, Par 72, SSS 73, Course record 65.

Club membership: 1300. **Visitors:** must contact Course Ranger in advance 01534 747166. Visitors may play after 2.30pm weekends and bank holidays. **Societies:** apply in writing. **Green Fees:** 18 holes £50 (weekends & bank holidays £55). **Cards:** 💳 💳 💳 💳 💳 **Prof:** Mike Deeley **Course Designer:** James Braid **Facilities:** 🏦 🍴 🛍 🍺 🍽 🏠 ⚒ 🏠 ⛳ 🏌 **Location:** W side of village off A13

Hotel
★★★★ **The Atlantic Hotel,**
Le Mont de la Pulente, ST BRELADE
☎ 01534 744101 – 50 en suite

SCOTLAND

ABERDEENSHIRE

CRUDEN BAY

Cruden Bay
Aulton Rd AB42 0NN
☎ 01779 812285 📄 01779 812945
e-mail: cbaygc@aol.com

A typical links course which epitomises the old fashioned style of rugged links golf. The drives require accuracy with bunkers and protecting greens, blind holes and undulating greens. The 10th provides a panoramic view of half the back nine down at beach level, and to the east can be seen the outline of the spectacular ruin of Slains Castle featured in Bram Stoker's *Dracula.* **The figure eight design of the course is quite unusual.**

Main Course:
18 holes, 6395yds, Par 70, SSS 72, Course record 65.
St Olaf Course: 9 holes, 5106yds, Par 64, SSS 65.

Club membership: 1100. **Visitors:** welcome on weekdays, at weekends only when there are no competitions, must pre-book **Societies:** weekdays only, telephone in advance. **Green Fees:** £55 per round/£75 per day (weekend £65 per round). **Cards:** 💳 💳 💳 💳 💳 **Prof:** Robbie Stewart **Course Designer:** Thomas Simpson **Facilities:** 🏦 🍴 🛍 🍺 🍽 🏠 ⚒ 🏠 ⛳ 🏌 **Conf:** Corporate Hospitality Days available **Location:** SW side of village on A975

Hotel
★★ 66% **Red House Hotel,** Aulton Rd, CRUDEN BAY
☎ 01779 812215 – 6 rms (5 en suite)

ANGUS

BARRY

Panmure
Burnside Rd DD7 7RT
☎ 01241 855120 📄 01241 859737
e-mail: secretary@panmuregolfclub.co.uk

18 holes, 6317yds, Par 70, SSS 71, Course record 62.

Location: S side of village off A930
Telephone for further details

Hotel
⌂ **Premier Travel Inn Dundee East,**
115-117 Lawers Dr, Panmurefield Village,
BROUGHTY FERRY
☎ 0870 9906324 – 60 en suite

EDZELL

Edzell
High St DD9 7TF
☎ 01356 647283 (Secretary) 📄 01356 648094
e-mail: secretary@edzellgolfclub.net

This delightful, gentle, flat course is situated in the foothills of the Scottish Highlands and provides good golf as well as conveying a feeling of peace and quiet to everyone who plays here. The village of Edzell is one of the most picturesque in Scotland.

Continued

Championship Course

Carnoustie Golf Links

Links Pde DD7 7JE
☎ 01241 853789 bookings 📄 01241 852720
e-mail: golf@carnoustiegolflinks.co.uk

This Championship Course has been voted the top course in Britain by many golfing greats and described as Scotland's ultimate golfing challenge. The course developed from origins in the 1560s; James Braid added new bunkers, greens and tees in the 1920s. The Open Championship first came to the course in 1931 and Carnoustie hosted the Scottish Open in 1995 and 1996, and was the venue for the 1999 Open Championship. The Burnside Course (6028 yards) is enclosed on three sides by the Championship Course and has been used for Open Championship qualifying rounds. The Buddon Course (5420 yards) has been extensively remodelled, making it ideal for mid to high handicappers.

WHERE TO STAY NEARBY

★★65%
Hotel Seaforth, Dundee Rd,
ARBROATH
☎ 01241 872232; 19 en suite

★★★★76%
Apex City Quay Hotel & Spa,
1 West Victoria Dock Rd, DUNDEE
☎ 01382 202404 & 0845 608 3456
📄 01382 201401
153 en suite

Championship
18 holes, 6941yds, Par 72, SSS 75, Course record 64

Burnside
18 holes, 6028yds, Par 68, SSS 69

Buddon Links
18 holes, 5420yds, Par 66, SSS 67

Visitors
Not before 2pm Sat, not before 11.30am Sun; must contact in advance; handicap certificate for Championship Course

Societies
Write or phone in advance

Green Fees
Terms on application

Cards
💳 💳 VISA ①

Professional
Colin Sinclair

Course Designer
James Braid

Facilities
sauna, solarium, gymnasium

Location
SW of town centre off A930

18 holes, 6367yds, Par 71, SSS 71, Course record 62.
West Water: 9 holes, 2057yds, Par 32, SSS 31.

Club membership: 855. **Visitors:** may not play 4.45-6.15pm weekdays & 7.30-10am, 12-2 weekends. Not before 2pm on 1st Sat each month. **Societies:** must contact secretary at least 14 days in advance. **Green Fees:** £38 per day; £28 per round (£48/£34 weekends). West Water: £15 per 18 holes, £10 per 9 holes. **Cards:** 💳 🖪 🗲 **Prof:** A J Webster **Course Designer:** Bob Simpson **Facilities:** Ⓐ 🍴 🏌 ♨ 🛒 🚂 🏡 ⛳ **Location:** N of Brechin on A90, take B966 signposted Edzell, continue 3.5m

Hotel
★★★ 65% **Glenesk Hotel,** High St, EDZELL
☎ 01356 648319 – 24 en suite

MONIFIETH

Monifieth
Princes St DD5 4AW
☎ 01382 532767 (Medal) & 532967 (Ashludie) 📄
01382 535816

The chief of the two courses at Monifieth is the Medal Course. It has been one of the qualifying venues for the Open Championship on more than one occasion. A seaside links, but divided from the sand dunes by a railway which provides the principal hazard for the first few holes. The 10th hole is outstanding, the 17th is excellent and there is a delightful finishing hole. The other course here is the Ashludie, and both are played over by a number of clubs who share the links.

Medal Course:
18 holes, 6655yds, Par 71, SSS 72, Course record 63.
Ashludie Course: 18 holes, 5123yds, Par 68, SSS 66.

Club membership: 1750. **Visitors:** must contact in advance. Restricted to after 2pm Sat, 10am Sun & after 9.30pm Mon-Fri. **Societies:** must contact in advance by telephone or writing to Medal Starter's Box, Princes St, Monifieth. **Green Fees:** terms on application. **Cards:** 💳 🖪 🗲 **Prof:** Ian McLeod **Facilities:** Ⓐ 🍴 by prior arrangement 🏌 ♨ 🛒 🚂 🏡 ⛳ **Location:** NE side of town on A930

Hotel
⬆ **Premier Travel Inn Dundee East,**
115-117 Lawers Dr, Panmurefield Village,
BROUGHTY FERRY
☎ 0870 9906324 – 60 en suite

MONTROSE

Montrose Golf Links
Traill Dr DD10 8SW
☎ 01674 672932 📄 01674 671800
e-mail: secretary@montroselinks.co.uk

The links at Montrose like many others in Scotland are on common land and are shared by three clubs. The Medal course at Montrose – the fifth oldest in the world – is typical of Scottish seaside links, with narrow, undulating fairways and problems from the 1st hole to the last. The Broomfield course is flatter and easier.

Medal Course:
18 holes, 6544yds, Par 71, SSS 72, Course record 63.
Broomfield Course: 18 holes, 4830yds, Par 66, SSS 63.

Club membership: 1300. **Visitors:** may not play on the Medal Course on Sat before 2.45pm & before 10am on Sun. Must have a handicap certificate for Medal Course. Contact in advance. No restrictions on Broomfield Course. Must contact in advance. **Societies:** must contact Secretary in advance. **Green Fees:** Medal: £50 per day; £40 per round (£58/£44 weekends). Broomfield: £18 per round (£20 weekends). **Cards:** 💳 🖪 🗲 **Prof:** Jason J Boyd **Course Designer:** W Park/Tom Morris **Facilities:** Ⓐ 🍴 🏌 ♨ 🛒 🚂 🏡 ⛳ **Location:** NE side of town off A92

Hotel
★★★ 74% **Best Western Links Hotel,**
Mid Links, MONTROSE
☎ 01674 671000 – 25 en suite

ARGYLL & BUTE

LUSS

Loch Lomond

Rossdhu House G83 8NT

☎ 01436 655555 📄 01436 655500

e-mail: info@lochlomond.com

A stunning and challenging golf course set in the heart of some of the most beautiful Scottish scenery. The exclusive club is strictly for members only. Nick Faldo called it the finest new course in Europe. It was designed by two Americans, Jay Morrish and Tom Weiskopf and was founded in 1993. There is a putting green, practice area and driving range. The clubhouse used to be the home of the chiefs of Clan Colquhoun.

Loch Lomond:
18 holes, 7100yds, Par 71, Course record 62.

Club membership: 650. no visitors strictly private. **Green Fees:** terms on application. **Prof:** Colin Campbell **Course Designer:** Tom Weiskopf **Facilities:** 🏖 🏠 ◇ ✓ 🎣 🎒 **Location:** Off A82 at Luss

Hotel
★★★★★ 70% **De Vere Cameron House,** BALLOCH
☎ 01389 755565 – 96 en suite

MACHRIHANISH

Machrihanish

PA28 6PT

☎ 01586 810213 📄 01586 810221

e-mail: secretary@machgolf.com

Magnificent natural links of championship status. The 1st hole is the famous drive across the Atlantic. Sandy soil allows for play all year round. Large greens, easy walking, windy. Fishing.

18 holes, 6225yds, Par 70, SSS 71.

Club membership: 1300. **Visitors:** no restrictions. **Societies:** apply in writing. **Green Fees:** Sun-Fri £40 per round/£60 per day. Sat £50/£75. (9-hole course £12 per day). **Cards:** 💳 💳 💳 💳 **Prof:** Ken Campbell **Course Designer:** Tom Morris **Facilities:** 🏖 🍴 🏖 💷 🍴 🎒 🏠 🎒 🚃 ✓ **Location:** 5m W of Campbeltown on B843

OBAN

Glencruitten

Glencruitten Rd PA34 4PU

☎ 01631 564604

There is plenty of space and considerable variety of hole on this downland course – popular with holidaymakers. In a beautiful, isolated situation, the course is hilly and testing, particularly the 1st and 12th (par 4s) and 10th and 17th (par 3s).

18 holes, 4452yds, Par 61, SSS 63, Course record 55.

Club membership: 500. **Visitors:** restricted Thu &

weekends. **Societies:** must contact in writing. **Green Fees:** not confirmed. **Course Designer:** James Braid **Facilities:** 🏖 🍴 🏖 💷 🍴 🎒 🏠 🎒 ✓ **Location:** NE side of town centre off A816

Hotel
★★★ 72% **Manor House Hotel,** Gallanach Rd, OBAN
☎ 01631 562087 – 11 en suite

CITY OF EDINBURGH

EDINBURGH

Royal Burgess

181 Whitehouse Rd, Barnton EH4 6BU

☎ 0131 339 2075 📄 0131 339 3712

e-mail: secretary@royalburgess.co.uk

No mention of golf clubs would be complete without the Royal Burgess, which was instituted in 1735, and is the oldest golfing society in the world. Its course is a pleasant parkland, and one with a great deal of variety. A club which anyone interested in the history of the game should visit.

18 holes, 6111yds, Par 68, SSS 69.

Club membership: 620. **Visitors:** must contact in advance, may not play at weekend. **Societies:** must contact in advance. **Green Fees:** terms on application. **Cards:** 💳 💳 💳 💳 💳 **Prof:** Steven Brian **Course Designer:** Tom Morris **Facilities:** 🏖 🏖 💷 🍴 🎒 🏠 🎒 ✓ **Conf:** Corporate Hospitality Days available **Location:** 5m W of city centre off A90

Hotel
★★★★ 70% **Menzies Belford Hotel,**
69 Belford Rd, EDINBURGH
☎ 0131 332 2545 – 146 en suite

CITY OF GLASGOW

GLASGOW

Haggs Castle

70 Dumbreck Rd, Dumbreck G41 4SN

☎ 0141 427 1157 📄 0141 427 1157

e-mail: secretary@haggscastlegolfclub.com

Wooded, parkland course where Scottish National Championships and the Glasgow and Scottish Open have been held.

18 holes, 6426yds, Par 72, SSS 71, Course record 63.

Club membership: 900. **Societies:** apply in writing. **Green Fees:** £40 per round; £50 per day. **Cards:** 💳 💳 💳 💳 **Prof:** Campbell Elliott **Course Designer:** James Braid **Facilities:** 🏖 🍴 🏖 💷 🍴 🎒 🏠 🎒 🚃 ✓ **Conf:** Corporate Hospitality Days available **Location:** 2.5m SW of city centre off M77 junct 1

Championship Course

Marriott Dalmahoy Hotel

Golf & Country Club, Kirknewton EH27 8EB
☎ 0131 3358010   📄 0131 335 3577
e-mail: golf.dalmahoy@marriotthotels.co.uk

The Championship East Course has hosted many major events including the Solheim Cup, the Scottish Seniors Open Championship and the PGA Championship of Scotland. The greens are large with immaculate putting surfaces and many of the long par 4 holes offer a serious challenge to any golfer. The short holes are well bunkered and the 15th hole in particular, known as the Wee Wrecker, will test your nerve and skill. The shorter West Course offers a different test with small greens requiring accuracy from a player's short game. The finishing holes with the Golgar burn meandering through the fairway create a tough finish.

WHERE TO STAY NEARBY

★★★★72%
Marriott Dalmahoy Hotel & Country Club, Kirknewton, EDINBURGH
☎ 0870 400 7299
43 en suite 172 annexe en suite

★★★★68%
Houstoun House, UPHALL
☎ 01506 853831 📄 01506 854220
24 en suite 47 annexe en suite

★★★★69%
Edinburgh Marriott Hotel, 111 Glasgow Rd, EDINBURGH
☎ 0870 400 7293 📄 0870 400 7393
245 en suite

East Course
18 holes, 7475yds, Par 72, SSS 72, Course record 62

West Course
18 holes, 5168yds, Par 68, SSS 66, Course record 60

Visitors
Subject to availability; weekends by application; phone to book tee times

Societies
Mon-Fri, phone or write for information

Green Fees
East Course £65 per 18 holes (£80 weekends and bank holidays); West Course £35 (£40 weekends and bank holidays)

Cards
💳

Professional
Neal Graham

Course Designer
James Braid

Facilities
sauna, solarium, gymnasium, beauty & hairdressing salon, fitness studio

Conferences
Facilities available

Corporate
Hospitality Days available

Location
7m W of city on A71

DUMFRIES & GALLOWAY

CUMMERTREES

Powfoot

DG12 5QE

☎ 01461 700276 📠 01461 700276

e-mail: bsutherland@powfootgolfclub.fsnet.co.uk

This British Championship Course is on the Solway Firth, playing at this delightfully compact semi-links seaside course is a scenic treat. Lovely holes include the 2nd, the 8th and the 11th, also the 9th with a World War II bomb crater.

18 holes, 6283yds, Par 71, SSS 70, Course record 63.

Club membership: 950. Visitors: contact in advance. May not play before 9am between 11am-1pm and after 3.30pm wekdays, no visitors Sat or before 1pm Sun. Societies: must book in advance. Green Fees: not confirmed. Cards: 💳 💳 Prof: Stuart Smith Course Designer: J Braid Facilities: ⊕ ⦿ ⛳ 🍺 🍴 ⛳ 🏌 🏠 🚂 🎯 Location: 0.5m off B724

Hotel

★★★ 68% Hetland Hall Hotel, CARRUTHERSTOWN ☎ 01387 840201 – 14 en suite 15 annexe en suite

DUNDEE CITY

DUNDEE

Downfield

Turnberry Av DD2 3QP

☎ 01382 825595 📠 01382 813111

e-mail: downfieldgc@aol.com

A 1999 Open Qualifying venue. A course with championship credentials providing an enjoyable test for all golfers.

18 holes, 6803yds, Par 73, SSS 73, Course record 65.

Club membership: 750. Visitors: must contact in advance, no visitors at weekends. Societies: must contact in advance. Green Fees: £38 per 18 holes (£47 per 36 holes). Cards: 💳 💳 💳 💳 💳 💳 Prof: Kenny Hutton Course Designer: James Braid Facilities: ⊕ ⦿ ⛳ 🍺 🍴 🏌 🏠 🎯 🎮 🚂 🎯 snooker room. Conf: Corporate Hospitality Days available Location: N of city centre, signposted on A90 Perth/Aberdeen road at junct with A923

EAST LOTHIAN

DUNBAR

Dunbar

East Links EH42 1LL

☎ 01368 862317 📠 01368 865202

e-mail: secretary@dunbargolfclub.sol.co.uk

Another of Scotland's old links. It is said that it was some Dunbar members who first took the game of golf to the North of England. A natural links course

on a narrow strip of land, following the contours of the sea shore. There is a wall bordering one side and the shore on the other side making this quite a challenging course for all levels of player. The wind, if blowing from the sea, is a problem.

18 holes, 6406yds, Par 71, SSS 71, Course record 64.

Club membership: 1000. Visitors: may not play Thu, between 12.30-2 weekdays, 12-2 weekends or before 9.30am any day. Societies: telephone in advance. Green Fees: £430 per round/£58 per day (weekend £53/£75). Cards: 💳 💳 💳 💳 💳 💳 Prof: Jacky Montgomery Course Designer: Tom Morris Facilities: ⊕ ⦿ ⛳ 🍺 🍴 🏌 🏠 🎯 🎯 Location: 0.5m E off A1087

GULLANE

Gullane

West Links Rd EH31 2BB

☎ 01620 842255 📠 01620 842327

e-mail: bookings@gullanegolfclub.com

Gullane is a delightful village and one of Scotland's great golf centres. Gullane Golf Club was formed in 1882. There are three Gullane courses of which numbers 1 and 2 are of championship standard. It differs from most Scottish courses in as much as it is of the upland links type and really quite hilly. The first tee is literally in the village. The views from the top of the course are magnificent and stretch far and wide in every direction – in fact, it is said that 14 counties can be seen from the highest spot.

Course No 1:
18 holes, 6466yds, Par 71, SSS 72, Course record 65.
Course No 2:
18 holes, 6244yds, Par 71, SSS 71, Course record 64.
Course No 3: 18 holes, 5252yds, Par 68, SSS 66.

Club membership: 1200. Visitors: advance booking recommended. Societies: advance booking advised. Green Fees: terms on application. Cards: 💳 💳 💳 💳 💳 Prof: Alasdair Good Course Designer: Various Facilities: ⊕ ⦿ ⛳ 🍺 🍴 🏌 🏠 🎯 🎮 🚂 🎯 🎯 Location: At west end of village on A198

Hotel

★★★★⟐🏰 Greywalls Hotel, Muirfield, GULLANE ☎ 01620 842144 – 17 en suite 5 annexe en suite

LONGNIDDRY

Longniddry

Links Rd EH32 0NL

☎ 01875 852141 📠 01875 853371

e-mail: secretary@longniddrygolfclub.co.uk

Undulating seaside links and partial parkland course with no par 5s. One of the numerous courses which stretch east from Edinburgh right to Dunbar. The inward half is more open than the wooded outward half, but can be difficult in prevailing west wind.

Continued

Championship Course

East Lothian   **GULLANE**

Honourable Company of Edinburgh Golfers
Muirfield

EH31 2EG
☎ 01620 842123   📄 01620 842977
e-mail: hceg@muirfield.org.uk

The course at Muirfield was designed by Old Tom Morris in 1891 and is generally considered to be one of the top ten courses in the world. The club itself has an excellent pedigree: it was founded in 1744, making it just 10 years older than the Royal and Ancient but not as old as Royal Blackheath. Muirfield has staged some outstanding Open championships. Perhaps one of the most memorable was in 1972 when Lee Trevino, the defending champion, seemed to be losing his grip until a spectacular shot brought him back to beat Tony Jacklin, who subsequently never won another Open.

WHERE TO STAY NEARBY

★★★
Greywalls Hotel,
Muirfield, GULLANE
☎ 01620 842144
17 en suite 5 annexe en suite

★★★72%
The Open Arms Hotel,
DIRLETON
☎ 01620 850241 📄 01620 850570
10 en suite

★★★64%
The Marine,
Cromwell Rd, NORTH BERWICK
☎ 0870 400 8129 📄 01620 894480
83 en suite

★★68%
Nether Abbey Hotel,
20 Dirleton Av, NORTH BERWICK
☎ 01620 892802 📄 01620 895298
13 en suite

---

18 holes, 6601yds, Par 70, SSS 73, Course record 63

Club Membership
700

Visitors
Tue, Thu only; must contact in advance; handicap certificate (men 18, women 24)

Societies
Tue, Thu; handicap limits (men 18, women 20); members of recognised golf course; groups up to 12 accepted

Green Fees
£150 per 36 holes, £120 per 18 holes

Cards
💳 VISA

Course Designer
Harry Colt

Facilities
🍴 🍺 🍽 ⛳ ♟ ✏ ⚒

Location
NE of village

18 holes, 6260yds, Par 68, SSS 70, Course record 63.

Club membership: 1140. **Visitors:** deposit required if booking more than 7 days in advance. May not play on competition days. **Societies:** Mon-Thu, apply in writing, handicap certificate required. **Green Fees:** £55 per day, £37.50 per round (weekends £48 per round). **Cards:** 💳💳💳 **Prof:** John Gray **Course Designer:** H S Colt **Facilities:** 🏌️🍴🛏️🏌️🍴 🏌️🏪🏌️🛒 **Conf:** Corporate Hospitality Days available **Location:** N side of village off A198

Hotel
★★★🏨 **Greywalls Hotel,** Muirfield, GULLANE
☎ 01620 842144 – 17 en suite 5 annexe en suite

NORTH BERWICK
North Berwick
Beach Rd EH39 4BB
☎ 01620 892135 📠 01620 893274
e-mail: secretary@northberwickgolfclub.com

Another of East Lothian's famous courses, the links at North Berwick is still popular. A classic championship links, it has many hazards including the beach, streams, bunkers, light rough and low walls. The great hole on the course is the 15th, the famous 'Redan'. Used by both the Tantallon and Bass Rock Golf Clubs.

West Links: 18 holes, 6420yds, Par 71, SSS 72, Course record 63.

Club membership: 730. **Visitors:** must contact in advance 01620 892135 (beyond 7 days) or 01620 892666 (within 7 days). **Societies:** must contact in advance. **Green Fees:** £80 per day; £55 per round (£75 weekends). **Cards:** 💳💳💳💳 **Prof:** D Huish **Facilities:** 🏌️🍴🛏️🏌️🍴🏪🛒🏌️ **Location:** W side of town on A198

Hotel
🅄 **The Marine,** Cromwell Rd, NORTH BERWICK
☎ 0870 400 8129 – 83 en suite

FIFE

CRAIL
Crail Golfing Society
Balcomie Clubhouse, Fifeness KY10 3XN
☎ 01333 450686 & 450960 📠 01333 450416
e-mail: crailgs@hotmail.com

Perched on the edge of the North Sea, the Crail Golfing Society's courses at Balcomie are picturesque and sporting. Crail Golfing Society began its life in 1786 and the course is highly thought of by students of the game both for its testing holes and the standard of its greens. Craighead Links has panoramic seascape and country views. With wide sweeping fairways and USGA specification greens it is a testing but fair challenge.

Balcomie Links:
18 holes, 5922yds, Par 69, SSS 70, Course record 62.
Craighead Links:
18 holes, 6700yds, Par 72, SSS 74, Course record 69.

Club membership: 1735. **Visitors:** must contact in advance, restricted 10am-noon & 2-4.30pm. **Societies:** must contact in advance, as much notice as possible for weekend play. **Green Fees:** per day: Balcomie/Balcomie £65, Craighead/Balcomie £55; per round £40 (weekends £78/£68/£50). **Cards:** 💳💳 💳💳💳 **Prof:** Graeme Lennie **Course Designer:** Tom Morris **Facilities:** 🏌️🍴🛏️🏌️🍴🏌️ 🏪🏌️🛒🏌️🏌️ **Location:** 2m NE off A917

Hotel
★★ 66% **Balcomie Links Hotel,** Balcomie Rd, CRAIL
☎ 01333 450237 – 15 rms (13 en suite)

Guesthouse
◆◆◆◆ **The Spindrift,** Pittenweem Rd, ANSTRUTHER
☎ 01333 310573 📠 01333 310573 – 8 rms (7 en suite)

ELIE
Golf House Club
KY9 1AS
☎ 01333 330301 📠 01333 330895
e-mail: sandy@golfhouseclub.freeserve.co.uk

One of Scotland's most delightful holiday courses with panoramic views over the Firth of Forth. Some of the holes out towards the rocky coastline are splendid. This is the course which has produced many good professionals, including the immortal James Braid.

18 holes, 6273yds, Par 70, SSS 70, Course record 62.

Club membership: 600. **Visitors:** advisable to contact in advance, limited availability Sat May-Sep and no visitors Sun May-Sep, ballot in operation for tee times during Jul and Aug. **Societies:** must contact in advance. **Green Fees:** not confirmed. **Cards:** 💳💳 💳💳 **Prof:** Robin Wilson **Course Designer:** James Braid **Facilities:** 🏌️🍴🛏️🏌️🍴🏌️🏪🏌️🛒🏌️🏌️ **Location:** W side of village off A917

Hotel
🏨 **The Inn at Lathones,** Largoward, ST ANDREWS
☎ 01334 840494 – 13 annexe en suite

LEVEN

Leven Links

The Promenade KY8 4HS
☎ 01333 428859 & 421390 📄 01333 428859
e-mail: secretary@leven-links.com

Leven has the classic ingredients which make up a golf links in Scotland; undulating fairways with hills and hollows, out of bounds and a 'burn' or stream. Turning into the prevailing west wind at the 13th leaves the golfer with a lot of work to do before one of the finest finishing holes in golf. A top class championship links course used for British Open final qualifying stages, it has fine views over Largo Bay.

18 holes, 6436yds, Par 71, SSS 70, Course record 61.

Club membership: 1000. **Visitors:** contact in advance. Limited availability Fri pm & Sat, contact for these times no more than 5 days in advance. **Societies:** apply in advance. **Green Fees:** £50 per day, £37 per round (weekends £60/£45). **Cards:** 💳 💳 💳 💳 **Course Designer:** Tom Morris **Facilities:** ⓣ ⓣ ⓣ ⓣ ⓣ ⓣ ⓣ

Hotel
★★★ 78% **Old Manor Hotel,**
Leven Rd, LUNDIN LINKS
☎ 01333 320368 – 24 en suite

LUNDIN LINKS

Lundin

Golf Rd KY8 6BA
☎ 01333 320202 📄 01333 329743
e-mail: secretary@lundingolfclub.co.uk

The Leven Links and the course of the Lundin Club adjoin each other. The course is part seaside and part inland. The holes are excellent but those which can be described as seaside holes have a very different nature from the inland style ones. The par 3 14th looks seawards across the Firth of Forth towards Edinburgh and the old railway line defines out of bounds at several holes. A number of burns snake across the fairways.

18 holes, 6371yds, Par 71, SSS 71, Course record 63.

Club membership: 850. **Visitors:** visitors welcome weekdays 9-3.30 (3pm Fridays) and Sat after 2.30pm, limited times on Sun. Book well in advance. **Societies:**

book well in advance by telephoning Secretary **Green Fees:** £50 per day; £42 per round. (£50 per round weekends). **Cards:** 💳 💳 💳 **Prof:** David Webster **Course Designer:** James Braid **Facilities:** ⓣ ⓣ ⓣ ⓣ ⓣ ⓣ **Location:** W side of village off A915

Hotel
★★★ 78% **Old Manor Hotel,**
Leven Rd, LUNDIN LINKS
☎ 01333 320368 – 24 en suite

ST ANDREWS

Dukes Course

Craigtoun KY16 8NS
☎ 01334 474371 📄 01334 479456
e-mail: reservations@oldcoursehotel.co.uk

Now owned and managed by the Old Course Hotel, with a spectacular setting above St Andrews. Blending the characteristics of a links course with an inland course, Dukes offers rolling fairways, undulating greens and a testing woodland section, and magnificent views over St Andrews Bay towards Carnoustie.

Dukes Course: 18 holes, 6749yds, Par 72, SSS 73, Course record 67.

Club membership: 500. **Visitors:** booking should be in advance to avoid disappointment through the hotel resort reservations team. **Societies:** apply in writing or fax in advance. **Green Fees:** From £75 per 18 holes. **Cards:** 💳 💳 💳 💳 💳 💳 💳 **Prof:** Ron Walker **Course Designer:** Peter Thomson **Facilities:** ⓣ ⓣ ⓣ ⓣ ⓣ ⓣ ⓣ ⓣ ⓣ ⓣ ⓣ ⓣ ⓣ sauna, solarium, gymnasium, computer swing analyses. **Conf:** facilities available **Corporate:** Hospitality Days available **Location:** Follow M90 from Edinburgh onto A91 to Cupar then to St Andrews turning off for Strathkiness

Hotel
★★★★★ **The Old Course Hotel,**
Golf Resort & Spa, ST ANDREWS
☎ 01334 474371 – 134 en suite

TAYPORT

Scotscraig

Golf Rd DD6 9DZ
☎ 01382 552515 📄 01382 553130
e-mail: scotscraig@scottishgolf.com

Combined with heather and rolling fairways, the course is part heathland, part links, with the greens being renowned for being fast and true.

18 holes, 6550yds, Par 71, SSS 72, Course record 62.

Club membership: 900. **Visitors:** restricted at weekends **Societies:** advance booking. **Green Fees:** £54 per day, £44 per round (weekends £60/£50). **Cards:** 💳 💳 💳 **Prof:** John Kelly **Course Designer:** James Braid **Facilities:** ⓣ ⓣ ⓣ ⓣ ⓣ ⓣ ⓣ ⓣ ⓣ ⓣ ⓣ ⓣ **Conf:** Corporate Hospitality Days available **Location:** S side of village off B945

Continued

Championship Course

St Andrews Links

Pilmour House KY16 9SF
☎ 01334 466666 📠 01334 479555
e-mail: linkstrust@standrews.org.uk

Golf was first played here around
1400 and the Old Course is
acknowledged worldwide as the
home of golf. The Old Course has
played host to the greatest
golfers in the world and many of
golf's most dramatic moments.
The New Course (6604 yards) was
opened in 1895, having been laid
out by Old Tom Morris. The
Jubilee was opened in 1897, and

is 6805 yards long from the medal tees. A shorter version of the
Jubilee Course is also available, known as the Bronze Course,
measuring 5674 yards. There is no handicap limit for the shorter
course and it is best for lower and middle-handicap golfers. The Eden
opened in 1914 and is recommended for middle to high handicap
golfers. The Strathtyrum has a shorter, less testing layout, best for
high handicap golfers. The 9-hole Balgrove Course, upgraded and
re-opened in 1993, is best for beginners and children. The facilities
and courses here make this the largest golf complex in Europe.

WHERE TO STAY NEARBY

★★★★★
The Old Course Hotel,
Golf Resort & Spa, ST ANDREWS
☎ 01334 474371
134 en suite

★★★
St Andrews Golf Hotel,
40 The Scores, ST ANDREWS
☎ 01334 472611 📠 01334 472188
21 en suite

★★★
**Rufflets Country House &
Garden Restaurant,**
Strathkinness Low Rd,
ST ANDREWS
☎ 01334 472594 📠 01334 478703
19 en suite 5 annexe en suite

★★★★★71%
**St Andrews Bay Golf Resort
& Spa,** St Andrews
☎ 01334 837000 📠 01334 471115
209 en suite 8 annexe en suite

★★★★71%
Macdonald Rusacks Hotel,
Pilmour Links, ST ANDREWS
☎ 0870 400 8128 📠 01334 477896
68 en suite

★★★71%
Scores Hotel, 76 The Scores,
ST ANDREWS
☎ 01334 472451 📠 01334 473947
30 en suite

Old Course
18 holes, 6609yds, Par 72,
SSS 72, Course record 62

New Course
18 holes, 6604yds, Par 71,
SSS 73

Jubilee Course
18 holes, 6742yds, Par 72,
SSS 73, Course record 63

Eden Course
18 holes, 6112yds, Par 70,
SSS 70

Strathtyrum Course
18 holes, 5094yds, Par 69,
SSS 69

Balgrove Course
9 holes, 1530yds, Par 30,
SSS 30

Visitors
Old Course: not Sun;
handicap (men 24, women
36); daily ballot or 2-year
booking. Other courses: 1-
month advance booking for
New, Jubilee, Eden, Strath;
no advance booking Sat

Societies
Book at least 1 month in
advance

Green Fees
£10–£115

Cards
💳

Facilities
🍴 🍽 🏌 ☕ 🍷 👕 ⛳

Corporate
Hospitality Days available

Location
Off A91

Hotel
★★★ 64% **Sandford Country House Hotel,**
Newton Hill, Wormit, DUNDEE
☎ 01382 541802 – 16 en suite

HIGHLAND

BOAT OF GARTEN
Boat of Garten
PH24 3BQ
☎ 01479 831282 📄 01479 831523
e-mail: boatgolf@enterprise.net

This heathland course was cut out from a silver birch forest though the fairways are adequately wide. There are natural hazards of broom and heather, good views and walking is easy. A round provides great variety.

18 holes, 5876yds, Par 70, SSS 69, Course record 67.

Club membership: 650. **Visitors:** must contact in advance. Handicap certificate required. Play restricted to 10am-4pm weekends & 9.20am-7pm weekdays **Societies:** must telephone or email in advance. **Green Fees:** £40 per day; £30 per round (£45/£35 weekends). **Cards:** 💳 💳 💳 💳 **Course Designer:** James Braid **Facilities:** ⓘ 🍴 🛍 🍺 🍽 🏌 🏠 🚩 🏌 🚜 🏌 🏌 **Conf:** Corporate Hospitality Days available **Location:** E side of village

Hotel
★★★ 76% **Boat Hotel,** BOAT OF GARTEN
☎ 01479 831258 – 28 en suite

DORNOCH
Royal Dornoch
Golf Rd IV25 3LW
☎ 01862 810219 ext.185 📄 01862 810792
e-mail: bookings@royaldornoch.com

The Championship Course was recently rated 9th among Britain's top courses and is a links of rare subtlety. It appears amicable but proves very challenging in play with stiff breezes and tight lies. The 18-hole Struie links course provides, in a gentler style, an enjoyable test of a golfer's accuracy for players of all abilities.

Championship: 18 holes, 6514yds, Par 70, SSS 73. Struie Course: 18 holes, 6276yds, Par 72, SSS 70.

Club membership: 1700. **Visitors:** Recommended to contact in advance for Championship Course **Societies:** must apply in advance. **Green Fees:** Championship course: £72 per round (£82 weekends). Struie course: £47 per day; £26 per round. **Cards:** 💳 💳 💳 💳 💳 **Prof:** A Skinner **Course Designer:** Tom Morris **Facilities:** ⓘ 🍴 🛍 🍺 🍽 🏌 🏠 🚩 🏌 🏌 **Conf:** Corporate Hospitality Days available **Location:** E side of town

NAIRN
Nairn
Seabank Rd IV12 4HB
☎ 01667 453208 📄 01667 456328
e-mail: secretary@nairngolfclub.co.uk

18 holes, 6430yds, Par 71, SSS 73, Course record 64. Newton: 9 holes, 3542yds, Par 58, SSS 57.

Course Designer: A Simpson/Old Tom Morris/James Braid **Location:** 16m E of Inverness on A96 Telephone for further details

MORAY

ELGIN

Elgin

Hardhillock, Birnie Rd, New Elgin IV30 8SX
☎ 01343 542338 📠 01343 542341
e-mail: secretary@elgingolfclub.com

Possibly the finest inland course in the north of Scotland, with undulating greens and compact holes that demand the highest accuracy. There are thirteen par 4s and one par 5 hole on its parkland layout, eight of the par 4s being over 400 yards in length.

Hardhillock:
18 holes, 6416yds, Par 68, SSS 69, Course record 63.

Club membership: 1000. **Visitors:** must contact in advance, weekend play only by prior arrangement. **Societies:** telephone secretary for details. **Green Fees:** £40 per day, £30 per round. **Cards:** 💳 💳 💳 💳 💳 💳 **Prof:** Kevin Stables **Course Designer:** John Macpherson **Facilities:** 🌐 🍴 🛍 ➖ 🍴 ⛳ 🏠 🍴 ⛏ 🚃 ⛳ 🏌 **Conf:** facilities available **Location:** 1m S on A941

Hotel

★★★ 74% **Mansion House Hotel,** The Haugh, ELGIN
☎ 01343 548811 – 23 en suite

FORRES

Forres

Muiryshade IV36 2RD
☎ 01309 672250 📠 01309 672250
e-mail: sandy@forresgolf.demon.co.uk

An all-year parkland course laid on light, well-drained soil in wooded countryside. Walking is easy despite some hilly holes. A test for the best golfers.

18 holes, 6240yds, Par 70, SSS 70, Course record 60.

Club membership: 1000. **Visitors:** welcome although club competitions take priority. Weekends may be restricted in summer. **Societies:** advised to telephone 2-3 weeks in advance. **Green Fees:** £26 per round/£34 per day. **Cards:** 💳 💳 💳 **Prof:** Sandy Aird **Course Designer:** James Braid/Willie Park **Facilities:** 🌐 🍴 🛍 ➖ 🍴 ⛳ 🏠 🍴 ⛏ 🚃 ⛳ **Conf:** Corporate Hospitality Days available **Location:** SE side of town centre off B9010

Hotel

★★★ 68% **Ramnee Hotel,** Victoria Rd, FORRES
☎ 01309 672410 – 20 en suite

LOSSIEMOUTH

Moray

Stotfield Rd IV31 6QS
☎ 01343 812018 📠 01343 815102
e-mail: secretary@moraygolf.co.uk

Two fine Scottish Championship links courses, known as Old and New (Moray), and situated on the Moray Firth where the weather is unusually mild.

Old Course:
18 holes, 6643yds, Par 71, SSS 73, Course record 65.
New Course:
18 holes, 6004yds, Par 69, SSS 69, Course record 62.

Club membership: 1550. **Visitors:** must contact in advance 01343 812018 Secretary. **Societies:** Contact in advance. **Green Fees:** terms on applications. **Cards:** 💳 💳 💳 💳 💳 💳 **Prof:** Alistair Thomson **Course Designer:** Tom Morris **Facilities:** 🌐 🍴 🛍 ➖ 🍴 ⛳ 🏠 🍴 ⛏ 🚃 ⛳ **Conf:** Corporate Hospitality Days available **Location:** N side of town

Hotel

★★★ 74% **Mansion House Hotel,** The Haugh, ELGIN
☎ 01343 548811 – 23 en suite

NORTH AYRSHIRE

IRVINE

Glasgow

Gailes KA11 5AE
☎ 0141 942 2011 📠 0141 942 0770
e-mail: secretary@glasgow-golf.com

A lovely seaside links. The turf of the fairways and all the greens is truly glorious and provides tireless play. Established in 1882, and is a qualifying course for the Open Championship.

Glasgow Gailes: 18 holes, 6535yds, Par 71, SSS 72, Course record 63.

Club membership: 1200. **Visitors:** prior booking through Secretary reccomended, no visitors before 2.30pm Sat & Sun. **Societies:** initial contact by telephone. **Green Fees:** £70 per day, £55 per round (£60 per round weekends). **Cards:** 💳 💳 💳 💳 **Prof:** J Steven **Course Designer:** W Park Jnr **Facilities:** 🌐 🍴 by prior arrangement 🛍 ➖ 🍴 ⛳ 🏠 🍴 ⛏ 🚃 ⛳ **Conf:** Corporate Hospitality Days available **Location:** Off A78 at Newhouse junct, South of Irvine

Hotel

★★★ 69% **Montgreenan Mansion House Hotel,** Montgreenan Estate, KILWINNING
☎ 01294 557733 – 21 en suite

Western Gailes

Gailes by Irvine KA11 5AE
☎ 01294 311649 📠 01294 312312
e-mail: enquiries@westerngailes.com

A magnificent seaside links with glorious turf and wonderful greens. The view is open across the Firth of Clyde to the neighbouring islands. It is a well-balanced course crossed by three burns. There are two par 5s, the 6th and 14th, and the 11th is a testing 445-yard par 4 dog-leg.

18 holes, 6639yds, Par 71, SSS 74, Course record 65.

Visitors: welcome Mon, Wed, Fri. Must contact in advance. Limited number of times on Sun pm must reserve in advance **Societies:** Mon/Wed/Fri, Sun pm must contact in advance. **Green Fees:** £95 per 18 holes, £140 per 36 holes (both including lunch). £100 Sun (no lunch). **Cards:** 🟢 💳 📇 💷 **Facilities:** ⊕ ⦿ by prior arrangement 🛍 ☕ 🍴 ⚡ 🏌 🏠 🏊 **Conf:** Corporate Hospitality Days available **Location:** 2m S off A737

Hotel
★★★ 69% **Montgreenan Mansion House Hotel,** Montgreenan Estate, KILWINNING
☎ 01294 557733 – 21 en suite

PERTH & KINROSS

BLAIRGOWRIE

Blairgowrie
Golf Course Rd, Rosemount PH10 6LG
☎ 01250 872622   📠 01250 875451
e-mail: admin@blairgowrie-golf.co.uk

Two 18-hole heathland courses, also a 9-hole course.

Rosemount Course:
18 holes, 6590yds, Par 72, SSS 73, Course record 64.
Lansdowne Course:
18 holes, 6802yds, Par 72, SSS 73, Course record 67.
Wee Course: 9 holes, 2327yds, Par 32.

Club membership: 1550. **Visitors:** must contact in advance & have handicap certificate, restricted Wed, Fri & weekends. **Societies:** must contact in advance. **Green Fees:** Rosemount: £65 per round; Lansdowne: £50 per round. **Cards:** 🟢 💳 📇 💷 **Prof:** Charles Dernie **Course Designer:** J Braid/P Allis/D Thomas/Old Tom Morris **Facilities:** ⊕ ⦿ 🛍 ☕ 🍴 ⚡ 🏌 🏠 🏊 ⚡ **Conf:** Corporate Hospitality Days available **Location:** Off A93 Rosemount

Hotel
★★★ 64% **Angus Hotel,** Wellmeadow, BLAIRGOWRIE
☎ 01250 872455 – 81 en suite

CRIEFF

Crieff
Ferntower, Perth Rd PH7 3LR
☎ 01764 652909   📠 01764 655096
e-mail: bookings@crieffgolf.co.uk

Set in the dramatic countryside of Perthshire, Crieff Golf Club was established in 1891. The Ferntower Championship Course has magnificent views over the Strathearn Valley and offers all golfers an enjoyable round. The short 9-hole Dornoch Course, which incorporates some of the James Braid designed holes from the original 18 holes, provides an interesting challenge for juniors, beginners and others short of time.

Ferntower Course:
18 holes, 6427yds, Par 71, SSS 72, Course record 64.
Dornock Course: 9 holes, 2372yds, Par 32.

Club membership: 720. **Visitors:** must contact professional in advance. **Societies:** must contact professional in advance. **Green Fees:** Ferntower: weekday per round: Mar-Apr £23 May & Oct £26 Jun-Sep £28 (weekends £28/£33/£38). Dornock £9 for 9 holes, £14 for 18 holes. **Cards:** 🟢 💳 💷 **Prof:** David Murchie **Course Designer:** James Braid **Facilities:** ⊕ ⦿ 🛍 ☕ 🍴 ⚡ 🏌 🏠 🏊 ⚡ 🏌 ⚡ 🏌 **Conf:** Corporate Hospitality Days available **Location:** 0.5m NE on A85

Hotel
★★★ 74% **Royal Hotel,** Melville Square, COMRIE
☎ 01764 679200 – 11 en suite

PITLOCHRY

Pitlochry
Golf Course Rd PH16 5QY
☎ 01796 472792   📠 01796 473947
e-mail: pro@pitlochrygolf.co.uk

A varied and interesting heathland course with fine views and posing many problems. Its SSS permits few errors in its achievement.

Pitlochry Golf Course:
18 holes, 5670yds, Par 69, SSS 69, Course record 63.

Club membership: 450. **Societies:** must contact in advance. **Green Fees:** £35 per day, £24 per round

Championship Course

AUCHTERARDER

Gleneagles Hotel

PH3 1NF

☎ 01764 662231 📠 01764 662134

e-mail: resort.sales@gleneagles.com

The PGA Centenary Course, designed by Jack Nicklaus and James Braid, and launched in style in May 1993, has an American-Scottish layout with many water hazards, elevated tees and raised contoured greens. It is the selected venue for the Ryder Cup 2014. It has a five-tier tee structure, making it both the longest and shortest playable course at the resort, as well as the most accommodating to all standards of golfer. The King's Course, with its abundance of heather, gorse, raised greens and plateau tees, is set within the valley of Strathearn with the Grampian mountains spectacularly in view to the north. The shorter Queen's Course, with fairways lined with Scots pines and water hazards, is set within a softer landscape and is considered an easier test of golf. You can improve your game at the golf academy at Gleneagles, where the philosophy is that golf should be fun and fun in golf comes from playing better. A complete corporate golf package is available.

WHERE TO STAY NEARBY

★★★★★
The Gleneagles Hotel,
AUCHTERARDER
☎ 01764 662231
270 en suite

★★76%
Cairn Lodge, Orchil Rd,
AUCHTERARDER
☎ 01764 662634 📠 01764 662866
10 en suite

★★★74%
Huntingtower Hotel,
Crieff Rd, PERTH
☎ 01738 583771 📠 01738 583777
31 en suite   3 annexe en suite

King's Course
18 holes, 6471yds, Par 70, SSS 73, Course record 60

Queen's Course
18 holes, 5965yds, Par 68, SSS 70, Course record 62

PGA Centenary Course
18 holes, 6551yds, Par 72, SSS 73, Course record 63

Visitors
8-week advance booking required; advance payment to secure tee times

Societies
Phone, e-mail or fax

Green Fees
May–Sept £110 before 3pm, £70 after 3pm, £40 after 5pm; reduced rates Oct–Apr

Cards

Professional
Russell Smith

Course Designers
James Braid, Jack Nicklaus

Facilities
squash, sauna, solarium, gymnasium, golf academy, shooting, falconry, off-road driving

Conferences
Facilities available

Corporate
Hospitality Days available

Location
2m SW of Auchterarder off A823

(£45/£30 weekends). **Cards:** 💳 💳 💳 💳 **Prof:**
Mark Pirie **Course Designer:** Willy Fernie **Facilities:**
🍴🏌️⛳🛏️⛳🏌️⛳ **Location:** Larchwood
Road from A924. golf club on left.

Hotel
★★★ 74% **Pine Trees Hotel,**
Strathview Ter, PITLOCHRY
☎ 01796 472121 – 20 en suite

SCOTTISH BORDERS

KELSO

Roxburghe
Heiton TD5 8JZ
☎ 01573 450333 📠 01573 450611
e-mail: golf@roxburghe.net

An exceptional parkland layout designed by
Dave Thomas and opened in 1997. Surrounded by
natural woodland on the banks of the River Teviot.
Owned by the Duke of Roxburghe, this course has
numerous bunkers, wide rolling and sloping
fairways and strategically placed water features.
The signature hole is the 14th.

Roxburghe Golf Course: 18 holes, 6925yds, Par 72, SSS
74, Course record 66.

Club membership: 310. **Visitors:** dress code (smart
casual, no jeans, no training shoes). Book in advance
Societies: please telephone in advance, a number of
packages available. **Green Fees:** £80 per day, £60 per
round. **Cards:** 💳 💳 💳 💳 💳 **Prof:** Craig
Montgomerie **Course Designer:** Dave Thomas
Facilities: 🍴🏌️⛳🛏️⛳🏌️⛳🏌️⛳
🏌️ Clay pigeon shooting, falconry, archery, mountain
bikes. **Conf:** facilities available **Corporate:** Hospitality
Days available **Location:** 5m E of Jedburgh on A698,
2m W of Kelso on A698

Hotel
★★★★🏌️ 76% **The Roxburghe Hotel & Golf
Course,** Heiton, KELSO
☎ 01573 450331 – 16 en suite 6 annexe en suite

SOUTH AYRSHIRE

BARASSIE

Kilmarnock (Barassie)
29 Hillhouse Rd KA10 6SY
☎ 01292 313920 📠 01292 318300
e-mail: secretarykbgc@lineone.net

**The club now has a 27-hole layout. Magnificent
seaside links, relatively flat with much heather
and small, undulating greens.**

18 holes, 6817yds, Par 72, SSS 74, Course record 63.
9 hole course: 9 holes, 2888yds, Par 34.

Club membership: 600. **Visitors:** limited availability
Wed & weekends and Fri am. Contact Secretary in
advance. **Societies:** must telephone in advance and
confirm in writing. **Green Fees:** £58 for up to 36
holes. **Cards:** 💳 💳 💳 **Prof:** Gregor Howie
Course Designer: Theodore Moone **Facilities:** 🍴🏌️
🛏️⛳🏌️⛳🏌️⛳ **Location:** E side of village on
B746, 2m N of Troon

Hotel
★★★★ 69% **Marine Hotel,** Crosbie Rd, TROON
☎ 01292 314444 90 en suite

PRESTWICK

Prestwick
2 Links Rd KA9 1QG
☎ 01292 477404 📠 01292 477255
e-mail: bookings@prestwickgc.co.uk

**Seaside links with natural hazards, tight fairways
and difficult, fast, undulating greens.**

18 holes, 6544yds, Par 71, SSS 73, Course record 67.

Club membership: 575. **Visitors:** restricted Thu and
Sun, no play on Sat. Must contact in advance and have
a handicap certificate. **Societies:** must contact in
writing. **Green Fees:** £100 per round/£150 per day
(Sundays £125 per round). **Cards:** 💳 💳 💳 💳 💳
Prof: D A Fleming **Course Designer:** Tom Morris
Facilities: 🍴🛏️⛳🏌️⛳🏌️⛳ **Conf:** Corporate
Hospitality Days available **Location:** In town centre
off A79

Hotel
★★★ 70% **Parkstone Hotel,** Esplanade, PRESTWICK
☎ 01292 477286 – 22 en suite

Championship Course

Royal Troon

Craigend Rd KA10 6EP
☎ 01292 311555　📄 01292 318204
e-mail: bookings@royaltroon.com

Troon was founded in 1878 with just 5 holes on linksland. In its first decade it grew from 5 holes to 6, then 12, and finally 18 holes. It became Royal Troon in 1978 on its 100th anniversary. Royal Troon's reputation is based on its combination of rough and sandy hills, bunkers, and a severity of finish that has diminished the championship hopes of many. The most successful players have relied on an equal blend of finesse and power. The British Open Championship has been played at Troon eight times – in 1923, 1950, 1962, 1973, 1982, 1989, 1997, and lastly in 2004 when it hosted the 133rd tournament. It has the shortest and longest holes of courses hosting the Open. Ten new bunkers and four new tees were added after the 1997 competition. It is recommended that you apply to the course in advance for full visitor information.

WHERE TO STAY NEARBY

★★★★69%
Marine Hotel,
Crosbie Rd, TROON
☎ 01292 314444
90 en suite

★★★75%
Piersland House Hotel,
Craigend Rd, TROON
☎ 01292 314747 📄 01292 315613
15 en suite 15 annexe en suite

★★★
Lochgreen House, Monktonhill
Rd, Southwood, TROON
☎ 01292 313343 📄 01292 318661
32 en suite 8 annexe en suite

Old Course
18 holes, 6641yds, Par 71, SSS 73, Course record 64

Portland
18 holes, 6289yds, Par 71, SSS 71, Course record 65

Club Membership
800

Visitors
Mon, Tue, Thu only May-Oct; must write in advance; letter of introduction from own club and handicap certificate (men under 20, women under 30). Under 16s may play Portland

Green Fees
£200 day package including coffee and lunch

Cards
💳 💳 💳 💳

Professional
R B Anderson

Course Designers
C Hunter, G Strath, W Fernie

Facilities
🍴 ⛳ ☕ 🍺 👕 🏠 🎯 🏌️

Location
S of town on B749. 5m from Prestwick airport

Championship Course

Westin Turnberry Resort

KA26 9LT
☎ 01655 331000 🖨 01655 331069
e-mail: turnberry@westin.com

For thousands of players of all nationalities, Turnberry is one of the finest of all golf destinations, where some of the most remarkable moments in Open history have taken place. The legendary Ailsa Course is complemented by the new highly acclaimed Kintyre Course, while the 9-hole Arran Course, created by Donald Steel and Colin Montgomerie, has similar challenges such as undulating greens, tight tee shots, pot bunkers and thick Scottish rough. With the famous hotel on the left and the magnificent Ailsa Craig away to the right, there are few vistas in world golf to match the 1st tee here. To help you prepare for your game the Colin Montgomerie Links Golf Academy, alongside the luxurious and extensive clubhouse, was opened in April 2000; it features 12 driving bays, 4 short-game bays, 2 dedicated teaching rooms and a group teaching room.

WHERE TO STAY NEARBY

★★★★★
The Westin Turnberry Resort, TURNBERRY
☎ 01655 331000
132 en suite 89 annexe en suite

★★★75%
Malin Court, TURNBERRY
☎ 01655 331457 🖨 01655 331072
18 en suite

★★★
Ladyburn, MAYBOLE
☎ 01655 740585 🖨 01655 740580
5 en suite

Ailsa Course
18 holes, 6440yds, Par 69, SSS 72, Course record 63

Kintyre Course
18 holes, 6376yds, Par 71, SSS 72

Arran Course
9 holes, 1996yds, Par 31, SSS 31

Visitors
Residents of the hotel have preferential booking

Societies
Apply in writing

Green Fees
Ailsa £130 per round (£175 weekends); Kintyre £105 per 18 holes

Cards
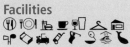

Professional
Paul Burley

Course Designers
Mackenzie Ross, Donald Steel

Facilities
🍴🍽️🛏️🍺🍷🛋️🏠 ⛳🛒🏌️🔍🏊🎵
sauna, solarium, gymnasium, Colin Montgomerie Links Golf Academy

Corporate
Hospitality Days available

Location
15m SW of Ayr on A77

SOUTH LANARKSHIRE

LANARK

Lanark
The Moor, Whitelees Rd ML11 7RX
☎ 01555 663219 & 661456 📄 01555 663219
e-mail: lanarkgolfclub@supanet.com

Lanark is renowned for its smooth fast greens, natural moorland fairways and beautiful scenery. The course is built is built on a substrate of glacial sands, providing a unique feeling of tackling a links course at 600 feet above sea level. The par of 70 can be a real test when the prevailing wind blows.

Old Course:
18 holes, 6306yds, Par 70, SSS 71, Course record 62.
Wee Course: 9 holes, 1489yds, Par 28.

Club membership: 880. **Visitors:** booking advisable, no visitors weekends. **Societies:** apply in advance. **Green Fees:** £45 per day; £35 per round. Wee Course; £7 per day. **Prof:** Alan White **Course Designer:** Tom Morris **Facilities:** ⑪ ⑩ 🏌 💼 🖥 🎍 👜 ⚙ 🏌 **Conf:** Corporate Hospitality Days available **Location:** E side of town centre off A73

Hotel
★★★ 66% **Cartland Bridge Hotel,**
Glasgow Rd, LANARK
☎ 01555 664426 – 20 rms (18 en suite)

STIRLING

BANNOCKBURN

Brucefields Family Golfing Centre
Pirnhall Rd FK7 8EH
☎ 01786 818184 📄 01786 817770
e-mail: brucefields@freenetname.co.uk

Gently rolling parkland with fine views. Most holes can be played without too much difficulty with the exception of the 2nd which is a long and tricky par 4 and the 6th, a par 3 which requires exact club selection and a straight shot.

Main Course:
9 holes, 2513yds, Par 68, SSS 68, Course record 66.

Club membership: 300. **Visitors:** no restrictions **Societies:** apply in writing. **Green Fees:** £17 per 18 holes, £10 per 9 holes (£19/£11 weekends). **Cards:** 💳 🖼 🗾 🖾 ⑤ **Prof:** Gregor Monks **Course Designer:** Souters Sportsturf **Facilities:** ⑪ ⑩ 🏌 💼 🖥 🎍 👜 ⚙ 🏌 golf academy, par 3 9-hole course. **Conf:** facilities available **Corporate:** Hospitality Days available **Location:** Exit at inerchange of M80/M9 (junct 9), from roundabout take A91, 1st left at sign for Brucefields

ISLAY, ISLE OF

PORT ELLEN

Machrie Hotel
Machrie PA42 7AN
☎ 01496 302310 📄 01496 302404
e-mail: machrie@machrie.com

Championship links course opened in 1891, where golf's first £100 Open Championship was played in 1901. Fine turf and many blind holes. Par 4.

18 holes, 6226yds, Par 71, SSS 71, Course record 66.

Club membership: 340. **Visitors:** no restrictions. **Societies:** apply in writing or telephone. **Green Fees:** £57 per day, £42 per round. **Cards:** 💳 🖼 🗾 🖾 ⑤ **Course Designer:** W Campbell **Facilities:** ⑪ ⑩ 🏌 💼 🖥 🎍 👜 ⚙ 🏌 🎍 snooker, table tennis. **Conf:** facilities available **Location:** 4m N off A846

Inn
◆◆◆◆◆ **The Harbour Inn and Restaurant,** BOWMORE
☎ 01496 810330 – 7 en suite

WALES

ANGLESEY, ISLE OF

BEAUMARIS

Princes
Henllys Hall LL58 8HU
☎ 01248 811717 📄 01248 811511
e-mail: henllys@hpbsite.com

18 holes, 6062yards.

Course Designer: Roger Jones **Location:** A545 to Beaumaris and through town. After 0.25m, Henllys Hall signed on left
Telephone for further details

Hotel
★★ 75% **Ye Olde Bulls Head Inn,**
Castle St, BEAUMARIS
☎ 01248 810329 – 12 en suite 1 annexe en suite

HOLYHEAD

Holyhead
Lon Garreg Fawr, Trearddur Bay LL65 2YL
☎ 01407 763279 📄 01407 763279
e-mail: mqrsec@aol.com

Treeless, undulating seaside course which provides a varied and testing game, particularly in a south wind. The fairways are bordered by gorse, heather and rugged outcrops of rock. Accuracy from most tees is paramount as there are 43 fairway and greenside bunkers and lakes. Designed by James Braid.

18 holes, 6058yds, Par 70, SSS 70, Course record 64.

Club membership: 1350. Visitors: must contact in advance. Societies: must contact in advance. Green Fees: £25 per day (£30 weekends & bank holidays). Prof: Stephen Elliot Course Designer: James Braid Facilities: ⊕ †⊙↓ ┗ ☞ ☜↓ 👤 🏠 ⛳ ◇ ✦ Location: A55 to rdbt at Hollyhead, left on B4545 to Trearddur Bay 1m

Hotel
★★★ 73% **Trearddur Bay Hotel,** TREARDDUR BAY
☎ 01407 860301 – 36 en suite

BRIDGEND

BRIDGEND

Southerndown
Ewenny CF32 0QP
☎ 01656 880476 📄 01656 880317
e-mail: southerndowngolf@btconnect.com

Downland-links championship course with rolling fairways and fast greens. Golfers who successfully negotiate the 4 par 3s still face a testing finish with 3 of the last 4 holes played into the prevailing wind. The par 3 5th is played across a valley and the 18th, with its split-level fairway, is a demanding finishing hole. Superb views.

18 holes, 6449yds, Par 70, SSS 72, Course record 64.

Club membership: 710. Visitors: must contact in advance & have handicap certificate. Societies: by arrangement with secretary. Green Fees: £45 (£60 weekends or 36 holes). Cards: 💳 💳 💳 💳 Prof: D G McMonagle Course Designer: W Park/W Fernie & others Facilities: ⊕ †⊙↓ ┗ ☞ ☜↓ 👤 🏠 ✦ 🏌 ✦ 🎯 Location: 3m SW of Bridgend on B4524

Hotel
★★★ 69% **Heronston Hotel,** Ewenny Rd, BRIDGEND
☎ 01656 668811 – 69 en suite 6 annexe en suite

PORTHCAWL

Royal Porthcawl
Rest Bay CF36 3UW
☎ 01656 782251 📄 01656 771687
e-mail: royalporthcawl@aol. com

One of the great links courses, Royal Porthcawl is unique in that the sea is in full view from every single hole. The course enjoys a substantial reputation with heather, broom, gorse and a challenging wind demanding a player's full skill and attention.

18 holes, 6440yds, Par 72, SSS 73.

Club membership: 800. Visitors: must contact in advance & produce handicap certificate. Limit men 20, ladies 30. Restricted at weekends & bank holidays. Societies: apply in writing/telephone/e-mail Green Fees: not confirmed. Cards: 💳 💳 💳 💳 💳 Prof: Peter Evans Course Designer: Ramsey Hunter Facilities: ⊕ †⊙↓ ┗ ☞ ☜↓ 👤 🏠 ☜ ◇ ✦ 🎯 Location: M4 junct

37, proceed to Porthcawl & Rest Bay

Hotel
★★★ 65% **Seabank Hotel,**
The Promenade, PORTHCAWL
☎ 01656 782261 – 67 en suite

CARDIFF

CARDIFF

St Mellons
St Mellons CF3 2XS
☎ 01633 680408 📄 01633 681219
e-mail: stmellons@golf2003.fsnet.co.uk

First opened in 1936, St Mellons is a parkland course on the eastern edge of Cardiff. The course is laid out in the shape of a clover leaf and provides one of the best tests of golf in South Wales. The course comprises 3 par 5s, 5 par 3s and 10 par 4s. The par 3s will make or break your card but the two finishing par 4 holes are absolutely superb.

18 holes, 6275yds, Par 70, SSS 70, Course record 63.

Club membership: 700. Visitors: must contact in advance. With member only at weekends. Societies: must contact in advance. Green Fees: £28 per round, £40 per day. Cards: 💳 💳 💳 💳 Prof: Barry Thomas Course Designer: Colt & Morrison Facilities: ⊕ †⊙↓ ┗ ☞ ☜↓ 👤 🏠 ☜ ✦ 🏌 ✦ Conf: Corporate Hospitality Days available Location: 2m from Junct 30 M4, 0.5m off A48

Hotel
★★★ 72% **St Mellons Hotel & Country Club,**
Castleton, CARDIFF
☎ 01633 680355 – 21 en suite 20 annexe en suite

CARMARTHENSHIRE

BURRY PORT

Ashburnham
Cliffe Ter SA16 0HN
☎ 01554 832269 & 833846

18 holes, 6916yds, Par 72, SSS 74, Course record 70.

Course Designer: J H Taylor Location: 5m W of Llanelli, A484 road
Telephone for further details

Hotel
★★ 70%
Ashburnham Hotel, Ashburnham Rd, Pembrey, LLANELLI
☎ 01554 834343 & 834455 📄 01554 834483
13 en suite

CONWY

CONWY

Conwy (Caernarvonshire)
Beacons Way, Morfa LL32 8ER
☎ 01492 592423 📠 01492 593363
e-mail: secretary@conwygolfclub.co.uk

Founded in 1890, Conwy has hosted national and international championships since 1898. Set among sandhills, possessing true links greens and a profusion of gorse on the latter holes, especially the 16th, 17th and 18th. This course provides the visitor with real golfing enjoyment against a background of stunning beauty.

18 holes, 6647yds, Par 72, SSS 72, Course record 64.

Club membership: 1050. Visitors: must to contact secretary in advance. Limited play weekends. Societies: must contact in advance. Green Fees: £42 per day; £35 per round (£48/£42 weekends & bank holidays). Cards: 💳 VISA 🅂 Prof: Peter Lees Facilities: ⊕ ⌖ 🝔 🍴 🟊 🏠 ⛳ 🏌 🛒 Location: 1m W of town centre on A55

Hotel
★★★ 73% The Groes Inn, Tyn-y-Groes, CONWY
☎ 01492 650545 – 14 en suite

LLANDUDNO

Llandudno (Maesdu)
Hospital Rd LL30 1HU
☎ 01492 876450 📠 01492 876450
e-mail: george@maesdugolfclub.freeserve.co.uk

Part links, part parkland, this championship course starts and finishes on one side of the main road, the remaining holes, more seaside in nature, being played on the other side. The holes are pleasantly undulating and present a pretty picture when the gorse is in bloom. Often windy, this varied and testing course is not for beginners.

18 holes, 6545yds, Par 72, SSS 72, Course record 62.

Club membership: 1120. Visitors: must book in advance. Societies: must apply in advance to Secretary. Green Fees: £30 per day, £25 per round (£35/£30 weekends). Cards: 💳 VISA 🅂 Prof: Simon Boulden Facilities: ⊕ ⌖ 🝔 🍴 🟊 🏠 ⛳ 🏌 🛒 snooker. Location: S side of town centre on A546

Hotel
★★★ 74% Imperial Hotel,
The Promenade, LLANDUDNO
☎ 01492 877466 – 100 en suite

North Wales
72 Bryniau Rd, West Shore LL30 2DZ
☎ 01492 875325 📠 01492 873355
e-mail: golf@nwgc.freeserve.co.uk

Challenging seaside links with superb views of Anglesey and Snowdonia. It possesses humpy, hillocky fairways, awkward stances and the occasional blind shot. Heather and gorse lurk beyond the fairways and several of the greens are defended by deep bunkers. The first outstanding hole is the 5th, a par 5 that dog-legs into the wind along a rollercoasting, bottleneck-shaped fairway. Best par 4s include the 8th, played through a narrow valley menaced by a railway line and the beach and the 11th, which runs uphill into the wind and where the beach again threatens. The finest par 3 is the 16th with a bunker to the left of a partially hidden, bowl-shaped green.

18 holes, 6287yds, Par 71, SSS 71, Course record 66.

Club membership: 670. Visitors: must contact in advance. Societies: must contact in advance. Green Fees: £40 per day, £30 per round (£50/£40 weekends and bank holidays). Mondays £20 per round/day. Cards: 💳 🅂 VISA 🝔 🅂 Prof: Richard Bradbury Course Designer: Tancred Cummins Facilities: ⊕ ⌖ 🝔 🍴 🟊 🏠 ⛳ 🏌 🛒 snooker. Location: W side of town on A546

Hotel
★★ St Tudno Hotel and Restaurant,
The Promenade, LLANDUDNO
☎ 01492 874411 – 19 en suite

GWYNEDD

HARLECH

Royal St Davids
LL46 2UB
☎ 01766 780361 📠 01766 781110
e-mail: secretary@royalstdavids.co.uk

Championship links, with easy walking and natural hazards, demanding strength and accuracy. Under the gaze of Harlech Castle, with a magnificent backdrop of the Snowdonia mountains.

18 holes, 6263yds, Par 69, SSS 71.

Club membership: 900. Visitors: pre-booking essential, must hold current handicap certificate. Societies: contact Secretary in advance. Handicap certificates required. Green Fees: £52 per day, £42 per round, £25 after 3pm (£62/£52 weekends & holidays, £30 after 3pm). Reduced winter rates. Cards: 💳 VISA 🝔 🅂 Prof: John Barnett Course Designer: Harold Finch-Hatton Facilities: ⊕ ⌖ 🝔 🍴 🟊 🏠 🏌 🛒 🏌 Conf: facilities available Corporate: Hospitality Days available Location: W side of town on A496

Hotel
★★ 64% Ty Mawr Hotel, LLANBEDR
☎ 01341 241440 – 10 en suite

Championship Course

ABERDYFI

Aberdovey

LL35 0RT
☎ 01654 767493   📠 01654 767027

Golf was first played at Aberdovey in 1886, and the club was founded six years later. The links has since developed into one of the finest championship courses in Wales. The club has hosted many prestigious events over the years, and is popular with golfing societies and clubs who regularly return here. Golfers can enjoy spectacular views and easy walking alongside the dunes of this characteristic seaside links. Fine holes include the 3rd, the 11th, and a good short hole at the 12th. The late Bernard Darwin, a former president and captain of the club, was a golf correspondent for *The Times*. Many of his writings feature the course, which he referred to as, 'the course that my soul loves best of all the courses in the world'; Darwin was a major contributor to its success. He would easily recognise the course today. In 1995 the old clubhouse was destroyed by fire, and rebuilt with the help of a National Lottery grant. The fine new clubhouse was opened by HRH the Duke of York in 1998.

18 holes, 6454yds, Par 71, SSS 72, Course record 66

Club Membership
1000

Visitors
Restricted weekends; handicap certificate; must contact in advance

Societies
Arrangement essential

Green Fees
£50 per day, £35 per round (£55/£42 weekends)

Cards
💳 💳 💳 💳

Professional
John Davies

Course Designer
J Braid

Facilities
🍴 🍽 🛋 ☕ 🍷 ⛳ 🏌 📷
🏌 🚗 🏌 snooker

Conferences
Facilities available

Location
0.5m W on A493

WHERE TO STAY NEARBY

★★★75%
Trefeddian Hotel,
ABERDYFI
☎ 01654 767213
59 en suite

★★74%
Penhelig Arms Hotel Restaurant, ABERDYFI
☎ 01654 767215 📠 01654 767690
10 en suite 5 annexe en suite

★★69%
Dovey Inn,
Seaview Ter, ABERDOVEY
☎ 01654 767332 📠 01654 767996
8 en suite

Championship Course

CHEPSTOW

Marriott St Pierre

Hotel Country Club, St Pierre Park NP16 6YA
☎ 01291 625261 📄 01291 627977
e-mail: golf.stpierre@marriotthotels.co.uk

Set in 400 acres of beautiful parkland, Marriott St Pierre offers two 18-hole courses. The Old Course is one of the finest in the country and has played host to many major championships. The par 3 18th is famous for its tee shot over the lake to an elevated green. The Mathern has its own challenges and is highly enjoyable for golfers of all abilities. The hotel has teaching professionals as well as hire of clubs and equipment. A new 13-bay driving range was added in 1998.

WHERE TO STAY NEARBY

★★★★70%
**Marriott St Pierre
Hotel & Country Club,**
St Pierre Park, CHEPSTOW
☎ 01291 625261
148 en suite

★★★66%
The Chepstow Hotel,
Newport Rd, CHEPSTOW
☎ 01291 626261 📄 01291 626263
31 en suite

★★68%
Castle View Hotel,
16 Bridge St, CHEPSTOW
☎ 01291 620349 📄 01291 627397
9 en suite 4 annexe en suite

★★61%
Beaufort Hotel,
Beaufort Square, CHEPSTOW
☎ 01291 622497 📄 01291 627389
22 en suite

Old Course
18 holes, 6733yds, Par 71, SSS 72, Course record 64

Mathern Course
18 holes, 5732yds, Par 68, SSS 67

Club Membership
800

Visitors
Advisable to contact in advance (up to 10 days)

Societies
Advance reservation only

Green Fees
Terms on application

Cards
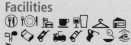

Professional
Craig Dun

Course Designer
H Cotton

Facilities
🍴🍽️🏌️💪🍷🏌️👔🛏️
🏌️🎁🏊🚕🏌️🎣🏌️🔍🏊
🧖 sauna, solarium, gymnasium, steam room, health and beauty suite, chipping green

Conferences
Facilities available

Corporate
Hospitality Days available

Location
M48 junct 2, A466 towards Chepstow, onto A48 towards Caldicot

MORFA NEFYN

Nefyn & District
LL53 6DA
☎ 01758 720966 📠 01758 720476
e-mail: nefyngolf@tesco.net

A 27-hole course played as two separate 18s, Nefyn is a cliff-top links where you never lose sight of the sea. A well-maintained course which will be a very tough test for the serious golfer, but still user friendly for the casual visitor. Every hole has a different challenge and the old 13th fairway is approximately 30 yards across from sea-to-sea. The course has an added bonus of a pub on the beach roughly halfway round for those whose golf may need some bolstering!

Old Course:
18 holes, 6201yds, Par 71, SSS 71, Course record 67.
New Course:
18 holes, 6317yds, Par 71, SSS 71, Course record 66.

Club membership: 800. **Visitors:** must contact in advance. **Societies:** apply by telephone. **Green Fees:** Sun-Fri £39 per day, £31 per round (£48/£37 Sat & bank holidays). **Cards:** 💳 **Prof:** John Froom **Course Designer:** James Braid **Facilities:** ⛳ 🍴 🍺 🚪 🏌 🏡 ⚙ ✈ 🛒 ✦ **Conf:** facilities available **Location:** 0.75m NW

Hotel
★★★✦🏨 75% **Porth Tocyn Hotel,** Bwlch Tocyn, ABERSOCH
☎ 01758 713303 – 17 en suite

MONMOUTHSHIRE

ABERGAVENNY

Monmouthshire
Gypsy Ln, LLanfoist NP7 9HE
☎ 01873 852606 📠 01873 850470
e-mail: secretary@mgcabergavenny.fsnet.co.uk

This parkland course is very picturesque, with the beautifully wooded River Usk running alongside. There are a number of par 3 holes and a testing par 4 at the 15th.

18 holes, 5806yds, Par 70, SSS 69, Course record 65.

Club membership: 700. **Visitors:** must play with member at weekends. Must contact in advance & have handicap certificate. **Societies:** must confirm in writing. **Green Fees:** terms on application. **Prof:** B Edwards **Course Designer:** James Braid **Facilities:** ⛳ 🍴 by prior arrangement 🚪 🍺 🏌 🏡 ✦ **Location:** 2m S off B4269

Hotel
★★ 72% **Llanwenarth Hotel & Riverside Restaurant,** Brecon Rd, ABERGAVENNY
☎ 01873 810550 – 17 en suite

MONMOUTH

Rolls of Monmouth
The Hendre NP25 5HG
☎ 01600 715353 📠 01600 713115
e-mail: enquiries@therollsgolfclub.co.uk

A hilly and challenging parkland course encompassing several lakes and ponds and surrounded by woodland. Set within a beautiful private estate complete with listed mansion and panoramic views towards the Black Mountains. The short 4th has a lake beyond the green and both the 17th and 18th holes are magnificent holes with which to end your round.

18 holes, 6733yds, Par 72, SSS 73, Course record 69.

Club membership: 160. **Visitors:** must telephone in advance. **Societies:** must contact in advance. **Green Fees:** £38 per day (weekends £42) (Mon special, £35 for round and lunch). **Cards:** 💳 **Facilities:** ⛳ 🍴 🚪 🍺 🏌 🏡 🏡 ⚙ 🛒 ✦ **Location:** 4m W on B4233

Hotel
★★ 65% **Riverside Hotel,** Cinderhill St, MONMOUTH
☎ 01600 715577 & 713236 📠 01600 712668
17 en suite

NEWPORT

NEWPORT

Newport
Great Oak, Rogerstone NP10 9FX
☎ 01633 892643 📠 01633 896676
e-mail: newportgolfclub.gwent@euphony.net

An undulating parkland course, in an ideal situation on an inland plateau 300ft above sea level with fine views over the surrounding wooded countryside. There are no blind holes, but plenty of natural hazards and bunkers.

18 holes, 6460yds, Par 72, SSS 71, Course record 63.

Club membership: 800. **Visitors:** must contact in advance, handicap certificate required. Not on Sat, limited time Sun. **Societies:** must contact in writing or telephone. **Green Fees:** not confirmed. **Prof:** Paul Mayo **Course Designer:** W Fernie **Facilities:** ⛳ 🍴 🚪 🍺 🏌 🏡 ✦ 🛒 ✦ **Location:** 1m NW of junct 27 on M4 on B4591 just beyond Promotive Garage

Hotel
★★★★★ 71% **The Celtic Manor Resort,** Coldra Woods, NEWPORT
☎ 01633 413000 – 400 en suite

Tredegar Park
Parc-y-Brain Rd, Rogerstone NP10 9TG
☎ 01633 894433 📠 01633 897152
e-mail: tpgc@btinternet.com

Continued

Championship Course

Celtic Manor Resort

Coldra Woods NP18 1HQ
☎ 01633 413000   📠 01633 410269
e-mail: golf@celtic-manor.com

This relatively new resort has quickly become a world-renowned venue for golf, set in 1,400 acres of beautiful, unspoiled parkland at the southern gateway to Wales. Boasting three championship courses, Celtic Manor offers a challenge for all levels of play, complemented by a golf school and one of the largest clubhouses in Europe, as well as extensive leisure facilities. The Wentwood Hills (par 72), a favoured course for championships, is home to the Wales Open and is due to host the Ryder Cup in 2010. Roman Road is a par 70 and is ideal for golfers of all levels, with a variety of tees, generous fairways and deep greens. For shorter round golfers, Coldra Woods, at par 59, is a challenging test of iron play.

WHERE TO STAY NEARBY

★★★★★71%
The Celtic Manor Resort,
Coldra Woods, NEWPORT
☎ 01633 413000
400 en suite

★★★68%
Newport Lodge Hotel,
Bryn Bevan, Brynglas Rd,
NEWPORT
☎ 01633 821818 📠 01633 856360
27 en suite

★★★66%
The Kings Hotel,
High St, NEWPORT
☎ 01633 842020 📠 01633 244667
61 en suite

Roman Road
18 holes, 6462yds, Par 70,
SSS 72, Course record 68

Coldra Woods
18 holes, 3807yds, Par 59,
SSS 61

Wentwood Hills
18 holes, 7097yds, Par 72,
SSS 75, Course record 61

Club Membership
580

Visitors
Subject to availability;
must book and pay in
advance; handicap
certificate for Roman
Road and Wentwood Hills

Societies
Phone for details in advance

Green Fees
Apr–Oct: Wentworth Hills
£95, Roman Road £60,
Coldra Woods £25

Cards

Professional
Kevin Carpenter

Course Designer
Robert Trent Jones

Facilities
🍽️🍴🛍️⛳🚩🏊🏠
🏌️💎🏌️🚗🔦🎣🐾🔍🚤
📞 sauna, solarium,
gymnasium, health spa,
golf academy with
18-hole course

Conferences
Facilities available

Corporate
Hospitality Days available

Location
M4 junct 24, A48 towards
Newport, 300yds right

18 holes, 6150yds, Par 72, SSS 72.

Course Designer: R Sandow **Location:** N of M4, Junct 27, B4591, club signposted from here Telephone for further details

Hotel
★★★ 66% **The Kings Hotel,** High St, NEWPORT
☎ 01633 842020 – 61 en suite

PEMBROKESHIRE

TENBY

Tenby
The Burrows SA70 7NP
☎ 01834 844447 842978 📄 01834 844447
e-mail: tenbygolfclub@ukn.co.uk

The oldest club in Wales, this fine old seaside links, with sea views and natural hazards, provides good golf all the year round.

18 holes, 6224yds, Par 69, SSS 71, Course record 65.

Club membership: 800. **Visitors:** subject to competition & tee reservation. **Societies:** must apply in advance. **Green Fees:** not confirmed. **Cards:** 💳 💳 💳 💳 💳 **Prof:** Mark Hawkey **Course Designer:** James Braid **Facilities:** ⊕ 🍴 🛍 💼 🗞 ⚐ 🏌 **Conf:** Corporate Hospitality Days available **Location:** Close to railway station in the town

Hotel
★★★ 75% **Atlantic Hotel,** The Esplanade, TENBY
☎ 01834 842881 & 844176 📄 01834 842881 ex 256
42 en suite

VALE OF GLAMORGAN

HENSOL

Vale Hotel Golf & Spa Resort
Hensol Park CF72 8JY
☎ 01443 665899 📄 01443 222220
e-mail: golf@vale-hotel.com

Two championship courses set in 200 acres of glorious countryside with views over Hensol Park lake and castle. The Wales National with greens constructed to USGA standard will prove a stern test for even the very best players. The aptly named Lake Course has water coming into play on 12 holes. The signature hole, the 12th, has an island green reached via a stone bridge. The club is also home to the Welsh PGA.

Lake: 18 holes, 6426yds, Par 72, SSS 71.
Hensol: 9 holes, 3115yds, Par 72, SSS 71.

Club membership: 1100. **Visitors:** must have a handicap certificate. May only play with member at weekends on Lake Course. **Societies:** apply in writing. **Green Fees:** not confirmed. **Cards:** 💳 💳 💳 💳 💳 💳 **Prof:** D Llewellyn/P Johnson/C Coombs **Course Designer:** Peter Johnson **Facilities:** ⊕ 🍴 🛍

🛍 🍴 🛋 🏠 ⚐ 🏌 ◇ 🛢 🏌 ⚒ 🎿 🐚 squash, sauna, solarium, gymnasium, many facilities in process of being built. **Conf:** facilities available **Corporate:** Hospitality Days available **Location:** 2 mins from junct 34 of M4

Hotel
★★★★ 73% **Vale Hotel Golf & Spa Resort,** Hensol Park, HENSOL
☎ 01443 667800 – 29 en suite 114 annexe en suite

NORTHERN IRELAND

CO ANTRIM

ANTRIM

Massereene
51 Lough Rd BT41 4DQ
☎ 028 94428096 📄 028 94487661
e-mail: info@massereene.com

The first 9 holes are parkland, while the second, adjacent to the shore of Lough Neagh, have more of a links character with sandy ground.

18 holes, 6602yds, Par 72, SSS 72, Course record 63.

Club membership: 969. **Visitors:** must contact in advance. **Societies:** book in advance. **Green Fees:** £12.50 per 9 holes (£15 weekends); £22 per 18 holes (£28 weekends). **Cards:** 💳 💳 💳 💳 💳 **Prof:** Jim Smyth **Course Designer:** F Hawtree/H Swan **Facilities:** ⊕ 🍴 🛍 💼 🗞 ⚐ 🏠 ⚐ 🏌 **Conf:** facilities available **Corporate:** Hospitality Days available **Location:** 1m SW of town

Hotel
★★★★ 59% **Galgorm Manor,** BALLYMENA
☎ 028 2588 1001 – 24 en suite

CO BELFAST

BELFAST

Malone
240 Upper Malone Rd, Dunmurry BT17 9LB
☎ 028 9061 2758 (Office) & 9061 4917 (Pro)
📄 028 9043 1394
e-mail: manager@malonegolfclub.co.uk

Co Antrim   **PORTRUSH**

Royal Portrush

Dunluce Rd BT56 8JQ
☎ 028 70822311   🖹 028 70823139
e-mail: rpgc@dnet.co.uk

Dunluce
18 holes, 6641yds, Par 72, SSS 73

Valley
18 holes, 6054yds, Par 70, SSS 72

Course Designer
Harry Colt

Location
0.5m from Portrush on Bushmills road.
Phone for further details

This course, designed by Harry S Colt, is considered to be among the best six in the UK. Founded in 1888, it was the venue of the first professional golf event in Ireland, held in 1895, when Sandy Herd beat Harry Vardon in the final. Royal Portrush is spectacular and breathtaking, one of the tightest driving courses known to golfers. On a clear day there's a fine view of Islay and the Paps of Jura from the 3rd tee, and the Giant's Causeway from the 5th. While the greens have to be 'read' from the start, there are fairways up and down valleys, and holes called Calamity Corner and Purgatory (for good reason). The 2nd hole, Giant's Grave, is 509 yards, but the 17th is even longer.

WHERE TO STAY NEARBY

★★★70%
Bayview Hotel, 2 Bayhead Rd,
PORTBALLINTRAE
☎ 028 2073 4100
25 en suite

Two parkland courses, extremely attractive with a large lake, mature trees and flowering shrubs and bordered by the River Lagan. Very well maintained and offering a challenging round.

Main Course: 18 holes, 6706yds, Par 71, SSS 72.
Edenderry: 9 holes, 6320yds, Par 72, SSS 70.

Club membership: 1450. **Visitors:** advisable to contact pro-shop in advance. Main Course: Unable to play Sat, before 3pm, Sun morning, Wed after 12 noon; Tue & Fri between 12 and 2pm **Societies:** apply in writing or fax to club manager. Large group normally Mon & Thu only. **Green Fees:** Main Course: £55 per day (£60 weekends); Edenderry: £20 per day (£25 weekends). **Cards:** 💳 💳 💳 💳 **Prof:** Michael McGee **Course Designer:** C K Cotton **Facilities:** 🍴 🍽 🛏 🛒 🍷 ⚐ ⛳ 💺 🏌 🔨 Outdoor bowling green. **Conf:** Corporate Hospitality Days available **Location:** 4.5m S opposite Lady Dixon Park

Hotel
★★★ 71% **Malone Lodge Hotel,**
60 Eglantine Av, BELFAST
☎ 028 9038 8000 – 51 en suite

NEWTOWNBREDA
The Belvoir Park
73 Church Rd BT8 7AN
☎ 028 90491693 📠 028 90646113

18 holes, 6516yds, Par 71, SSS 71, Course record 65.

Course Designer: H Holt **Location:** 2m from city centre off Saintfield/Newcastle rd
Telephone for further details

Hotel
★★★ 77% **Clandeboye Lodge Hotel,**
10 Estate Rd, Clandeboye, BANGOR
☎ 028 9185 2500 – 43 en suite

CO DOWN
HOLYWOOD
The Royal Belfast
Station Rd, Craigavad BT18 0BP
☎ 028 9042 8165 📠 028 9042 1404
e-mail: royalbelfastgc@btclick.com

On the shores of Belfast Lough, this attractive course consists of wooded parkland on undulating terrain which provides a pleasant, challenging game.

18 holes, 6185yds, Par 70, SSS 69.

Club membership: 1200. **Visitors:** may not play on Wed or Sat before 4.30pm; must be accompanied by a member or present a letter of introduction from their own golf club. Must contact in advance. **Societies:** must contact in writing/by telephone. **Green Fees:** £45 (£55 weekends & bank holidays). **Cards:** 💳 💳 💳 💳 **Prof:** Chris Spence **Course Designer:** H C

Colt **Facilities:** 🍴 🍽 🛏 🛒 🍷 ⚐ 🏌 🍷 ⛳ ⚑ 🔨 💺 squash. **Conf:** Corporate Hospitality Days available **Location:** 2m E on A2

Hotel
★★★ 78% **The Old Inn,**
15 Main St, CRAWFORDSBURN
☎ 028 9185 3255 – 31 en suite 1 annexe en suite

CO LONDONDERRY
CASTLEROCK
Castlerock
65 Circular Rd BT51 4TJ
☎ 028 7084 8314 📠 028 7084 9440
e-mail: info@castlerockgc.co.uk

A most exhilarating course with three superb par 4s, four testing short holes and five par 5s. After an uphill start, the hazards are many, including the river and a railway, and both judgement and accuracy are called for. The signature hole is the 4th, Leg of Mutton. A challenge in calm weather, any trouble from the elements will test your golf to the limits.

Mussenden Course:
18 holes, 6499yds, Par 73, SSS 71, Course record 64.
Bann Course:
9 holes, 2938yds, Par 34, SSS 33, Course record 60.

Club membership: 1250. **Visitors:** contact in advance, limited number of places at weekends. Must be members of a recognised club. **Societies:** must contact in advance. **Green Fees:** £50 per day (£70 per round weekends and bank holidays). **Cards:** 💳 💳 💳 **Prof:** Ian Blair **Course Designer:** Ben Sayers **Facilities:** 🍴 🍽 🛏 🛒 🍷 ⚐ 🏌 ⛳ **Location:** 6m from Coleraine on A2

Guesthouse
♦♦♦♦♦ **Greenhill House,**
24 Greenhill Rd, Aghadowey, COLERAINE
☎ 028 7086 8241 – 6 en suite

PORTSTEWART
Portstewart
117 Strand Rd BT55 7PG
☎ 028 70832015 & 70833839 📠 028 70834097
e-mail: bill@portstewartgc.co.uk

Strand Course:
18 holes, 6784yds, Par 72, SSS 72, Course record 67.
Old Course: 18 holes, 4733yds, Par 64, SSS 62.
Riverside: 9 holes, 2622yds, Par 32.

Course Designer: Des Giffin
Telephone for further details

Guesthouse
♦♦♦♦ **Harbour Heights,** 17 Kerr St, PORTRUSH
☎ 028 7082 2765 – 10 rms (9 en suite)

Championship Course

Royal County Down

36 Golf Links Rd BT33 0AN
☎ 028 43723314   🖹 028 43726281
e-mail: golf@royalcountydown.org

The Championship Course is consistently rated among the world's top ten courses. Laid out beneath the imperious Mourne Mountains, the course has a magnificent setting as it stretches out along the shores of Dundrum Bay. As well as being one of the most beautiful courses, it is also one of the most challenging, with great swathes of heather and gorse lining fairways that tumble beneath vast sandhills, and wild tussock-faced bunkers defending small, subtly contoured greens. The Annesley Links offers a less formidable yet extremely characterful game, played against the same incomparable backdrop. Recently substantially revised under the direction of Donald Steel, the course begins quite benignly before charging headlong into the dunes. Several charming and one or two teasing holes have been carved out amid the gorse, heather and bracken.

WHERE TO STAY NEARBY

★★65%
Enniskeen House Hotel,
98 Bryansford Rd, NEWCASTLE
☎ 028 4372 2392
12 en suite

Championship Course
18 holes, 7065yds, Par 71, SSS 74, Course record 66

Annesley
18 holes, 4681yds, Par 66, SSS 63

Club Membership
450

Visitors
Not Wed, Sat on Championship Course; not Sat on Annesley; advisable to contact in advance

Societies
Phone for availability & confirm in writing

Green Fees
Championship Course £115 weekdays, £100 pm (£130 Sun)

Cards

Professional
Kevan Whitson

Course Designer
Tom Morris

Facilities

Location
N of town centre off A2

REPUBLIC OF IRELAND

CO CARLOW

CARLOW

Carlow
Deerpark
☎ 059 9131695 📄 059 9140065
e-mail: carlowgolfclub@eircom.net

Created in 1922 to a design by Cecil Barcroft, this testing and enjoyable course is set in a wild deer park, with beautiful dry terrain and a varied character. With sandy sub-soil, the course is playable all year round. There are water hazards at the 2nd, 10th and 11th and only two par 5s, both offering genuine birdie opportunities.

18 holes, 5974mtrs, Par 70, SSS 71, Course record 65.

Club membership: 1200. Visitors: are welcome, although play is limited on Tue and difficult on Sat & Sun. Must contact in advance. Societies: must book in advance. Green Fees: not confirmed. Cards: 💳 💳
Prof: Andrew Gilbert Course Designer: Cecil Barcroft Facilities: ⊕ ⊙ 🛒 💺 🍴 🏖 🏠 🏌 Location: 3.2km N of Carlow on N9

Hotel
★★★ Seven Oaks Hotel, Athy Rd, CARLOW
☎ 059 913 1308 – 59 en suite

CO CAVAN

BALLYCONNELL

Slieve Russell Hotel Golf & Country Club

☎ 049 9525090 📄 049 9526640
e-mail: slieve-russell@quinn-hotels.com

An 18-hole course opened in 1992 and rapidly establishing itself as one of the finest parkland courses in the country. The complex incorporates a 9-hole par 3 course and driving range. On the main course, the 2nd plays across water while the 16th has water surrounding the green. The course finishes with a 519-yard, par 5 18th.

18 holes, 6614yds, Par 72, SSS 72, Course record 65.

Club membership: 400. Visitors: must book in advance for Saturdays. Telephone in advance. Societies: write or telephone in advance Green Fees: €65 (€80 Sat) (special rates in winter). Cards: 💳 💳 💳 💳 Prof: Liam McCool Course Designer: Paddy Merrigan Facilities: ⊕ ⊙ 🛒 💺 🍴 🏖 🏠 🏌 ❤ 🏌 ⛳ sauna, solarium, gymnasium, New spa for 2005. Conf: facilities available Corporate Hospitality Days available Location: 2.4km E of Ballyconnell

Hotel
★★★★ 70% Slieve Russell Hotel Golf and Country Club, BALLYCONNELL
☎ 049 9526444 – 157 en suite

CO CLARE

LAHINCH

Lahinch
☎ 065 7081592 📄 065 81592
e-mail: info@lahinchgolf.com

Old Course: 18 holes, 6696yds, Par 72, SSS 73.
Castle Course: 18 holes, 5594yds, Par 70, SSS 70.

Course Designer: Alister MacKenzie Location: 2m W of Ennisstymon on N67
Telephone for further details

Hotel
🏨 Kincora Country House & Gallery Restaurant, LISDOONVARNA
☎ 065 7074300 – 14 en suite

CO CORK

BLARNEY

Muskerry
Carrigrohane
☎ 021 4385297 📄 021 4516860
e-mail: muskgc@eircom.net

An adventurous game is guaranteed at this course, with its wooded hillsides and the meandering Shournagh River coming into play at a number of holes. The 15th is a notable hole – not long, but very deep – and after that all you need to do to get back to the clubhouse is stay out of the water.

18 holes, 5520mtrs, Par 71, SSS 70.

Club membership: 851. Visitors: may not play Wed afternoon & Thu morning. Some limited play at weekends after 3.30pm & members hour 12.30-1.30pm daily. Must contact in advance. Societies: must telephone in advance and then confirm in writing. Green Fees: €35 per round(€40 weekends). Cards: 💳 💳 💳 Prof: W M Lehane Course Designer: Dr A McKenzie Facilities: ⊕ ⊙ 🛒 💺 🍴 🏖 🏠 🏌 Location: 4km W of Blarney

Hotel
★★★★ Hayfield Manor, Perrott Av, College Rd, CORK
☎ 021 4845900 – 88 en suite

CORK

Cork

Little Island

☎ 021 4353451   📄 021 4353410

e-mail: corkgolfclub@eircom.net

This championship-standard course is kept in superb condition and is playable all year round. Memorable and distinctive features include holes at the water's edge and in a disused quarry. The 4th hole is considered to be among the most attractive and testing holes in Irish golf.

18 holes, 5910mtrs, Par 72, SSS 72, Course record 67.

Club membership: 750. **Visitors:** may not play 12.30-2pm or on Thu (Ladies Day), and only after 2pm Sat & Sun. **Societies:** must contact in advance. **Green Fees:** €80 (€90 weekends and bank holidays). **Cards:** 💳 💳 💳 💳 **Prof:** Peter Hickey **Course Designer:** Alister Mackenzie **Facilities:** ⛳ 🍴 🏌 💪 🍷 🍽 🛒 🏠 🛎 🛺 ✏ 🏴 **Conf:** Corporate Hospitality Days available **Location:** 8km E, on N25 of Cork City

MALLOW

Mallow

Ballyellis

☎ 022 21145   📄 022 42501

e-mail: golfmall@gofree.indigo.ie

Mallow Golf Club was first established in the late 1800s. A well wooded parkland course overlooking the Blackwater Valley, Mallow is straightforward, but no less of a challenge for it. The front 9 is by far the longer, but the back 9 is demanding in its call for accuracy and the par 3 18th provides a tough finish.

18 holes, 5769mtrs, Par 72, SSS 71, Course record 67.

Club membership: 1250. **Visitors:** must contact in advance. **Societies:** apply in advance. **Green Fees:** €35 per round (€40 weekends & public holidays). **Cards:** 💳 💳 **Prof:** Sean Conway **Course Designer:** D W Wishart **Facilities:** ⛳ 🍴 🏌 💪 🍷 🍽 🛒 🏠 🛎 ✏ 🏴 🏌 squash. **Location:** 1m E of Mallow town

Hotel

★★★🏨🏨 **Longueville House Hotel,** MALLOW

☎ 022 47156 & 47306   📄 022 47459 – 20 en suite

MONKSTOWN

Monkstown

Parkgariffe, Monkstown

☎ 021 4841376   📄 021 4841722

e-mail: office@monkstowngolfclub.com

Undulating parkland course with five tough finishing holes.

18 holes, 5441mtrs, Par 70, SSS 68, Course record 66.

Club membership: 960. **Visitors:** must contact in advance. Not Tue or before 2pm weekends. **Societies:** apply in writing or telephone. Large groups (24+) should book before Xmas. **Green Fees:** €40 per day (weekend €47). **Cards:** 💳 💳 **Prof:** Batt Murphy **Course Designer:** Peter O'Hare & Tom Carey **Facilities:** ⛳ 🍴 🏌 💪 🍷 🍽 🛒 🏠 🛎 ✏ 🏴 **Conf:** Corporate Hospitality Days available **Location:** 800mtrs SE of Monkstown village

Hotel

★★★★ 67% **Carrigaline Court Hotel,** CARRIGALINE

☎ 021 4852100 – 91 en suite

YOUGHAL

Youghal

Knockaverry

☎ 024 92787 & 92861   📄 024 92641

e-mail: youghalgolfclub@eircom.ie

For many years the host of various Golfing Union championships, Youghal offers a good test of golf and is well maintained for year-round play. The Parkland Course has recently been extended with the addition of two new holes. There are panoramic views of Youghal Bay and the Blackwater estuary.

18 holes, 6175mtrs, Par 72, SSS 72, Course record 71.

Club membership: 994. **Visitors:** Should contact in advance for weekends and ladies day (Wed) **Societies:** must apply in writing a few months in advance. **Green Fees:** €30 per round (€40 weekends) (discount if with member). **Cards:** 💳 💳 **Prof:** Liam Burns **Course Designer:** Cd. Harris **Facilities:** ⛳ 🍴 🏌 💪 🍷 🍽 🛒 🏠 🛎 ✏ **Location:** Located on the N25 main road from Rosslare, between Waterford and Cork City

Hotel

🏨 **Ahernes,** 163 North Main St, YOUGAL

☎ 024 92424 – 13 en suite

CO DONEGAL

BUNCRANA

North West

Lisfannon, Fahan, buncrana

☎ 074 9361715   📄 074 9363284

e-mail: nwgc@tinet.ie

A traditional-style links course on gently rolling

sandy terrain with some long par 4s. Good judgement is required on the approaches and the course offers a satisfying test coupled with undemanding walking.

18 holes, 5968yds, Par 70, SSS 70, Course record 64.

Club membership: 580. **Visitors:** contact in advance for weekends. Wed - Ladies Day **Societies:** telephone in advance. **Green Fees:** €25 (€30 weekends). **Prof:** Seamus McBriarty **Course Designer:** Thompson Davy **Facilities:** ⊕ ⊗ ⓘ ⓛ ⓦ ⓕ ⓐ ⓔ ⓕ ⓕ **Location:** 1.6km S of Buncanna

Guesthouse
◆◆◆◆ **Mount Royd Country Home**, CARRIGANS
☎ 074 914 0163 – 4 en suite

BUNDORAN

Bundoran
☎ 071 9841302 📄 071 9842014
e-mail: bundorangolfclub@eircom.net

This popular course, acknowledged as one of the best in the country, runs along the high cliffs above Bundoran beach and has a difficult par of 70. Designed by Harry Vardon, it offers a challenging game of golf in beautiful surroundings and has been the venue for a number of Irish golf championships.

18 holes, 5688mtrs, Par 70, SSS 70, Course record 67.

Club membership: 770. **Visitors:** must contact in advance for prior booking. **Societies:** must contact in advance. **Green Fees:** not confirmed. **Prof:** David T Robinson **Course Designer:** Harry Vardon **Facilities:** ⓛ ⓦ ⓕ ⓐ ⓔ ⓟ ⓢ ⓕ **Location:** Just off Main St, Bundoran on the Sligo/Derry road, 35km N of Sligo

Hotel
★★★ 79% **Sand House Hotel**, ROSSNOWLAGH
☎ 071 985 1777 – 55 en suite

LAGHEY

Donegal
Murvagh
☎ 074 9734054 📄 074 9734377
e-mail: info@donegalgolfclub.ie

This massive links course was opened in 1973 and provides a world-class facility in peaceful surroundings. It is a very long course with some memorable holes, including five par 5s, calling for some big hitting.

18 holes, 6243mtrs, Par 73, SSS 73, Course record 69.

Club membership: 750. **Visitors:** must contact in advance, limited availability at weekends & Mon **Societies:** must contact in advance. **Green Fees:** €50 Mon-Thu; €65 Fri-Sun. **Cards:** ⬛ ⬛ **Prof:** Leslie Robinson **Course Designer:** Eddie Hackett **Facilities:** ⊕ ⊗ ⓛ ⓦ ⓕ ⓐ ⓔ ⓟ ⓢ ⓕ **Conf:** Corporate Hospitality Days available **Location:** 10km S of Donegal on Ballyshannon road

Hotel
★★★ 79% **Sand House Hotel**, ROSSNOWLAGH
☎ 071 985 1777 – 55 en suite

CO DUBLIN

CASTLEKNOCK

Elm Green
☎ 01 8200797 📄 01 8226662
e-mail: elmgreen@golfdublin.com

18 holes, 5796yds, Par 71, SSS 66, Course record 65.

Course Designer: Eddie Hackett **Location:** Off Navan Rd, 15 mins from city centre
Telephone for further details

Hotel
★★★ 70% **Finnstown Country House Hotel**, Newcastle Rd, Lucan, DUBLIN
☎ 01 6010700 – 25 en suite 28 annexe en suite

DONABATE

Island
Corballis
☎ 01 8436205 📄 01 8436860
e-mail: info@theislandgolfclub.com

A genuine old links course surrounded by the Irish Sea, Donabate beach and the Broadmeadow estuary, nestling between the highest sand dunes of any links course in Ireland. The rugged beauty cannot fail to impress. An Irish qualifying course for the Open Championship from 2005.

18 holes, 6206mtrs, Par 71, SSS 63.

Club membership: 1020. **Visitors:** must contact in advance. **Societies:** Contact club office **Green Fees:** €110 per 18 holes. **Cards:** ⬛ ⬛ ⬛ ⬛ **Prof:** Kevin Kelliher **Course Designer:** Martin Hawtree **Facilities:** ⊕ ⊗ ⓛ ⓦ ⓕ ⓐ ⓔ ⓟ ⓕ ⓢ ⓕ **Conf:** facilities available **Corporate:** Hospitality Days available **Location:** Take main Dublin/Belfast road N1, pass airport, take turn for Donabate/Portrane, follow signs

Hotel
★★★ 67% **Deer Park Hotel & Golf Courses**, HOWTH
☎ 01 8322624 – 80 en suite

Co Dublin   **PORTMARNOCK**

Portmarnock

☎ 01 8462968   📄 01 8462601
e-mail: emer@portmarnockgolfclub.ie

Universally acknowledged as one of the truly great links courses, Portmarnock has hosted many great events from the British Amateur Championships of 1949 and the Canada Cup in 1960, to 12 stagings of the revised Irish Open. Founded in 1894, the serpentine championship course offers a classic challenge: surrounded by water on three sides, no two successive holes play in the same direction. Unlike many courses that play nine out and nine home, Portmarnock demands a continual awareness of wind direction. Extraordinary holes include the 14th, which Henry Cotton regarded as the best hole in golf; the 15th, which Arnold Palmer regards as the best par 3 in the world; and the 5th, regarded as the best on the course by the late Harry Bradshaw. Bradshaw was for 40 years Portmarnock's golf professional and runner-up to A D Locke in the 1949 British Open, playing his ball from an empty bottle of stout.

WHERE TO STAY NEARBY

★★★★
**Portmarnock
Hotel & Golf Links,**
Strand Rd, PORTMARNOCK
☎ 01 8460611
99 en suite

Old Course
18 holes, 7182yds, Par 72, SSS 73

New Course
9 holes, 3370yds, Par 37

Club Membership
1100

Visitors
Not Wed; restricted Sat, Sun, public holidays; contact in advance and confirm in writing; handicap certificate

Societies
Must contact in advance in writing

Green Fees
€165 (€190 weekends and public holidays)

Cards
💳 💳 VISA 💳

Professional
Joey Purcell

Course Designer
W Pickeman

Facilities
🍴 🍽 by prior arrangement 🛒 ☕ 🍷 ⛱ 🏠 ⛳ 🎱 🛺 ✏

DUBLIN

Grange
Rathfarnham
☎ 01 4932889

18 holes, 5517mtrs, Par 68, SSS 69.

Location: 6m from city centre
Telephone for further details

Hotel
★★★ 70% **Jurys Montrose Hotel,**
Stillorgan Rd, DUBLIN
☎ 01 2693311 – 178 en suite

Royal Dublin
North Bull Island Reserve, Dollymount
☎ 01 8336346 📄 01 8336504
e-mail: jlambe@theroyaldublingolfclub.com

A popular course with visitors for its design subtleties, the condition of the links and the friendly atmosphere. Founded in 1885, the club moved to its present site in 1889 and received its Royal designation in 1891. A notable former club professional was Christy O'Connor, who was appointed in 1959 and immediately made his name. Along with its many notable holes, Royal Dublin has a fine and testing finish. The 18th is a sharply dog-legged par 4, with out of bounds along the right-hand side. The decision to try the long carry over the 'garden' is one many visitors have regretted.

18 holes, 6002mtrs, Par 72, SSS 71, Course record 63.

Club membership: 1250. **Visitors:** must contact in advance & have handicap certificate. May not play Wed, Sat until 4pm. Restricted Sun. **Societies:** must book one year in advance. **Green Fees:** €125 all week. **Cards:** 💳 💳 💳 **Prof:** Leonard Owens **Course Designer:** H S Colt **Facilities:** 🏤 🍴 🛍 🍺 🍽 🏌 🏕 ⛳ 🛒 🏌 🎯 **Conf:** facilities available Corporate Hospitality Days available **Location:** 3.5m NE of city centre

Hotel
★★★ 67% **Longfield's Hotel,**
Fitzwilliam St Lower, DUBLIN 2
☎ 01 6761367 – 26 en suite

St Margaret's Golf & Country Club
St Margaret's
☎ 01 8640400 📄 01 8640289
e-mail: sales@stmargaretsgolf.com

18 holes, 6917yds, Par 73, SSS 73, Course record 69.

Course Designer: Craddock/Ruddy **Location:** 9m NW of city centre. From main airport roundabout take exit for Belfast, after 500yds take 1st exit from roundabout to St Margarets just past Coachman's Inn
Telephone for further details

Hotel
★★★ 71% **Marine Hotel,** Sutton Cross, DUBLIN 13
☎ 01 8390000 – 48 en suite

MALAHIDE

Malahide
Beechwood, The Grange
☎ 01 8461611 📄 01 8461270
e-mail: malgc@clubi.ie

Main Course: 18 holes, 6066mtrs, Par 71.

Course Designer: E Hackett **Location:** 1.6km from coast road at Portmarnock Telephone for further details

Hotel
★★★★ **Portmarnock Hotel & Golf Links,**
Strand Rd, PORTMARNOCK
☎ 01 8460611 – 99 en suite

CO GALWAY

BALLYCONNEELY

Connemara
☎ 095 23502 & 23602 📄 095 23662
e-mail: links@iol.ie

This championship links course is situated on the verge of the Atlantic Ocean in a most spectacular setting, with the Twelve Bens Mountains in the background. Established as recently as 1973, it is a tough challenge, due in no small part to its exposed location, with the back 9 the equal of any in the world. The last six holes are exceptionally long and offer a great challenge to golfers of all abilities. When the wind blows, club selection is crucial. Notable holes are the 13th (200yd par 3), the long par 5 14th, the 15th with a green nestling in the hills, the 16th guarded by water and the 17th and 18th, both par 5s over 500yds long.

Championship:
18 holes, 6666yds, Par 72, SSS 73, Course record 64.
New: 9 holes, 3012yds, Par 35.

Club membership: 970. Visitors: advisable to book in advance. Sun am members only Societies: telephone or e-mail in advance. Green Fees: not confirmed. Cards: ▢▢ Prof: Hugh O'Neill Course Designer: Eddie Hackett Facilities: ⓉⓄ ⅃ ☕🍴 ⚒💈🏌 Conf: Corporate Hospitality Days available Location: 14.5km SW of Clifden

Hotel
★★★★ 69% Abbeyglen Castle Hotel, Sky Rd, CLIFDEN
☎ 095 21201 – 44 en suite

BEARNA

Bearna Golf and Country Club
Corboley
☎ 091 592677 📄 091 592674
e-mail: info@bearnagolfclub.com

Set amid the beautiful landscape of the west of Ireland and enjoying commanding views of Galway Bay, the golf course covers more than 100 hectares of unique countryside. This has resulted in generously proportioned fairways, many elevated tees and some splendid carries. Water comes into play at thirteen holes and the final four holes provide a memorable finish. New lakes developed on holes 6, 7 and 10 in 2003 with many other improvements.

18 holes, 5746mtrs, Par 72, SSS 72, Course record 68.

Club membership: 600. Visitors: must telephone in advance. Can play at any time Societies: contact in advance. Green Fees: €35 Mon-Thu (€40 Fri, 50 Sat-Sun and bank holidays). Cards: ▢▢ ▢▢ ▢▢ Prof: Declan Cunningham Course Designer: Robert J Brown Facilities: ⓉⓄ ⅃ ☕🍴 ⚒💈🏌 Conf: facilities available Location: 5m W Galway City on Spiddal Rd.

Hotel
★★★★ 70% Galway Bay Hotel Conference & Leisure Centre, The Promenade, Salthill, GALWAY
☎ 091 520520 – 153 en suite

GALWAY

Galway
Blackrock, Salthill
☎ 091 522033 📄 091 529783
e-mail: galwaygolf@eircom.net

Designed by Dr Alister McKenzie, this course is inland by nature, although some of the fairways run close to the ocean. The terrain is of gently sloping hillocks with plenty of trees and furze bushes to catch out the unwary. Although not a long course, it provided a worthy challenge as the venue of the Celtic International Tournament in 1984 and continues to delight the visiting golfer.

18 holes, 6376yds, Par 70, SSS 71, Course record 67.

Club membership: 1050. Visitors: preferred on weekdays, except Tue. Societies: must apply in writing. Green Fees: not confirmed. Cards: ▢▢ ▢▢ Prof: Don Wallace Course Designer: McKenzie Facilities: ⓉⓄ ⅃ ☕🍴 ⚒💈🏌 Conf: Corporate Hospitality Days available Location: 3.2km W in Salthill

Hotel
★★★ 60% Lochlurgain Hotel, 22 Monksfield, Upper Salthill, GALWAY
☎ 091 529595 – 13 en suite

ORANMORE

Galway Bay Golf & Country Club
Renville
☎ 091 790503 📄 091 792510
e-mail: gbaygolf@iol.ie

18 holes, 6533mtrs, Par 72, SSS 73, Course record 68.

Course Designer: Christy O'Connor Jnr Location: N18 S towards Limerick/Shannon, turn right for Oranmore at rdbt, through village, follow signs Telephone for further details

CO KERRY

GLENBEIGH

Dooks
☎ 066 9768205 📄 066 9768476
e-mail: office@dooks.com

Old-established course on the sea shore between the Kerry mountains and Dingle Bay. Sand dunes are a feature (the name Dooks is a derivation of the Gaelic word for sand bank) and the course offers a fine challenge in a superb Ring of Kerry location. Recently redesigned by Martin Hantree.

18 holes, 6271yds, Par 71, SSS 70.

Club membership: 900. Visitors: must contact in advance. Members time reserved. Societies: contact in advance. Green Fees: €58 per 18 holes. Cards: ▢▢ ▢▢ ▢▢ Course Designer: Martin Hantree Facilities: ⓉⓄ ⅃ ☕🍴 ⚒💈🏌 Conf: Corporate Hospitality Days available Location: On N70, between Killorglin and Glenbeigh

Hotel
★★★ 70% Gleneagle Hotel, KILLARNEY
☎ 064 36000 – 250 en suite

Ballybunion

Sandhill Rd

☎ 068 27146 📄 068 27387 e-mail: bbgolfgc@ioe.ie

Having excellent links, Ballybunion is recognised for its fine development of the natural terrain. Mr Murphy built the Old Course in 1906. With large sand dunes and an Atlantic backdrop, Ballybunion offers the golfer an exciting round of golf in a scenic location. But be warned, the Old course is difficult to play in the wind. President Clinton played Ballybunion on his historic visit to Ireland in 1998. Although overshadowed by the Old Course, the Cashen Course designed by Robert Trent Jones is also world class, characterised by narrow fairways, small greens and large dunes.

WHERE TO STAY NEARBY

◆◆◆◆◆
Cashen Course House,
Golf Links Rd, Ballybunion
☎ 068 27351
9 en suite

◆◆◆◆
The Tides Guest House,
BALLYBUNION
☎ 068 27980 📄 068 27923
5 en suite

★★★68%
The White Sands Hotel,
BALLYHEIGUE
☎ 066 7133102 📄 066 7133357
81 en suite

★★★★70%
Ballygarry House Hotel,
Killarney Rd, Tralee
☎ 066 7123322 📄 7127630
46 en suite

★★★67%
Abbey Gate Hotel,
Maine St, TRALEE
☎ 066 7129888 📄 066 7129821
100 en suite

Old Course
18 holes, 6603yds, Par 71, SSS 72, Course record 67

Cashen
18 holes, Par 72, SSS 71, Course record 69

Club Membership
1500

Visitors
Not weekends; contact in advance

Societies
Apply in advance

Green Fees
Old Course €135 per round; Cashen Course €95 per round; both courses €180

Cards

Professional
Brian O'Callaghan

Course Designer
Simpson

Facilities
sauna

Ring of Kerry Golf & Country Club

Templenoe
☎ 064 42000 ▤ 064 42533
e-mail: reservations@ringofkerrygolf.com

A world-class golf facility with spectacular views across Kenmare Bay. Opened in 1998, the club has gone from strength to strength and is fast becoming a 'must play' course for golfers visiting the area. Every hole is memorable.

18 holes, 6330yds, Par 72, SSS 73, Course record 68.

Club membership: 250. **Visitors:** advisable to pre-book at weekends. **Societies:** book beforehand by telephone, in writing or by e-mail. **Green Fees:** 18 holes €80; 36 holes €120 any day. **Cards:** 💳 🏧 💳 **Prof:** Adrian Whitehead **Course Designer:** Eddie Hackett **Facilities:** ⓣ ⍥ by prior arrangement 🏌 🛒 🍴 ⛳ 🏪 ⛳ ♟ ♛ **Conf:** facilities available **Corporate:** Hospitality Days available **Location:** 6.5km W of Kenmare

Hotel
★★★★☆🏨 **Sheen Falls Lodge,** KENMARE
☎ 064 41600 – 66 en suite

Killarney Golf & Fishing Club

Mahony's Point
☎ 064 31034 ▤ 064 33065
e-mail: reservations@killarney-golf.com

The three courses are parkland with tree-lined fairways; many bunkers and small lakes provide no mean challenge. Mahoney's Point Course has a particularly testing par 5, 4, 3 finish and the courses call for great skill from the tee. Killarney has been the venue for many important events, including the 1996 Curtis Cup, and is a favourite of many famous golfers.

Mahony's Point:
18 holes, 5826mtrs, Par 72, SSS 72, Course record 64.
Killeen:
18 holes, 6001mtrs, Par 72, SSS 72, Course record 68.
Lackabane: 18 holes, 6011mtrs, Par 72, SSS 72.

Club membership: 1600. **Visitors:** advisable to contact in advance. Neat casual dress required in the clubhouse and on the course. **Societies:** must telephone in advance/apply in writing. **Green Fees:** per 18 holes: Mahony's Point €80, Killeen €85, Lackabane €60. **Cards:** 💳 🏧 💳 💳 **Prof:** Tony Coveney **Course Designer:** H Longhurst/Sir Guy Campbell **Facilities:** ⓣ ⍥ 🏌 🛒 🍴 🛒 🏪 ⛳ ♟ ♛ sauna, gymnasium. **Conf:** Corporate Hospitality Days available **Location:** On N72, Ring of Kerry road

Hotel
★★★★★ **Aghadoe Heights Hotel,** KILLARNEY
☎ 064 31766 – 75 en suite

Tralee

West Barrow
☎ 066 7136379 ▤ 066 7136008
e-mail: info@traleegolfclub.com

The first Arnold Palmer designed course in Europe, this magnificent 18-hole links is set in spectacular scenery on the Barrow peninsula, surrounded on three sides by the sea. Perhaps the most memorable hole is the par 4 17th which plays from a high tee, across a deep gorge to a green perched high against a backdrop of mountains. The back 9 are very difficult and challenging. Not suitable for beginners.

18 holes, 5970mtrs, Par 71, SSS 71, Course record 66.

Club membership: 1306. **Visitors:** may play before 4.20pm on weekdays but only between 7.30-10.30am on Wed & 11am-1.30pm on Sat & 11.30am-1pm bank holidays. Must have a handicap certificate and contact in advance. May not play Sun. **Societies:** weekdays only; must contact in writing. **Green Fees:** €160 per round. **Cards:** 💳 🏧 💳 **Prof:** David Power **Course Designer:** Arnold Palmer **Facilities:** ⓣ ⍥ 🏌 🛒 🍴 🛒 🏪 ⛳ ♟ **Location:** 13km NW of Tralee off Spa-Fenit Road

Hotel
★★★ 69% **Meadowlands Hotel,** Oakpark, TRALEE
☎ 066 7180444 – 58 en suite

Waterville House & Golf Links

☎ 066 9474102 ▤ 066 9474482
e-mail: wvgolf@iol.ie

On the western tip of the Ring of Kerry, this course is highly regarded by many top golfers. The feature holes are the par 5 11th, which runs along a rugged valley between towering dunes, and the par 3 17th, which features an exceptionally elevated tee. Needless to say, the surroundings are beautiful.

18 holes, 6640yds, Par 72, SSS 72, Course record 65.

Visitors: preferable to contact in advance. **Societies:** must contact secretary/manager in advance. **Green Fees:** not confirmed. **Cards:** 6 8 3 4 **Prof:** Liam Higgins **Course Designer:** Eddie Hackett/Tom Fazio **Facilities:** ⓣ ⍥ 🏌 🛒 🍴 🛒 🏪 ⛳ ♟ ♛ 🚂 🏪 ⛳ sauna. **Location:** on the ring of Kerry route (N70) 400m from Waterville Village.

Hotel
★★★ 66% **Derrynane Hotel,** CAHERDANIEL
☎ 066 9475136 – 73 en suite

Championship Course

The K Club

☎ 01 6017300   🖹 01 6017399
e-mail: golf@kclub.ie

The K Club is the venue for the Ryder Cup in 2006, the first time that Ireland has hosted the event. The course reflects the personality of its architect, Arnold Palmer, covering 89 hectares of Kildare woodland, with 14 man-made lakes and the River Liffey providing the water hazards. From the instant you arrive at the 1st tee, you are enveloped by a unique atmosphere: the courses are both cavalier and charismatic. The Palmer Course is one of Europe's most spectacular courses, charming, enticing, and invariably bringing out the very best in your game. The best way to describe the Smurfit Course is that of an inland links, but its attributes do not stop there. The course has many dramatic landscapes with dunes moulding throughout, while some 6 hectares of water have been worked in to the design, especially through the final holes 13 to 18; a watery grave awaits many on the home stretch. The course is entirely different from the Palmer Course located just across the River Liffey.

WHERE TO STAY NEARBY

★★★★★
The K Club, STRAFFAN
☎ 01 6017200
69 en suite 10 annexe en suite

Palmer Course
18 holes, 6526 mtrs,
Par 74, SSS 72,
Course record 65

Smurfit Course
18 holes, 6636 mtrs,
Par 72, SSS 72

Club Membership
540

Visitors
Restricted at members' times; contact in advance to book tee times

Societies
Phone and write in advance

Green Fees
Terms on application

Cards

Professionals
John McHenry,
Peter O'Hagan

Course Designer
Arnold Palmer

Facilities
🍴 🍽 🏋 ☕ 💺 🍸 👔 🏠
🔧 🛒 ✂ 🛏 🚿 ⛲ 🥾
sauna, solarium, gymnasium

Conferences
Facilities available

Corporate
Hospitality Days available

Location
M4 junct 3, R406 to Straffan, entrance to hotel on right in village

Championship Course

Mount Juliet

Hotel & Golf Club
☎ 056 7773064 📄 056 7773078 e-mail: golfinfo@mountjuliet.ie

Venue for the American Express Championship in 2002 and 2004, Mount Juliet's superb 18-hole course was designed by Jack Nicklaus. It has also hosted many prestigious events including the Irish Open on three occasions. The course has a cleverly concealed drainage and irrigation system, perfect even when inclement weather would otherwise halt play. It takes advantage of the estate's mature landscape to provide a world-class 72-par challenge for professionals and high-handicap golfers alike. A unique 3-hole golfing academy has been added to allow novice and experienced players ample opportunity to improve their game, while a new 18-hole putting course provides an extra dimension of golfing pleasure and is the venue for the National Putting Championship.

WHERE TO STAY NEARBY

★★★★
Mount Juliet Conrad Hotel, THOMASTOWN
☎ 056 777 3000
32 en suite
27 annexe en suite

★★★★71%
Kilkenny River Court Hotel, The Bridge, John St, KILKENNY
☎ 056 772 3388 📄 056 772 3389
90 en suite

★★★75%
Newpark Hotel, KILKENNY
☎ 056 776 0500 📄 056 776 0555
111 en suite

★★★65%
Langtons Hotel, 69 John St, KILKENNY
☎ 056 776 5133 📄 056 776 3693
14 en suite   16 annexe en suite

---

18 holes, 6926yds, Par 72, SSS 73, Course record 62

Club Membership
500

Visitors
Must contact in advance

Societies
Book in advance by phone or writing

Green Fees
£140 (£155 weekends)

Cards
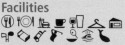

Professional
Sean Cotter

Course Designer
Jack Nicklaus

Facilities
🍴🍽️🧺☕🍺🛒🧥📦
⛳🔑🏌️🎣🔍🏊📞
sauna, solarium, gymnasium, archery, clay shooting, equestrian

Conferences
Facilities available

Corporate
Hospitality Days available

Location
4km S of Thomastown off N9

CO KILKENNY

KILKENNY

Kilkenny

Glendine

☎ 056 7765400   📄 056 7723593

e-mail: enquiries@kilkennygolfclub.com

One of Ireland's most pleasant inland courses, noted for its tricky finishing holes and its par 3s. Features of the course are its long 11th and 13th holes and the challenge increases year by year as thousands of trees planted over the last 30 years or so are maturing. As host of the Kilkenny Scratch Cup annually, the course is permanently maintained in championship condition. The Irish Dunlop Tournament and the Irish Professional Matchplay Championship have also been held here.

18 holes, 5925mtrs, Par 71, SSS 70, Course record 68.

Club membership: 1368. **Visitors:** must contact in advance. **Societies:** must contact in advance. **Green Fees:** not confirmed. **Cards:** 💳 💳 **Prof:** Jimmy Bolger **Facilities:** 🏋 🍴 🍺 💼 🛍 🏌 🏠 ⛳ 🏌 🛒
🏌 **Location:** 1.6km from centre on Castlecomer road

Hotel

★★★ 65% **Langtons Hotel,** 69 John St, KILKENNY
☎ 056 776 5133 – 14 en suite 16 annexe en suite

CO LOUTH

BALTRAY

County Louth

☎ 041 9881530   📄 041 9881531

e-mail: reservations@countylouthgolfclub.com

Generally held to have the best greens in Ireland, this links course was designed by Tom Simpson to have well guarded and attractive greens without being overly dependant on bunkers. It provides a good test for the modern champion, notably as the annual venue for the East of Ireland Amateur Open.

18 holes, 6673yds, Par 72, SSS 72, Course record 64.

Club membership: 1342. **Visitors:** must contact in advance. **Societies:** by prior arrangement. **Green Fees:** €110 per round (€130 weekends). **Cards:** 💳 💳 💳 **Prof:** Paddy McGuirk **Course Designer:** Tom Simpson **Facilities:** 🏋 🍴 🍺 💼 🏌 🏠 ⛳ ◇ 🏌 🚗 🏌 🍴 **Location:** 8km NE of Drogheda

CO MAYO

WESTPORT

Westport

Carrowholly
☎ 098 28262 & 27070 📄 098 27217
e-mail: wpgolf@eircom.net

This is a beautiful course with wonderful views of Clew Bay, with its 365 islands, and the holy mountain called Croagh Patrick, famous for the annual pilgrimage to its summit. Golfers indulge in a different kind of penance on this challenging course with many memorable holes. Perhaps the most exciting is the par 5 15th, 580 yards long and featuring a long carry from the tee over an inlet of Clew Bay.

18 holes, 6667yds, Par 73, SSS 71, Course record 65.

Club membership: 600. Visitors: must contact in advance. No visitors during members times. Societies: apply in writing or telephone/email well in advance. Green Fees: €38/€45 per round (weekends €42/€55). Cards: 💳 💳 💳 Prof: Alex Mealia Course Designer: Fred Hawtree Facilities: ⑪ ⑩ 🍴 🏌 🛒 🍴 ⚞ 🏕 🍴 ⛳ 🚗 ⛳ 🏌 Conf: Corporate Hospitality Days available Location: 4km from town on Newport road

Hotel
★★★ 76% Hotel Westport Conference & Leisure Centre, Newport Rd, WESTPORT
☎ 098 25122 – 129 en suite

CO MEATH

KELLS

Headfort

☎ 046 9240146 📄 046 9249282
e-mail: hgcadmin@eircom.net

The Old Course is a delightful parkland course which is regarded as one of the best of its kind in Ireland. There are ample opportunities for birdies, but even if these are not achieved, provides for a most pleasant game. The New Course is a challenging course with water featuring on 13 of its 18 holes. Not a course for the faint hearted, this is a course for the thinking golfer.

Headfort Golf Club-Old Course:
18 holes, 5973mtrs, Par 72, SSS 71.
Headfort Golf Club-New Course:
18 holes, 6164, Par 72, SSS 74.

Club membership: 1608. Visitors: Must contact in advance, timesheets in operation Societies: must apply in writing. Green Fees: Old Course: €45 per round (€50 Fri-Sun). New Course: €60 per round (€65 Fri-Sun). Cards: 💳 💳 💳 Prof: Brendan McGovern Course Designer: Christy O'Connor jnr Facilities: ⑪ ⑩ 🏌 🛒 🍴 ⚞ 🏕 🍴 ⛳ 🏌 Location: 800m 0n N3, E of Kells

Hotel
★★★ 64% Ardboyne Hotel, Dublin Rd, NAVAN
☎ 046 902 3119 – 29 en suite

CO SLIGO

ENNISCRONE

Enniscrone

☎ 096 36297 📄 096 36657
e-mail: enniscronegolf@eircom.net

27 holes, 6698yds, Par 73, SSS 72, Course record 70.

Course Designer: E Hackett/Donald Steel Location: 800m S on Ballina road Telephone for further details

SLIGO

County Sligo

Rosses Point
☎ 071 9177134 or 9177186 📄 071 9177460
e-mail: cosligo@iol.ie

Now considered to be one of the top links courses in Ireland, County Sligo is host to a number of competitions, including the West of Ireland Championships and Internationals. Set in an elevated position on cliffs above three large beaches, the prevailing winds provide an additional challenge. Tom Watson described it as 'a magnificent links, particularly the stretch of holes from the 14th to the 17th.' All Ireland Golf Club of the Year 2002.

18 holes, 6043mtrs, Par 71, SSS 72, Course record 67. Bomore: 9 holes, 2785mtrs, Par 35, SSS 69.

Club membership: 1175. Visitors: must contact in advance, available most days except Captains and Presidents days. Deposit required to secure. Societies: must contact in writing & pay a deposit. Green Fees: Championship Course:€65 per 18 holes Mon-Thu (€80 Fri-Sun and bank holidays). Cards: 💳 💳 💳 Prof: Jim Robinson Course Designer: Harry Colt Facilities: ⑪ ⑩ 🏌 🛒 🍴 ⚞ 🏕 🍴 ⛳ 🏌 Conf: facilities available Corporate: Hospitality Days available Location: Off N15 to Donegal

CO TIPPERARY

CLONMEL

Clonmel

Lyreanearla, Mountain Rd
☎ 052 24050 & 21138 📄 052 83349
e-mail: cgc@indigo.ie

Set in the scenic, wooded slopes of the Comeragh Mountains, this is a testing course with lots of open space and plenty of interesting features. It provides an enjoyable round in exceptionally tranquil surroundings.

18 holes, 6347yds, Par 72, SSS 71.

Club membership: 950. Visitors: must contact in

advance. **Societies:** apply in advance by writing or phone. **Green Fees:** not confirmed. **Cards:** 💳 **Prof:** Robert Hayes **Course Designer:** Eddie Hackett **Facilities:** ⑨ ⑩ by prior arrangement ⬛ 🏌 🏌 ⛳ 🏠 🍴 🚃 ✍ **Location:** 5km from Clonmel off N24

Hotel
★★★ 74% **Hotel Minella,** CLONMEL
☎ 052 22388 – 70 en suite

CO WATERFORD

WATERFORD

Waterford Castle
The Island, Ballinakill
☎ 051 871633 📄 051 871634
e-mail: golf@waterfordcastle.com

A unique 320-acre island golf course surrounded by the River Suir and accessed by private ferry. The course has four water features on the 2nd, 3rd, 4th and 16th holes with a Swilken Bridge on the 3rd hole. Two of the more challenging holes are the par 4s at the 9th and 12th, the 9th being a 414-yard uphill, dog-leg right. The 456-yard 12th is a fine test of accuracy and distance. The views from the course are superb.

18 holes, 5827mtrs, Par 72, SSS 71, Course record 70.

Club membership: 770. **Visitors:** must contact in advance, pre-booking required. **Societies:** apply in advance. **Green Fees:** Winter €45-€50; Summer €50-€60. **Cards:** 💳 💳 💳 **Course Designer:** Des Smyth **Facilities:** ⑨ ⑩ ⬛ 🏌 🏌 ⛳ 🍴 🏳 ✍ 🚃 ✍ 🏴 🏊 **Conf:** facilities available **Corporate:** Hospitality Days available **Location:** 3.2km E of Waterford City, on Island approached by private ferry

Hotel
★★★★ **Waterford Castle Hotel,**
The Island, WATERFORD
☎ 051 878203 – 19 en suite

CO WESTMEATH

MULLINGAR

Mullingar
☎ 044 48366 📄 044 41499

18 holes, 6406yds, Par 72, SSS 71, Course record 63.

Course Designer: James Braid **Location:** 4.8km S Telephone for further details

Hotel
🏨 **Crookedwood House,** Crookedwood, MULLINGAR
☎ 044 72165 – 8 en suite

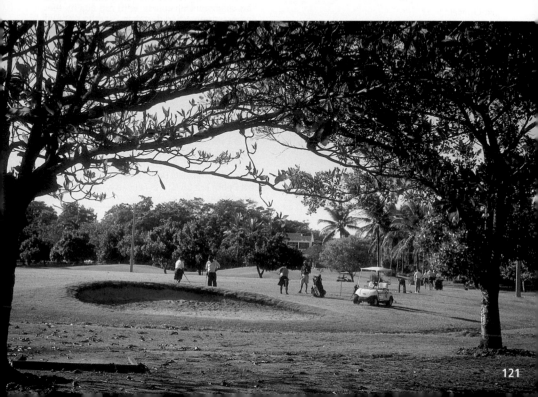

CO WEXFORD

GOREY

Courtown

Kiltennel
☎ 055 25166 055 25553
e-mail: courtown@iol.ie
18 holes, 5898mtrs, Par 71, SSS 71, Course record 65.

Course Designer: Harris & Associates **Location:** 4.8km from town, off Courtown Road
Telephone for further details

Hotel
★★★▲🏠 **Marlfield House Hotel,** GOREY
☎ 055 21124 – 20 en suite

ROSSLARE

Rosslare

Rosslare Strand
☎ 053 32203 053 32263
e-mail: office@rosslare.com

This traditional links course is within minutes of the ferry terminal at Rosslare. Many of the greens are sunken and are always in beautiful condition, but the semi-blind approaches are among features of this course which provide a healthy challenge. Celebrating 100 years of golf in 2005.

Old Course:
18 holes, 6608yds, Par 72, SSS 72, Course record 66.
Burrow: 12 holes, 3956yds, Par 46.

Club membership: 1000. **Visitors:** telephone 053 32203 ext 3 in advance. **Societies:** apply in writing/telephone. **Green Fees:** terms on application. **Cards:** 💳 VISA **Prof:** Johnny Young **Course Designer:** Hawtree/Taylor **Facilities:** ⑪ 🍽 ⓑ ⬤ ⬤ ⑪ ⚲ 🏠 ⑪ ⬤ 🛒 ⚲ sauna. **Conf:** Corporate Hospitality Days available **Location:** 10km N of Rosslare Ferry Terminal

Hotel
★★★★ **Kelly's Resort Hotel,** ROSSLARE
☎ 053 32114 – 118 annexe en suite

CO WICKLOW

BRITTAS BAY

The European Club
☎ 0404 47415 0404 47449
e-mail: info@europeanclub.com

A links course that runs through a large dunes system. Since opening in 1992 it is rapidly gaining recognition as one of Irelands best courses. Notable holes include the 7th, 13th and 14th.

20 holes, 7210yds, Par 71, SSS 73, Course record 67.

Club membership: 100. **Visitors:** pre-booking advised especially for weekends, no denim. **Societies:** must book in advance. **Green Fees:** not confirmed.

Cards: 💳 VISA **Course Designer:** Pat Ruddy
Facilities: ⑪ 🍽 ⓑ ⬤ ⚲ 🏠 ⑪ ⚲ 🛒 ⚲ **Conf:** Corporate Hospitality Days available **Location:** 1.6km from Brittas Bay Beach

Farmhouse
◆◆◆◆ **Kilpatrick House,** Redcross, WICKLOW
☎ 0404 47137 – 4 rms (3 en suite)

ENNISKERRY

Powerscourt

Powerscourt Estate
☎ 01 2046033 01 2761303
e-mail: golfclub@powerscourt.ie

A free draining course with links characteristics. This championship course, with top quality tees and exceptional tiered greens, is set in some of Ireland's most beautiful parkland. The course has an abundance of mature trees and natural features, with stunning views of the sea and Sugarloaf mountain.

East Course: 18 holes, 5930mtrs, Par 72, SSS 72.
West Course: 18 holes, 5906mtrs, Par 72, SSS 72.

Club membership: 920. **Visitors:** necessary to book in advance. **Societies:** necessary to book in advance. **Green Fees:** terms on application. **Cards:** 💳 ⬤ VISA ⑪ 🛒 ⑤ **Prof:** Paul Thompson **Course Designer:** Peter McEvoy **Facilities:** ⑪ 🍽 ⓑ ⬤ ⑪ ⚲ 🏠 ⑪ ◇ 🛒 ⚲ 🏴 **Conf:** facilities available Corporate Hospitality Days available **Location:** 19km S of Dublin just off N11 to Enniskerry, follow signs for Powerscourt Estate

Hotel
★★★ 65% **Royal Hotel & Leisure Centre,** Main St, BRAY
☎ 01 2862935 – 91 en suite

Druids Glen Golf Club

Newtown Mount Kennedy

☎ 01 2873600 📄 01 2873699 e-mail: info@druidsglen.ie

Druid's Glen from the 1st tee to the 18th green creates an exceptional golfing experience, with its distinguished surroundings and spectacular views. This masterpiece of inspired planning and golfing architecture was designed by Tom Craddock and Pat Ruddy. It is the culmination of years of preparation, creating a unique inland course that challenges and satisfies in equal parts. Special features include an island green on the 17th hole and a Celtic Cross on the 12th. Druid's Glen hosted the Murphy's Irish Open in 1996, 1997, 1998 and for an unprecedented fourth time in 1999. In 2000 Druid's Glen won the title of European Golf Course of the Year and in 2002 it hosted the Seve Trophy. The world's top professionals and club golfers alike continue to enjoy the challenge here. A variety of teeing positions are available and there is a practice area, including three full-length academy holes. Individual and corporate members enjoy generous reserved tee times; visitors are very welcome but it is recommended that you book well in advance.

WHERE TO STAY NEARBY

Ⓤ Marriott Druids Glen Hotel & Country Club,
Newtown Mount Kennedy
☎ 01 2870800
148 en suite

★★★67%
Hunter's Hotel, RATHNEW
☎ 0404 40106 📄 0404 40338
16 en suite

★★★★64%
Glenview Hotel,
Glen O' the Downs, DELGANY
☎ 01 2873399 📄 01 2877511
70 en suite

---

18 holes, 6547yds, Par 71, SSS 73, Course record 62

Club Membership
219

Visitors
Advance booking essential

Societies
Advance booking essential

Green Fees
Terms on application

Cards

Professional
George Henry

Course DesignerS
Tom Craddock, Pat Ruddy

Facilities
sauna, gymnasium.

Location
32km S of Dublin. 5km off N11, S of Glen of the Downs